W9-CVA-761

TWO BLADES OF GRASS

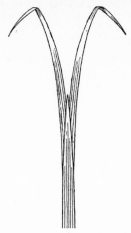

TWO BLADES OF GRASS

A HISTORY OF SCIENTIFIC DEVELOPMENT
IN THE U.S. DEPARTMENT OF AGRICULTURE

BY

T. SWANN HARDING

NORMAN

UNIVERSITY OF OKLAHOMA PRESS

1947

*D*edicated to those sincere, kindly, self-effacing, unavaricious humanitarians of highest integrity, the scientists who made the Department of Agriculture great as a research institution, and to my colleagues in information work in the various agencies of the Department, who so cheerfully and generously helped me to gather together the material comprising this book.

GENESIS OF THE BOOK

During 1933, not long after Henry A. Wallace became secretary and Rexford Guy Tugwell under secretary of agriculture, the latter became interested in the monetary value of research performed by Department of Agriculture scientists. As a result it was decided to have a survey made of Department publications reporting outstanding research achievements.

At that time I was editor of scientific publications of the Department, in the Division of Publications, Office of Information, of which Milton S. Eisenhower was director. The assignment was given to me, partly because of my fairly long service—I had first entered the Department of Agriculture in the Bureau of Chemistry in 1910, while Harvey W. Wiley was still its chief, though I was assigned to research and never worked on projects in the sector which ultimately became the Food and Drug Administration. My researches at this time were on the identification and production of rare sugars. In 1918 I went into private employment but returned to the Department in 1922, entering the Bureau of Animal Industry, where I was assigned to assist with a project on the nutrition of dairy cattle then being carried on at Beltsville, Maryland. In 1923 my division of the bureau became the Bureau of Dairy Industry; then, in 1928, I was appointed editor of scientific publications.

The survey interested me greatly, and it seemed that the method of presenting the value of research was both valid and interesting to a wide public. Therefore, instead of letting the project lapse after the report had been made, I continued it in my spare time. Gradually my interest extended to the entire history of the Department as an institution, and the material I had gathered ultimately appeared as No. 2 in an Agriculture History Series issued by the Bureau of Agricultural Economics, my contribution bearing the title, *Landmarks in the History of the Department of Agriculture.*

Thereafter I kept up my personal investigations—getting all the information that I could obtain from workers in the various scientific bureaus. The material came to me in fairly formal statements, informal memoranda, by word of mouth, and, in many instances, through personal acquaintance and experience with the scientists who were most concerned, a number of whom I knew and interviewed. The drafts prepared to represent the work of each bureau were checked and rechecked with bureau personnel for accuracy.

My desire to make a popular presentation of this material for the general public instead of a highly documented monograph, such as the volumes which comprise the Agricultural History Series, together with the Department's curtailment of publishing to wartime necessities, prompted me to ask permission, which was granted, to find an outside publisher for the material. In 1945 Ladd Haystead, of *Fortune* magazine, suggested that I submit the material to the University of Oklahoma Press, which had released a number of notable books in the field of agriculture.

The director of the press naturally wanted to know what kind of book this was to be. After trying to describe it in a satisfactory manner, I was finally cornered, gave up, and said that I would put the material in book form to let him see for himself. In rewriting, I completely rearranged my previous manuscript, for as it stood it was ill-organized for a book, consisting largely of notes and references with only a few chapters forming any coherent account in logical or chronological order. Helen W. Atwater, daughter of Dr. W. O. Atwater, had written the story of the Bureau of Human Nutrition and Home Economics in a brief report, and the late Clark F. Hunn of Forest Service had produced an excellent discussion of the work of that agency. However, these accounts also had to be torn asunder, rearranged, and rewritten for book purposes, though the respective bureaus retain the originals, which may be consulted by anyone interested. In preparing this book, I also found invaluable as an original source of information A. C. True's "A History of Agricultural Experimentation and Research in the United States, 1607–1925," U.S.D.A. *Miscellaneous Publication No. 251* (1937).

Here, then, is the book which grew out of Dr. Tugwell's desire to prove, as he well knew could be proved, that research performed by Department of Agriculture scientists has been almost incredibly valuable to the American public, both in scientific advancement and in monetary terms.

I want especially to thank Milton Eisenhower for giving me the original assignment; my supervisor at that time, M. C. Merrill, for saying that I did a good job with it and for assistance to me in preparing the appendix, "The Publication of Research"; Eisenhower's successors, Morse Salisbury and Keith Himebaugh for encouraging me in carrying to project further; Gove Hambidge for reading the entire original manuscript for overall clearance by the Agricultural Research Administration; Dallas Burch for doing the same thing again when the notes were more completely organized; and other workers in the bureaus of Agricultural Research Administration, in Forest Service, and in Soil Conservation Service for permitting me to badger them into sending me basic material. I am also deeply indebted to Anna Jim Holman for reading all the proofs and to Mrs. Mabel Hunt Doyle for making the index. Finally, Ladd Haystead has my gratitude for directing me to the publisher.

The title derives from a statement made (page 16) in the first Annual Report of the first Commissioner of Agriculture, Isaac Newton, who wrote, under date of January 1, 1863: "It should be the aim of every young farmer to do not only as well as his father, but to do his best; 'to make two blades of grass grow where but one grew before.' " That scientific research in the field of agriculture was the primary factor making this possible none can doubt.

T. SWANN HARDING

Falls Church, Virginia
December 10, 1946

THE CHAPTERS

THE ILLUSTRATIONS

RESEARCH in the natural sciences, the foundation for the phenomenal productivity of American farms today, has been an integral part of the work of the United States Department of Agriculture since its activities began in the Patent Office in 1839. I am glad to see in this volume an account of the Department of Agriculture as a research institution, and of its distinguished scientific workers. The author is a veteran employee of the Department, having entered it in 1910 and served consecutively as a research chemist, its editor of scientific publications, and an information specialist. His career has afforded him an excellent opportunity to make this out-of-hours project both interesting and accurate.

CLINTON P. ANDERSON

TWO BLADES OF GRASS

PART I : PRELIMINARIES

CHAPTER I

How It All Started

HERE IS AN ARTICLE with a profoundly repulsive scientific title: "Nutrient-Solution Purification for Removal of Heavy Metals in Deficiency Investigations with *Aspergillus Niger.*" It was published during 1935 in the *Journal of Agricultural Research,* a Department of Agriculture periodical devoted to just such esoteric and otherworldly material. Its author was a Department scientist named R. A. Steinberg, who had been trying to grow a fungus on a culture solution, and this highly technical paper told how he could purify his nutrient solutions.

What could all this possibly have to do with the price of peanuts? It might have a very great deal to do with it eventually; for it developed that the scientist's fungus needed, in order to thrive, certain so-called "trace" elements, minute quantities of various minerals present in such tiny traces that their presence could scarcely be detected. It was found that many of these trace elements were also essential to plant life and to the lives of animals pastured on or fed the plants. Soon other scientists discovered that minute traces of certain minerals, long regarded as soil or plant poisons, must be added to the soil to enable fruits, vegetables, and cereals to grow thereon.

Thus zinc used on the soil of old orchards in Georgia and California, which seemed to be petering out, put new life into them. Truck crops could now be grown on Florida muck land, high in organic matter, since it was known what trace elements should be added. Obscure tree, plant, and animal deficiency conditions, which caused poor growth and ill health and could terminate fatally, could now be diagnosed and wholly cured. Land long thought worthless became productive. Hydroponics came along, the growing of vegetables in water cultures containing minerals—an excellent procedure for emergency use, as by the armed forces on barren Ascension Island—and so on and on.

In short, each and every one of us benefits because a worker at pure research let his curiosity get the better of him in order to find out what was needed to make a mold grow. Little food as we have, or think we have, in this postwar period, it is much more than we would have otherwise by reason of his work and because his many colleagues also performed their parts in laboratory and field investigations.

This is only one example in a single scientific periodical of the hundreds of valuable papers expounding research performed by federal and state agricultural scientists. Research of this nature is not only of value to farmers and the agricultural industry; it also affects all of us, urban or rural, personally, every day of our lives. The *Journal of Agricultural Research* contains many other notable papers, basic to entire fields of industry, nutrition, or medical science, or which have actually founded new industries or aided in the institution of totally new and extremely beneficial activities.

Much of this research also has huge monetary value, though the dividends therefrom are paid socially rather than to individuals, because the findings themselves are usually made institutionally and at public expense. An example is the research explained in an article by the late Maurice C. Hall which appeared in the *Journal of Agricultural Research* during 1921 concerning the use of carbon tetrachloride for the removal of hookworms. As a result of its publication and of additional work by Hall and his colleagues, millions of human beings have been successfully treated with consequent enormous improvement in their health and work efficiency. Those who know most about such things estimate the value of this work to the American public at $75,000,000, and that is a conservative figure. It is also of interest that the American hookworm of man was discovered and identified by Charles Wardell Stiles in the same Bureau of Animal Industry where Hall later worked.

Dividends are large on every dollar invested in agricultural research. Overall returns probably average 500 per cent, though a return of 10,000 per cent on the original investment is not unusual. For instance, it cost the Bureau of Animal Industry about $1,500,-

ooo to eradicate contagious pleuropneumonia from this country when, before 1884, it was wiping out our cattle industry. During the period that this work was being carried on, say five or six years, cattle growers saved $41,000,000 in exports to Great Britain alone because of the investigations by scientists in this bureau.

It cost about $65,000 to make the basic discoveries which enabled this same bureau to fight cattle-tick fever successfully. That work has been worth around $40,000,000 a year, every year since, to the stockholders in that great corporation, the United States of America. Around 1938 it cost about $10,000 to show that phenothiazine was a versatile drug for the control of livestock parasites. This discovery has proved to be worth more than $10,000,000 a year to stockmen. Thus dividends are cumulative and perpetual.

That is why many private industrial concerns expend 4 or 5 per cent of their gross income on research, some of it pure investigation into basic principles without immediate practical application in mind. In the prewar year of 1938 it is estimated that the federal government spent 2 per cent of its income in this way. While industry spent 1.7 per cent of its gross 1938 income on research, the comparable figure for agriculture was 0.37 per cent—spent almost wholly upon work carried on by federal and state institutions, for agricultural research is in the main carried on governmentally.

This vast federal-state network consists of the Department of Agriculture, with its near-by Agricultural Research Center and Plant Industry Station, both at Beltsville, Maryland, the state agricultural experiment stations and land-grant colleges, the Department's four huge regional research laboratories in the four major regions of the nation, and the nine Bankhead-Jones (Jones was the former war food administrator) laboratories which typify federal-state co-operation at its closest. In addition, the Department and the states have a number of widely scattered substations and experimental farms for various specific purposes.

The major agencies in the Department of Agriculture which perform research are the Forest Service, the Soil Conservation Service, the Agricultural Research Administration, and, in the field of the social sciences, the Bureau of Agricultural Economics. The agencies comprising the Agricultural Research Administration are the bureaus of Agricultural and Industrial Chemistry, Animal Industry, Dairy Industry, Entomology and Plant Quarantine, Human Nutrition and Home Economics, Plant Industry, Soils, and Agricultural Engineering, and the Office of Experiment Stations. The last administers the federal side of the Hatch Act of 1887 and later acts which provide federal funds to aid state agricultural experiment stations.

Certain agencies which at one time formed part of the Department of Agriculture and have since been transferred elsewhere should be considered in this connection, also, as the research performed in them while part of the Department contributes to the institution's history. These are the Biological Survey, now part of Fish and Wildlife Service in the Department of the Interior; the Bureau of Public Roads, now the Public Roads Administration in the Federal Works Agency; the Food and Drug Administration, now in the Federal Security Agency; and the Weather Bureau, now in the Department of Commerce.

The Agricultural Research Center alone, where a staff of over 2,000 persons work in large, well-equipped buildings scattered over part of a 14,000-acre plot, is almost certainly the largest agricultural research institution in the world. Yet it forms only part of the Department of Agriculture, which has an additional big establishment in Washington, D. C., and far-flung laboratories and experiment stations all over the country. At Beltsville each bureau of the Agricultural Research Administration carries on investigations, while the entire Bureau of Plant Industry, Soils, and Agricultural Engineering has its headquarters at Plant Industry Station there.

All this vast organization sprang from small beginnings. When the Department of Agriculture was created in response to a law signed by President Lincoln on May 15, 1862, the incumbent head of the Agricultural Division in the Patent Office, from which the Department sprang, became the first Commissioner of Agriculture. He and his two or three clerks and assistants brought the Department into being in two basement rooms of an old building which still stands and is now occupied by the Civil Service Commission.

As created, the Department was an autonomous bureau with a commissioner at its head, who did not attain Cabinet status until 1889. Isaac Newton, this first commissioner, made reference to science in his first annual report as the *"what* and *how* to do . . . the concentrated experience of the ages . . . classified knowledge illustrated in practice and confirmed by experience, and as certain and eternal as truth itself." Applied chemistry stood foremost in his mind as the greatest aid to the farmer, and he quoted Sir Humphry Davy: "Nothing is impossible to labor aided by science."

Newton's initial appointments were of persons singularly well qualified for his day, as we shall see somewhat later. Among them were a botanist, a statistician, an entomologist, a chemist, a chief clerk, and a few laborers. Even by 1868 the Department had fewer than fifty employees. Newton also established an agricultural library and a museum.

Much earlier than Newton, however, various individuals in the Patent Office had sought to aid farmers by collecting and disseminating plants, seeds, agricultural statistics, and reports of farm inventions. This they did on woefully small appropriations and, originally, on none at all and without authorization by Congress.

In 1836 a rather remarkable individual resigned his position as mayor of Hartford, Connecticut, to become Commissioner of Patents under a new law which went into effect in Jackson's administration. This was Henry Leavitt Ellsworth, son of the third Chief Justice of the Supreme Court, president of a big life-insurance company, gentleman, and scientific farmer, farm-club organizer, and a man of independent means.

Before his time certain individuals like Benjamin Franklin and Thomas Jefferson had sent back to this country from abroad plants, seeds, and accounts of agricultural inventions which they thought might prove useful here. This work was not regularized, even though George Washington in his last message to Congress recommended agriculture as a fit subject upon which to expend federal funds. True, our consuls had been instructed in 1819 to send back plants, seeds, and news of agricultural inventions, and both houses of Congress had set up agricultural committees by 1825. But little was really accomplished for agriculture.

That little was effected through the Patent Office, which was in the Department of State until 1849, when the Department of Interior was established and the patent work was transferred there. However, so many of our farmers were convinced that the growth, culture, and manufacture of silk and silkworms would redeem agriculture here, that Congress took heed. It directed Richard Rush, secretary of the treasury, to make a study of the matter and, in 1828, the legislative, not the executive, branch of the federal government issued the first technical publication in the field of agriculture.

It was a manual on the subject of silk, the most comprehensive publication of the sort then available in this country. Almost immediately Count von Hazzi, a German nobleman, found out about it and petitioned Congress to publish also as a document his "Treatise on the Rearing of Silkworms," and this, too, was done.

For many years our more aristocratic gentlemen farmers, of whom George Washington and Thomas Jefferson were typical, had been intensely interested in applications of science to agriculture. Impetus was early given to the thinking of these persons by books such as Sir Humphry Davy's *Elements of Agricultural Chemistry* (1813), embodying the substance of a series of lectures he gave in 1803 for the British Agricultural Board. Influential also was Justus von Liebig's *Chemistry in its Application to Agriculture and Physiology*, which appeared in 1840.

Furthermore, the period between 1800 and 1840 was one of considerable technological progress. In 1831 William Manning patented his mowing machine, while Obed Hussey and Cyrus McCormick made the reaper practicable between 1833 and 1844. John Deere of Illinois produced the first steel plow from a saw blade in 1837. The stationary thresher and fanning mill, introduced in the thirties, reduced the time required for threshing, gathering, winnowing, and sacking an acre of wheat from twenty-six hours in 1839 to a mere four hours in 1840.

Meanwhile, both transportation and incipient methods of food processing and preservation were making strides. The year 1839 marked the end of the canal era and the beginning of the railroad-construction period. Better means of transportation, coupled with new refrigeration methods, soon greatly expanded the market for agricultural products. Technological progress also did much to open vast rich western lands to cultivation, which put them into severe competition with the eroded and seemingly exhausted soil of the East.

Then there was the depression of 1837–42, by far the most extended period of acute financial misfortune the nation underwent before the Civil War. Hundreds of banks closed their doors, and interest rates rose as high as 30 per cent. Speculative manias abounded, and farmers were by no means immune to them. Mulberry trees and silkworm production, broomcorn, the Chinese tree corn, Rohan potatoes, Merino sheep, shorthorn cattle, Berkshire hogs, the importation of camels and ostriches—each had partisans who regarded it as magic to solve farm problems.

No wonder Henry L. Ellsworth wanted to do something for farmers when he became commissioner of patents. Fortunately he was an entertaining as well as an informative writer. His reports had to be issued in editions of 25,000, enormous for those days, and John Quincy Adams half-querulously complained that reading these reports so absorbed him as to make him miss his appointments by as much as four hours.

In his first annual report Ellsworth remarked that, of late, inventors had "directed their attention, with peculiar interest, to the improvement of the implements of *agriculture*, and many labor-saving machines have been patented, which are of the highest utility to husbandmen. These are rapidly increasing; and it is scarcely possible to conjecture to what extent the labor of the agriculturist may be diminished, and the products of the country increased, by these improvements."

He went on to say that horsepower was already being widely used for sowing, mowing, and reaping, and "inventors are sanguine in the belief (and probably not without reason) that the time is not far distant when ploughing machines will be driven by steam, and steampower applied to many other operations of the husband-ryman. . . . A subject intimately connected with this, is the aid which husbandry might derive from the establishment of a regular system for the selection and distribution of grain and seeds of the choicest varieties for agricultural purposes."

During 1836–37, Ellsworth, at his own expense and without Congressional authorization, distributed seeds and plants that were gratuitously transmitted to him for the purpose. Soon the function of seed distribution was to be regularized under Congressional authority. For a long time this work consumed most of the federal funds allocated to agriculture. Ultimately it became a disgrace, as certain heads of the Department declared, but it did not cease until June 30, 1923.

Ellsworth felt that some place in Washington should be legally designated as a repository for seeds and plants as well as for agricultural information. He told of the introduction of new varieties of wheat which stood our severe northern winters and pushed the wheat belt farther north. He thought that wheat varieties could be produced by selection which would increase yields by 20 per cent. The same sort of thing had been done with corn by private individuals.

He believed that a 10 per cent increase in wheat yields would provide the nation with an additional income of from $15,000,000 to $20,000,000 annually. He felt that the same technique of increasing crop yields could be applied to other cereals and to vegetables and fruits. He declared that the federal government should take the sciences under its wing and use them to effect results of this kind.

In his annual reports for 1837 and 1839, dated January 1, 1838, and January 1, 1840, respectively, Ellsworth requested Congress to provide funds to be used for the collection and dissemination of agricultural seeds, plants, and statistics. Upon inquiry by Chairman Isaac Fletcher of the House Committee on Patents, he wrote a letter dated January 22, 1839, which so logically supported his claims that Congress, then considering the bill for the 1840 Census, attached thereto a provision permitting the Patent Office to expend the sum of $1,000 for agricultural purposes.

This was the first federal aid to agriculture, and the Agricultural Division of the Patent Office was established. Thereafter, other small appropriations were made, though the next grant of $1,000 did not come until 1842. In 1843 and 1844 the sum was doubled; it rose to $3,000 in 1845; but no grant at all was made for 1846, and the work was temporarily discontinued. However, the sum of $3,000 was granted for 1847 and $3,500 for 1848 and 1849, and there were no lapses from 1849 on.

In subsequent reports Ellsworth made it clear that he realized the value of the experimental method. At one point he exclaimed: "If the application of the sciences be yet further made to husbandry, what vast improvements may be anticipated!" This led to a eulogy of agricultural chemistry, which Ellsworth held to be of supreme importance to prevent farmers from groping along as they had in the past. Chemistry would prove which croplands would bear to advantage and which soils and manures were best. Chemistry had already shown how pork fat could be converted to stearine for use in making candles, thus providing an acceptable substitute for spermaceti. It had demonstrated that ten gallons of oil could be produced from one hundred bushels of corn meal. One concern even then (this was 1841) was attempting to secure the privilege of supplying all the lighthouses on the "upper lakes with this article."

A new method of trebling the sugar content of cornstalks had been announced. In Delaware, experiments had shown that one thousand pounds of sugar could thus be produced per acre of corn. The farmer merely permitted the stalks to mature, removing the ears before they were well formed; thus the stalk sugar increased to three times that contained by beets. Experiments should be continued on this project, upon which German chemists were already at work.

In the volume containing Ellsworth's annual report for 1842 there are articles describing experiments on making cornstalk sugar and giving information about foreign agricultural markets, agricultural statistics, improvements in fencing farmlands and building farmhouses, the effect of railroads upon agriculture and on our farm exports and imports as affected by the British Corn Laws.

In his annual report dated January 31, 1844, Ellsworth declared that an overall 10 per cent increase in crop yields, made possible by the application of scientific methods, would increase the farmers' annual income by $30,000,000. He was pleading now for the establishment of a federal government bureau to aid agriculture. The volume containing his report ran to some 330 pages and included extensive discussions of various crops, abundant agricultural statistics, and informative letters from farm correspondents.

Ellsworth's final report, dated January 28, 1845—he relinquished office April 30 of that year—covered 520 pages, with index, and was the most comprehensive of all. In it he declared that the science of agriculture had become a major study in the Patent Office.

Abandoned and worn-out lands were being reclaimed. Guesswork and hereditary notions were yielding to scientific analysis and the application of scientific principles.

But science must always persevere. It must never give up. Some people had at first claimed that cornstalk sugar was grape sugar, but science had shown it to be the equal of the best table sugar. Several grains had been analyzed. Dyspeptics would soon learn from the analyses of certain meals which of them contained excessive oil and therefore gave them indigestion. New methods of farm fencing and of building farmhouses of unburnt brick were discussed. Ellsworth stated that the productivity of the soil could be greatly increased by better manure, tillage, drainage, subsoiling aids, and deep plowing, for roots went down much further into the earth than had been thought.

The navy could often pick up valuable seeds in foreign ports for almost nothing, but an appropriation should be made available to package, box, and ship them from the American ports where they were put ashore, so that farmers could benefit. Potato diseases and the Hessian fly were causing much anxiety and should have attention.

In this fashion agricultural science got its start in the federal government. But duly organized agricultural research carried on in well-equipped institutions by well-trained personnel remained in the future. That future we shall trace in the following pages.

CHAPTER 2

Agricultural Science
in the Patent Office

Henry L. Ellsworth resigned as commissioner of patents on April 30, 1845, and went to live on his farm at Lafayette, Indiana, in the vicinity of which he had acquired 110,000 acres of public land. Here he remained until he returned to Fair Haven, Connecticut, a few months before his death on December 27, 1858. He had managed to get recognition from the federal government that agriculture was, as George Washington had said, worthy of government aid. Washington had told Congress on December 7, 1796:

> It will not be doubted that with reference either to individual or national welfare agriculture is of primary importance. In proportion as nations advance in population and other circumstances of maturity this truth becomes more apparent and renders the cultivation of the soil more and more an object of public patronage. Institutions for promoting it grow up, supported by the public purse; and to what object can it be dedicated with greater propriety?

While not all of Ellsworth's successors by any means had the intelligent interest in agriculture possessed by him, some measure of Patent Office aid was given to farmers during their administrations. Too much of this assistance went out in the form of free seed and not enough of it was directed toward scientific investigation. To be sure, such investigation must necessarily have been somewhat rudimentary, as science had not then attained maturity, but helpful beginnings could have been made.

Ellsworth's immediate successor, Edmund Burke, served until 1849, the year in which the Department of the Interior was created. The Patent Office became part of this new department. In December, 1849, President Taylor recommended the establishment of a bureau of agriculture in this Department, because he felt that current assistance to farmers was wholly inadequate, but Congress took no action.

Burke said that agriculture was "the great transcendent interest of the Union." He also wrote: "No occupation offers a greater field for experiment, and for the application of science directed by sound judgment. Experience has proved that every grain, vegetable and fruit, is susceptible of improvement by scientific cultivation." He then recounted the magic transformations already wrought by science in the potato, the peach, the apple, and other fruits and vegetables.

In 1848 a Congressional appropriation was made especially to finance analyses of various cereal grains produced in this country and flour manufactured here for export. The objective was to show the effects of soil and climate upon different varieties of grain, and of sea voyages upon the quality of flour. Professor Lewis C. Beck, a "practical analytical chemist" of Rutgers College, New Brunswick, New Jersey, was engaged to make these analyses.

Professor Beck's report on flour was printed in the annual Patent Office book, which also ran a report by Charles L. Fleischmann, who had been engaged to study sugar culture in Louisiana. The Patent Office book also contained considerable other material in the field of agricultural chemistry. Soon Part II of the annual report, concerned with agriculture, quite outgrew Part I, the report of the Patent Office proper, and it became necessary to employ a qualified individual to prepare Part II.

A little while before the Patent Office became a part of the Department of the Interior, English-born Thomas Ewbank, whose primary interests were industry, manufacturing, and mechanics, became commissioner of patents. He suggested that a "practical and scientific agriculturist" be engaged to prepare the separate annual report on agricultural matters. Daniel Lee, M.D., former editor of the *Genesee Farmer*, and professor of agriculture at the University of Georgia, was employed.

Lee's main passion was the conservation of soil nutrients. Regardless of the subject upon which he started out to write, even if it were agricultural statistics, he always managed to get to his favorite subject and to enlarge upon it. However, agricultural statistics were omitted from the annual reports now because it was felt that those published heretofore had been unreliable and that time and paper would be wasted in printing "crude guesses."

Lee's reports were filled not only with his own writings but with numerous essays on agricultural subjects and considerable discussion of agricultural education by others. Over and over he implored Congress to make an appropriation to prevent the universal impoverishment of American soils, but in vain. As he wrote:

Neither the earnest recommendation of the illustrious farmer of Mt. Vernon, nor the prayers of two generations of agriculturists, nor the painful fact that nearly all tilled lands were becoming less and less productive, could induce any legislature to foster the study of agriculture as a science.

He remarked with some asperity that not even an appropriation of a thousand million dollars, however judiciously expended, could be expected to restore fertility to the hundred million acres of partly exhausted soil then in the United States. Meanwhile soils, marls, and fertilizers should be analyzed, insect ravages demanded attention, farm animals ought to be improved, and rural science must come into its own.

These early reports were filled also with articles on the cultivation of special crops, on cattle breeding, and, of course, on soil destruction and agricultural education, along with replies to inquiries which were published to inform others. Before Lee left the work, some meteorological statistics appeared in the annual book and agricultural statistics, presumably more reliable, made their reappearance. Finally there was constant emphasis upon the necessity for setting up some sort of agricultural bureau in the federal government.

In his final reports Lee spoke of himself as having been in charge of the "agricultural department" of the Patent Office, and begged permission to expend $200 on experiments to find the best methods "to deodorize and concentrate night soil, that it might be put up in bags and sent far out into the country for agricultural purposes." But not a dollar could he get although, he complained, the sum of $100,000 was freely appropriated for the publication, binding, and distribution of an annual book on agriculture, while soil exhaustion continued unimpeded.

Lee originally received a salary of $2,000 a year, but this was reduced to $1,500, probably as an inducement for him to resign. Thereupon his successor, Daniel Jay Browne, was appointed by Commissioner Charles Mason at the same rate, though he was raised to $2,000 by 1855.

At the early age of twenty-six Browne had precociously founded a journal called the *Naturalist*. He was a New Hampshire-born and farm-bred agricultural and scientific writer. He went to Harvard and then occupied considerable time in foreign travel. He later employed himself in various pursuits concerned with the promotion of agriculture, meanwhile writing books and articles.

In 1852 he had become agricultural statistician for the Bureau of the Census and in 1853 the agricultural clerk of the Patent Office, where he prepared and edited the reports until his resignation in 1859. In 1855 he was sent to Europe to collect agricultural information, plants, and seeds; hence he was the first paid federal plant explorer. His activities aroused adverse criticism, largely of seedsmen opposed to governmental distribution of free seed, and of those persons who opposed federal aid to agriculture. This opposition led to Congressional investigation; Browne was exonerated, but, as criticism continued, he resigned.

During this period the appropriation for agricultural work became as much as $35,000. A two-acre tract between Four and One-half and Sixth streets and Missouri Avenue was set aside (1856) for the study of sorghums, and the seed produced was distributed. The annual reports also began to mention the introduction of the soybean, and a wide variety of agricultural subjects was discussed.

It was Charles Mason also who first employed that distinguished all-around agricultural scientist of the day, Townend Glover. In 1855 arrangements were made with the Smithsonian Institution to publish meteorological statistics. That same year a chemist and a botanist were employed, though not on a permanent basis.

Old Red Brick Building, 1867–1930, planned by Isaac Newton

U. S. Department of Agriculture buildings in Washington today

Glover was born in Brazil of British parents. He grew up in England, was originally trained as a painter, and a number of his paintings were hung in European galleries. He came to the United States in 1836 and settled in New York state, where he began to carry on experiments of his own in the growing of fruits and vegetables and the study of soils and insects. He made extraordinarily artistic colored models of fruits and vegetables, his collection being later sold to the federal government for $10,000.

In 1853 the Patent Office hired Glover to go to Europe and collect entomological and agricultural data. Later he was professor of entomology at the Maryland Agricultural College and subsequently, as will be seen, the first entomologist of the Department of Agriculture. As such he visited Brazil and brought back disease-resistant sugar canes to help replace inferior varieties then being grown in Louisiana.

Glover worked for many years on a comprehensive insect encyclopedia, which, however, he never completed. He was awarded a medal by Napoleon III of France for his work in entomology. He was witty, eccentric, and a good caricaturist. One of the many extraordinary professional men who worked in the field of federal agriculture during early days, he did not retire until 1878, when his health failed.

During Mason's term of office the following subjects were discussed in the agricultural reports of the Patent Office: cattle diseases, the importation of camels, gophers, birds, bees, Indian corn, bread crops, textiles, forage crops, fertilizers, fruits, vegetables, climatology, tobacco, sugar cane, sorghum, broomcorn, tomatoes, capers, okra, nuts, wine, gardening, and hedges for "live fences." This list is genuinely indicative of the Department's future field.

Mason argued strenuously that there was strong justification for the expenditure of Patent Office funds in aid of agriculture. After a short interval he was followed in office by Joseph Holt of Kentucky, appointed patent commissioner by President Buchanan in repayment of a political debt. Browne continued to edit the agricultural reports, which now began to contain considerable discussion of the tea plant.

On January 3, 1859, a Washington meeting of prominent agriculturists enthusiastically approved the agricultural work of the

Patent Office and recommended its extension. About this time steam tractors were being given unsuccessful trials and Grimm alfalfa was being introduced. Meanwhile, various vociferous groups and individuals were loudly and potently agitating for free land, agricultural colleges, and additional federal farm aid.

There was consistent opposition by the Southern delegation to Congress, which based on the doctrine of states' rights its hostility to legislation in this field. A land-grant–college bill did get through Congress during Buchanan's administration, but the President vetoed it out of deference to the opposition. He regarded federal grants to the states as not only extravagant but unconstitutional as well.

On March 23, 1859, President Buchanan appointed William Darius Bishop, a former railroad president and member of Congress, to be commissioner of patents. He served only until February 13, 1860, and was followed in office by Philip F. Thomas, who resigned on December 13, 1860, and then by David H. Holloway, who served from March 28, 1861, until August 16, 1865. During Holloway's term the agricultural work was transferred from the Patent Office to an independent agency under a commissioner of agriculture.

The 1860 agricultural report was prepared and edited by Thomas G. Clemson, who signed himself superintendent of the Agricultural Division. This was somewhat less grand than the title Browne used on occasion—superintendent of the Agricultural Division of the Patent Office. However, Clemson at times called himself "Superintendent of the Agricultural Affairs of the United States"!

Clemson, of course, was the famous founder of Clemson College in South Carolina. He had studied chemistry in France under masters like Gay-Iussac, worked as a mining engineer, married John C. Calhoun's daughter, and settled down to plantation life, which he left only when President Taylor sent him on a mission to Belgium. From 1853 until 1861 he lived in Bladensburg, Maryland, and was instrumental in founding the Maryland Agricultural College in 1858.

In 1859 the Secretary of the Interior placed Clemson in charge of the Agricultural Division of the Patent Office. He resigned on March 4, 1861, because of the impending Civil War, his Southern sympathies inducing him to take up residence in South Carolina. He was a member of many learned societies, an excellent amateur violinist and artist, and a collector of art. He was a much more distinguished personage than his immediate successor, Isaac Newton, who ultimately became first commissioner of agriculture.

The agricultural reports of these days mention continual trials of steam plows, traction engines, and steam cultivators, stressing the labor and man-power savings incident to their use. Farm technology was on the march and during the man-power shortage of the Civil War period it made great strides. One year the report also featured a long article by Samuel D. Backus, a New York architect, entitled "Some Hints Upon Farm Houses."

However, the Agricultural Division of the Patent Office could give relatively little general, much less scientific, aid to farmers. It had, to be sure, come a long way since 1842, when it employed only one clerk and issued a twenty-page annual report. It was now spending $53,000 a year—too much of it on free-seed distribution—and boasted besides its superintendent, four clerks, including translators and writers, a curator and gardener, and a few laborers.

But agitation was rife for the creation of an agricultural department in the federal government. The reports now stressed the fact that seed distribution was insufficient and should, in fact, be curtailed. Agricultural societies began to appeal to Congress for aid of another kind; they wanted something done about soil exhaustion and greater attention given the advances of farm technology. Above all it was felt that a good federal chemical laboratory could greatly aid farmers.

English husbandry, irrigation, grasses for the South, the diseases of domestic animals, bee culture, fish propagation, insects injurious to vegetation, wine making, grape culture, the forests and trees of North America, tea culture, Chinese agricultural methods, and the rapid spread of contagious pleuropneumonia among cattle were all discussed in these final agricultural reports from the Patent Office.

The new commissioner of patents took office, David P. Holloway. He had been a journalist interested in agriculture for years. He had been elected to the House of Representatives and had served as chairman of the Committee on Agriculture. He made very effective pleas for increased federal aid to agriculture in his annual reports. Meanwhile, Isaac Newton, born of Quaker stock in New Jersey, who had become an outstanding farm manager in Pennsylvania and was a friend of Abraham Lincoln, took charge of the Agricultural Division after Clemson's departure for the South.

Holloway's report for 1861, issued in 1862, was by far the most complete agricultural manual so far put out by the Patent Office. It consisted in the main of essays on current progress in American agriculture. It was in this report that the Commissioner launched his fervent plea for the establishment of a federal institution to serve agriculture. Three-fourths of this country's citizens were still farmers, and Holloway undoubtedly reflected a rising tide of public opinion. He came out pointedly for scientific investigations of our soils, crops, and cultural methods. Thus he coupled successful farming with wise land use.

He also held that worthless breeds of cattle must be supplanted by shorthorns on rich pasture. Agricultural tools and implements should be improved and made more widely available. Indeed, the federal government should have in it a Ministry of Industry, composed of three bureaus—agricultural, mechanical, and commercial. The subject matter discussed elsewhere in the book containing Holloway's report clearly indicates the subjects upon which farmers wanted aid: flax and hemp; sheep and wool production; artificial manures; hog cholera; raspberry and strawberry culture; worn-out lands of New Jersey; consumption of milk; cotton in Missouri; destruction of harmful insects; growing pears; farming in New England; hop culture; sorghum culture and sugar making; recent progress of agricultural science; Sandomir wheat; reclaiming salt marshes; cultivation of lupine; the general subject of food; silk-worms of China; horses of New England; wheat growing in Prussia; model dairy farms; select cattle breeds; grape growing and wine making; and fruit culture.

One article also discussed the relationship between entomology and soil productivity. Another bore the quaint title: "Something of the Philosophy and Chemistry of Manures."

It was a time of great change. When thousands of farmers went off to war, the farm use of labor-saving machinery increased rapidly. Whereas 20,000 mowers were manufactured in 1861, the number rose to 70,000 in 1865. The same advance was true of other equipment used in the effort to secure increased farm production with fewer hands. Meanwhile, the urban industrial population was increasing, as is customary during war.

Prominent among the pressure groups demanding that a Department of Agriculture be established was the United States Agricultural Society, which had been organized in 1852 and passed out of existence in 1862 after the law founding the Department was signed. It numbered among its members many men of national prominence. Time after time it insisted that the Department be created because agricultural work in the Patent Office was inadequate and insufficient.

In 1859 an advisory Board of Agriculturists met at the request of the House Committee on Agriculture. After discussion it made a report recommending the creation of a Department of Agriculture with a Cabinet officer at the head. Though that recommendation became known, the report itself was suppressed.

In 1861 Caleb B. Smith, Lincoln's secretary of the interior, advocated the establishment of a Bureau of Agriculture and Statistics, to be located in his own department. Lincoln, in his first message to Congress, repeated this proposal almost verbatim, sandwiching it in between more important matters in a rather diffident and perfunctory way. But, since the Southern delegation was no longer there, Congress took heed.

When the bill reached the House committee, Charles B. Calvert and Owen Lovejoy, prominent in the United States Agricultural Society, and others sought to provide for an independent department, with a commissioner at the head—still a compromise proposal. The President did not object. Existing farm journals insisted on competent nonpolitical leadership, but politics had the upper hand. Indeed, supporters of Isaac Newton are said to have lobbied the bill so effectively that no one else had a chance to head the new department other than the incumbent superintendent of the Patent Office's Agricultural Division.

The law passed and was signed by President Lincoln on May 15, 1862. The Department had an independent bureau status with a commissioner at its head who did not sit in the President's Cabinet. That commissioner was, of course, Isaac Newton. On May 20 of the same year the Homestead Act was passed; and on July 2, 1862, the Land-Grant College Act, fathered by Justin Smith Morrill of Vermont, became law. The last act endowed the state agricultural colleges with public land almost double the area of Morrill's native state.

We now turn to the scientific work carried on by the Department of Agriculture from its creation until 1889, when its head was promoted to Cabinet rank and it became a full-fledged executive department.

CHAPTER 3

Early Research in the
Department of Agriculture

Isaac Newton had some admirers, among whom was that very important personage, Abraham Lincoln, who never turned against his friend; but Newton also had many enemies and detractors, some of whom called him illiterate as well as incompetent. Acrimonious discussion about him and his activities raged at times. He did lean towards nepotism in appointing his staff, and other abuses almost certainly existed. In 1867 President Johnson sought to remove Newton from office, but the Senate refused to confirm the appointment of his successor.

Meanwhile Newton died, in a sense in the service of science. It was he who selected the present site of the Department buildings as an experimental farm. This was at some distance from his office in the old Patent Office (now the United States Civil Service) building. In July, 1866, he heard an approaching thunderstorm as he sat in that office and remembered that some wheat samples which had been cut on the experimental farm had not been put in out of the rain. He rushed over a mile to attend to them, bustled about helping, and suffered sunstroke. He lingered for a year, dying in office on July 19, 1867.

Newton was a good Pennsylvania dairy farmer who had made sound political connections and knew how to use them. No New Deal or long-term plan had been formulated for the new department. Its creation was almost wholly casual. Public farm aid was not a national pulse-quickening subject in those days. Gentlemen farmers in the main led the agitation for the Department's establishment, a subject that farm journals themselves appeared to mention only perfunctorily.

Gentlemen farmers had few aims in common with ordinary dirt farmers. Agricultural educators ranged from enthusiasts for manual-labor schools to highly specialized chemists imbued with the minutiæ of Germanic laboratory techniques and the wonders these were expected to accomplish and reveal. Thus the Department was launched under political rather than scientific auspices and concerned itself largely with distributing exotic seed, losing the respect of scientists and farm journalists alike. No controls were lodged in the new department despite urgent need of food during the Civil War.

Regardless of such inauspicious beginnings, the Department became a great and useful public institution and a scientific research agency second to none, but that was mostly in the future. Yet, however careless of ethical considerations Newton sometimes was in his clerical appointments, his scientific appointments were uniformly of men who had good professional standing and ranked with the best of their day. For that and for the formulation of his objectives as the Department's head he deserves considerable credit.

As was indicated earlier Townend Glover became the first Department entomologist, and, it will be noted, the scientists were so called for some years yet—the entomologist, the chemist, the statistician, and so on. Only afterward did sections, divisions, and, considerably later, bureaus come into existence. That Glover was exceptional goes without saying. He was as near an all-around agricultural scientist as existed at the time.

The first Department chemist, Charles M. Wetherill, was quite as distinguished in his own line. He had graduated from the University of Pennsylvania and then had done postgraduate work under no less an authority than Liebig himself. He next engaged in research in his own private laboratory in Philadelphia. Wetherill was appointed Department of Agriculture chemist in 1862, but served for only a little more than a year because Newton became irritated with Lincoln for borrowing him for special service in the War Department. The second or third time he was borrowed for this purpose, Newton discharged him, whereupon Wetherill was called to the chair of chemistry at Lehigh University, serving there until his death.

Wetherill's name appears on the first scientific paper ever issued by the Department, a six-page leaflet entitled "Report on the Chemical Analysis of Grapes." Therein Wetherill contended that our grapes were quite as good for wine making as any to be found in Europe. He also contrived therein to appeal to Congress to give his chemical division sufficient money to enable it to render adequate service. Wetherill instituted a chemical study of sorghum, sorghum syrup, and sorghum sugar.

His immediate successor, Henri Erni, who served until 1866, carried on investigations on soils, fertilizers, sugar beets, and fermentation processes. Erni was a Swiss who had investigated alcoholic fermentation in a Zurich laboratory and who, later, was at various times a member of the staffs of Yale Scientific School, the University of Vermont, and Shelby Medical College at Nashville, Tennessee. He later became a patent examiner after leaving the Department of Agriculture.

The Department's third chemist, also appointed by Newton, served from 1866 until 1871. His name was Thomas Antisell, and he was born in Dublin, Ireland. He had studied in Paris and Berlin under men like Dumas and Berzelius, and had then been sentenced to exile for being a member of the Young Ireland party. He had come to the United States in 1848, where he served as a professor of chemistry, practiced medicine, became a federal surveyor, and was a surgeon in the Union Army during the Civil War. Thereafter he settled in Washington, became connected with Georgetown University, and, subsequently, chemist for the Department of Agriculture. He was also professor of chemistry at Maryland Agricultural College and later served the Japanese government for five years with great honors.

In the capacity of chemist for the Department he undertook investigations on marls, "green sands," phosphates, tanning materials, sweet potatoes, peanuts, and meat extracts and other foods. In his report for 1869 Antisell called attention to the extensive adulteration of fertilizers and feedstuffs and to the need for controlling the purity of these products by chemical means. The future regulatory activities of the Department in the food field were here foreshadowed.

After Antisell's resignation Ryland T. Brown assumed office, working mainly on cassina and the agricultural value of sewage, from 1871 to 1873, when William McMurtrie became chemist, serving until 1878. McMurtrie was New Jersey–born and had graduated as a mining engineer from Pardee Scientific School, Lafayette College. While at postgraduate work he was appointed assistant to Antisell, and he received his Ph.D. degree from Lafayette in 1875. He initiated investigations on cereals, insecticides, sugar corn, bat guano, and mildew and rot.

He was also at one time special agent for the Department, charged with the function of collecting information on the wine, oil, sugar, and silk industries. He finally became professor of chemistry at the University of Illinois. His *Report on the Culture of the Sugar Beet and the Manufacture of Sugar Therefrom*, published in 1880 in France and the United States, was outstanding. He also wrote valuable reports on sumac, wine grapes, raw silk, wool, and other animal fibers.

He was followed in office by Peter Collier, a native of New York and a Yale graduate, and for a while instructor and professor at Sheffield Scientific School under the famous Professor S. W. Johnson. In 1870 Collier had received the M.D. degree from the University of Vermont, and he was for a while head of the medical faculty there, a training that doubtless influenced the type of investigations he made in the Department. President Grant appointed him, in 1873, one of six scientists to attend the Vienna Exposition. In 1877 he became USDA chemist, his main duty being to investigate sorghum.

Collier also made wide investigations of various well and mineral waters, baking powders, tea and coffee substitutes, butter and oleomargarine, veterinary remedies, grasses, and numbers of other products employed or produced by agriculture. But his comprehensive 570-page work on sorghum for syrup, sugar, and fodder was most notable. After leaving the Department, Collier became director of the New York (Geneva) Agricultural Experiment Station, where he served until fatal illness overtook him in 1887. He was followed in office by Harvey Washington Wiley, whose career will be treated later.

Of course, only the first three of these chemists were appointed by Newton, but the three were all good men, and two of them were outstanding.

In his first annual report Newton declared that the farmer must be enabled "to make two blades of grass grow where one grew before," and he used the words in quotation marks. He invoked the spirit and method of science in aid of farmers. He declared that his Department would:

Test by experiment the use of agricultural implements and the value of seeds, soils, manures, and animals; undertake the chemical investigation of soils, grains, fruits, vegetables, and manures, publishing the results; promote botany and entomology and establish a library and a museum.

The Department's first botanist and gardener was Scottish-born William Saunders, who had started to prepare for the ministry, changed to horticulture, and studied in St. Andrews and Edinburgh, finally working in Kew Gardens. He came to the United States in 1844 as manager of the estates of Johns Hopkins in Baltimore. To say that he was distinguished would be an understatement. He was an exceptional man in his field.

He did notable work in designing parks and setting out trees. He laid out the park system of Washington, D. C., and supervised the planting of 80,000 trees in the city. He introduced seedless or navel oranges from Brazil and got them started here; he first imported camphor trees and had them planted in the South; and he was a founder of the Patrons of Husbandry or the Grange. He served the Department faithfully and well until his death in 1890.

Newton first appointed to the post of statistician Lewis Bollman, a farmer, college teacher, and journalist, who did not remain long with the Department. He was succeeded by Jacob R. Dodge, also a journalist, who entered the Department as a clerk in 1863, began to edit the statistical reports, and succeeded Bollman as statistician in 1867. His varied crop and other statistical reports were outstanding; his reputation became national, then international, and he frequently attended meetings in foreign countries. He remained with the Department until his retirement in 1893, though he spent the period from the summer of 1879 until the summer of 1883 superintending compilation of agricultural statistics for the Tenth Census. He died in Massachusetts nearly a decade after his resignation, and was certainly pre-eminent in his field.

The earliest bound volume of Department publications in the Department library begins with a circular by the Commissioner himself on the "Present Agricultural, Mineral, and Manufacturing Resources of the United States." It is followed by a "Catalogue of Plants, Bulbs, Tubers, Etc. for Distribution from the U. S. Propagating Garden," by William Saunders. Then comes the pamphlet mentioned earlier on the analysis of grapes by Charles M. Wetherill.

Early in Newton's administration meteorological data supplied by Joseph Henry of the Smithsonian Institution began to appear in the annual book issued by the Department of Agriculture. Publication of weather material of this sort continued until the work in meteorology was transferred to the Army Signal Corps in 1870.

Agricultural information appeared to flow into the Department from hundreds of voluntary correspondents and crop reporters. Seed distribution flourished, but Newton contended that facilities must be provided for experimentation and laboratory work. The half-dozen rooms occupied by the Department in the basement of the Patent Office overflowed.

Reservation No. 2, originally intended for the Department's experimental grounds, was used by the army as a cattle yard. However, Newton finally got hold of it, started experiments on it, and also planned and almost completed the Department's original Old Red Brick Building, which was finally occupied a year after his death.

The early publications were chiefly in the form of scientific reports and the annual, later monthly, reports. Distribution of the latter, however, was effected politically, and many who really deserved and could have used copies did not get them. In time scientific bulletins began to be issued from the various semi-autonomous sections and divisions of the Department, later by the bureaus, finally by the Department as a whole again.

Before Newton died, he had a force of laborers clearing the reservation for the experimental plots, and soon sixty-seven varieties of potatoes and of spring wheat and fifty-five of fall wheat were under test there. The Commissioner also managed to rent two rooms near his office to house part of his personnel overflow. Townend Glover was sent to an international entomological exhibit in Paris at a cost of only $500. William Saunders began tests with oranges, tea, coffee, silk, figs, olives, cinchona, various fruits and nuts, suitable grasses, new cultural methods—even reforestation and land reclamation.

Newton's successor, Horace Capron, was very well qualified. Upon resigning as commissioner, he went as special agricultural adviser to the Japanese government, and is said to have revolutionized farming in Japan. Under him experiments continued in the effort to find new and better plant varieties and to improve cultural methods. Yet scant efforts were made to enable farmers better to adjust to advancing technology and to great changes that were taking place in marketing methods.

Capron manifested great interest in steam plowing. It was stated in Department reports that a single steam plow would do the work of twenty horses and would drastically cut both production costs and labor requirements. Capron also remarked that the Department's seed establishment had grown "into a sort of fungus, of little value in itself, while it absorbs largely the nutriment required to sustain the vital functions of the department." On January 13, 1868, the Department of Agriculture had forty-seven employees, including a statistician, an entomologist, a chemist and assistant chemist, and the superintendent of the experimental garden.

The annual book issued at this time contained discussions of citrus fruits, China grass, water use, the necessity for crop diversification, silk culture, practical entomology, and fish culture, as well as state agricultural reports and reviews of agricultural books. During Capron's term the setting up of Divisions of Botany and Entomology was announced, while the experimental plots were landscaped to form the Department building's grounds, and the experiments were moved elsewhere.

The third commissioner, Frederick Watts, who assumed office in the middle of 1871, served for about six years, but he was seventy years of age when he was appointed. His primary interest was railroading, and he permitted Department work rather to slide along as best it might under the supervision of his son, who, in turn, delegated his responsibility to the chief clerk. Watts practiced picayune economy but had a little interest in farm buildings. He did establish the Division of Microscopy under that unusual and rather notable character, Thomas Taylor. Taylor was Scottish born, studied science at Glasgow University, and came to the United States during the Civil War, where he experimented with projectiles and took an M.D. degree at Georgetown University, later practicing medicine out of hours while working for the government. Taylor proved to be a remarkable scientist for his day. He investigated and made interesting discoveries about cranberry rot, mushroom culture, grape mildew, peach yellows, and plum diseases, and in every instance gave growers assistance which benefited them financially.

Later Taylor discovered how to recognize certain fats microscopically in mixtures of fats, oils, and waxes. Soon he could detect adulterated butter and lard. His work continued until July 1, 1895, when the Division of Microscopy was dispersed, the work on food adulteration going to the Division of Chemistry, where Dr. Wiley took it over. The work on fungi then went to the Division of Vegetable Pathology and that on fibers to the Office of Fiber Investigation.

In Watts's term, however, the divisions other than Microscopy were: Chemistry, Horticulture, Entomology, Statistics, Seeds, and Botany. Watts was annoyed because private individuals wanted the Department chemist to test mine ore samples, wines, and patent medicines for them, and even to issue certificates of merit. Since there had been loud complaints about frauds in commercial fertilizers, chemist McMurtrie was instructed to devote his time instead to analyzing them and preparing the results for publication.

On July 1, 1877, William G. Le Duc was appointed commissioner of agriculture. As commissioner he established a tea farm and manifested considerable interest in sugar beets, sorghum, and animal diseases. He also promoted work in irrigation. He was strong, fearless, capable, and progressive. Le Duc deplored the small appropriations received by the Department. Increasing spread of animal diseases, particularly of contagious pleuropneumonia, turned his attention strongly to methods of control. In 1878 Congress appropriated the sum of $10,000 to meet this need, and a veterinarian was engaged to study the diseases of hogs and other domestic animals. Then in 1879 a Veterinary Division was established.

Congress also increased the appropriations for study of the history and habits of insects. Dr. Franklin B. Hough was appointed forest commissioner, and the first formal work in forestry was undertaken.

Meanwhile the Division of Chemistry needed more space, more equipment, and better pay for its staff. The chemist had received only $1,900 of his annual salary of $2,000 and his assistant only $1,400 of his $1,600 because of deficient appropriations. Le Duc thought even the full salaries inadequate.

During this time chemists McMurtrie and Collier engaged in some interesting and revealing work. For one thing the Washington City Health Department had called on them to analyze cream puffs and coffee suspected of being poisoned, and tea and bologna suspected of adulteration. The chemists also examined certain coffee and tea substitutes, as well as a tonic called "Boneset," some baking powders, and some samples of butter and oleomargarine. Peter Collier worked co-operatively with the botanist on forage grasses.

In 1880 Collier's report covered 147 closely printed pages with 14 large graphs in color folded in. Le Duc stated that the Division of Chemistry was then "confined to a room in the present building, 20 feet square, with two basement rooms of the same size, and a small closet." We shall hear more about this basement crowding later. It came to a crisis in the administration of Secretary Rusk when the chemists were finally moved to other quarters.

Commissioner Le Duc, however, felt that this "national laboratory of a great people" should immediately have better facilities. Before he left office, the chemist had eleven assistants, mostly young graduates of chemical schools there to complete their education. The chemist was making analyses of stock feeds, veterinary remedies, and magic metal polish, publishing the results with the full names of the makers and their label claims.

This quotation from the annual report of Le Duc for 1880 is also revealing:

We have had frequent communications respecting the adulteration of foods, in respect of which our correspondents err in presuming that the remedy therefor lies with this de-

31

partment. Inquiries are made whether, if there be no more ready remedy, it is not within the power of Congress to pass a stringent law making it a crime to manufacture spurious articles or to adulterate genuine ones. Admitting the subject to be one of great and universal interest, we have only been able to say to our correspondents, that under the present standard of commercial morality, nothing is safe from adulteration; that the action of the general government is limited to imported articles, and chiefly to drugs; that the power of the government ceases with the custom-house; and that the general regulation of the subject is left to the several States, in most of which there are laws designed to remedy the evil, which, however, can only be done effectually by a rigid system of inspection. Merely prohibitory laws are of little value against human ingenuity and cupidity.

Naturally this subject will require more extended discussion when the career of Harvey W. Wiley is examined. Even at this early date, however, the public was not satisfied with state regulation in this field, and federal intervention was demanded. New methods of food processing, preservation, and transportation provided new opportunities for misbranding, fraud, and adulteration.

George B. Loring, the next commissioner of agriculture, had been educated as a physician, later devoting himself to politics and agriculture. His appointment followed his defeat for re-election to the House in 1880. He served from the middle of 1881 until the spring of 1885. During his term of office the Bureau of Animal Industry had to be created by act of Congress because state control of contagious pleuropneumonia proved so inadequate that the entire cattle industry appeared doomed.

In 1883 a study of butter and its adulteration led to the observation that this investigation was "to aid the dairy interest in establishing a standard of good butter and to protect consumers against fraud," the first hint that this industry was expecting aid from the Department. It is notable that Harvey W. Wiley came to the Department as an assistant chemist in 1883 and became the chemist and head of the Division of Chemistry soon afterward.

Loring had a habit of referring to his various divisions—and

The Department's personnel about 1887

Maj. H. A. Meyers, William Saunders, Col. E. M. Whitaker, Maj. G. B. Newton, Commissioner of Agriculture Isaac Newton, W. E. Gardiner, J. R. Dodge, Thomas Antisell, Isaac Newton, Jr., Townend Glover

Secretary Tama Jim Wilson, who built natural science into the U.S.D.A., and his bureau chiefs, about 1911–12

Top row: C. C. Clark, Carl L. Alsberg, L. W. Page, A. Zappone, Victor H. Olmstead, C. B. Lower
Middle row: W. P. Jones, L. O. Howard, H. W. Henshaw, A. C. True, A. D. Melvin, B. T. Galloway
Bottom row: Henry Graves, Milton Whitney, Asst. Sec'y Willet M. Hayes, Secretary Wilson, Willis L. Moore, Joseph A. Arnold   *U.S.D.A. photographs*

some of them were scarcely large enough to justify the bureaucratic term—as "bureaus," though this they did not become in any case until the administration of "Tama" Jim Wilson as secretary, beginning in 1897. In Loring's time Congress made a special appropriation of $15,000 for an investigation of silk culture.

This brings us to the last Commissioner and the first Secretary of Agriculture, the Missouri farm-journal publisher, Norman J. Colman. He was actually appointed to the office because of his broad knowledge of agriculture, and he was certainly the most competent individual so far to head the Department. He was largely instrumental in effecting passage of the Hatch Act, providing federal aid to the state experiment stations and resulting in the creation of the Office of Experiment Stations in the Department. Colman also agitated for passage of the bill to give the Department's head a seat in the Cabinet; it was passed in 1889 and he became secretary for twenty-one days.

It should be said here that the Department's policy of making two blades of grass grow where one grew before, while eminently successful, did not suffice to solve farmers' problems. Indeed, as early as 1890, with the frontier gone, agricultural overproduction became a threat. Yet the Department's sole remedy was to evolve scientific methods which further increased production or else decreased the per-unit cost of production.

Farmers intensified their efforts, followed instructions, made their land yield just as much as possible, yet did not always prosper. Scientifically approved cultural practices, the prevention of crop and animal damage by insects and disease, the selection of better varieties, strains, and breeds, all were important yet insufficient. With the frontier closed it was also impossible to move on to richer land beyond the horizon. That is why the social sciences soon began to infiltrate the Department, getting their start in its scientific agencies.

CHAPTER 4

A Few Connecting Links

Before we move on to a consideration of Department accomplishments in the different fields of science from 1880 on we should briefly examine the careers of the secretaries of agriculture and then look into two or three problems which early occupied the attention of the Department's staff and see what became of them.

The first secretary of agriculture by appointment, Jeremiah M. Rusk, served from March, 1889, until March, 1893. His administration was marked by the eradication from this country of the destructive cattle disease, contagious pleuropneumonia. It was he also who, fearful of the noxious fumes and frequent explosions contrived by the chemists in the basement beneath him, got them out of there into a remodeled residence. They had at times caused the Commissioner of Agriculture to rush outdoors with his guests to get a breath of air, while at least once they had blown the Commissioner clear out of his chair.

During Rusk's administration the first meat-inspection legislation was passed, the importance of publicity was recognized, contacts with the press were established, and Farmers' Bulletins began to appear, because the Secretary was determined that scientific knowledge should be so popularized that the public could profit most from it. Rusk also reorganized the Department and placed its scientific work under an assistant secretary provided by Congress.

Rusk's successor was J. Sterling Morton, who served from March, 1893, until March, 1897. He was a man of strong and independent views and extremely economical. He had a passion for planting trees and was the father of Arbor Day. He fought free seed distribution unsuccessfully, established a Division of Publications, reorganized the Division of Statistics, and established a Division of Agrostology to study forage plants. During his term also a Division of Soils was established in the Weather Bureau, a Dairy Division in the Bureau of Animal Industry, and an Office of Road Inquiry became an independent unit.

James (Tama Jim) Wilson of Iowa took over in March, 1897, and served as secretary of agriculture until March, 1913. It was he who drew together numerous autonomous sections and divisions and formed the first bureaus in the Department. He also enormously increased the Department's staff of scientific workers and really put scientific research on the map. He made the Department a notable research institution.

Wilson's successor, the World War I secretary of agriculture, David F. Houston, served from March, 1913, until February, 1920. Much of his agricultural thinking was far in advance of his time, but the war deflected him from many accomplishments he would otherwise have made. However, he did so reorganize the Department that it could cope with the rising economic and social problems it had too long ignored or given scant attention. He also fostered study of rural credit and agricultural marketing facilities.

His dynamics carried over into the administrations of Edwin T. Meredith (February, 1920–March, 1921), Henry C. Wallace (March, 1921–October, 1924), and Howard M. Gore (November, 1924–March, 1925). Increasing attention was given right along to the farmer's economic and social problems. The administrations of William M. Jardine (March, 1925–March, 1929) and Arthur M. Hyde (March, 1929–March, 1933) constituted a period of consolidation and reorganization, also an effort to use scientific research as a method of producing agricultural commodities of higher quality which would bring price premiums, and to combat the idea that such research necessarily resulted in market gluts and overproduction.

This brings us to the administrations of Henry A. Wallace (March, 1933–September, 1940) and Claude R. Wickard (September, 1940–June 30, 1945), as well as that of the present incumbent, Clinton P. Anderson, which began July 1, 1945. These are sufficiently recent not to need exposition here.

It seems appropriate here also hastily to review certain organizational changes in the scientific agencies. In 1889, when the head of the Department assumed his seat in the Cabinet, his agency consisted of the following: Divisions or Sections of Statistics, Entomology, Chemistry, Silk Culture, Botany, Vegetable Pathology, Economic Ornithology and Mammalogy, Microscopy, Forestry, Gardens, Grounds and Horticulture, and Pomology; also the Office of Experiment Stations and the Bureau of Animal Industry. The Weather Bureau became part of the Department in 1891, when this work was transferred to it from the War Department.

In 1898, when James Wilson was secretary, the Department's scientific agencies were: Bureau of Animal Industry, Office of Experiment Stations, Weather Bureau, Division of Gardens and Grounds, Division of Chemistry, Division of Entomology, Division of Statistics, Division of Botany, Division of Forestry, Biological Survey, Division of Pomology, Office of Fiber Investigations, Division of Vegetable Physiology and Pathology, Office of Road Inquiry, Division of Agrostology, and the Division of Soils.

In 1901 the Bureaus of Chemistry, Soils, Forestry, and Plant Industry were created, the last by consolidating several smaller agencies in somewhat the same line of work. The Division of Entomology became the Bureau of Entomology in 1904, and the Division of Biological Survey attained bureau status two years later. The Bureau of Public Roads was established in 1918, the Bureau of Home Economics in 1923, and the Bureau of Dairying (name later changed to Bureau of Dairy Industry) in 1924. The Bureau of Agricultural Engineering became a separate agency in 1931.

In 1927 regulatory work was separated from research in the Bureau of Chemistry. The former was placed in the Food, Drug, and Insecticide Administration (later Food and Drug Administration), and the latter was combined with the Bureau of Soils to become the Bureau of Chemistry and Soils. At the same time the Federal Horticultural Board became a separate administrative unit known as the Plant Quarantine and Control Administration, which, in 1934, was combined with the Bureau of Entomology, to become the Bureau of Entomology and Plant Quarantine.

A worthy successor to Tama Jim Wilson, who built the biological and physical sciences into an integral part of the structure of the Department, was Henry A. Wallace, who served as secretary from March 4, 1933, until September 4, 1940. He greatly expanded and modernized the Department's scientific agencies and redirected a great deal of effort toward basic research. He also converted the *Yearbook of Agriculture* into a cyclopedic compendium of information on a specific scientific subject each year, a basic anthology written by a large group of experts inside and outside the Department.

Himself a gifted research worker, he furthered in every possible way the development of fundamental scientific investigations in the field of so-called pure science, without in any way neglecting practical projects in the field of applied science. This was most fortunate, as, without continual progress in the former, irrespective of immediate applications or strict monetary values, progress in applied science soon languishes. The Department owes much to the impetus Wallace gave in this direction, a trend likewise promoted by his successors.

In 1938 the Bureau of Agricultural Engineering was combined with part of the Bureau of Chemistry and Soils, the unit being designated as the Bureau of Agricultural Chemistry and Engineering. In February, 1943, all nutrition work was transferred from the Bureau of Agricultural Chemistry and Engineering to the Bureau of Home Economics. At the same time the agricultural engineering work and work on weed eradication and effluent contaminants went to the Bureau of Plant Industry. The names of the affected bureaus then became: Bureau of Agricultural and Industrial Chemistry, Bureau of Human Nutrition and Home Economics, and Bureau of Plant Industry, Soils, and Agricultural Engineering.

Meanwhile, the Agricultural Research Administration was created by Executive Order on February 23, 1942, taking supervision over all Department research work except that in Forest Service, Soil Conservation Service, and the Bureau of Agricultural Economics.

The Bankhead-Jones Act of 1935 provided for scientific, technical, economic, and other research into laws and principles underlying basic agricultural problems in their broadest aspects. It called also for research to improve the quality of agricultural products, to develop new and improved methods for their production and distribution to discover new uses for farm products and by-products and materials manufactured therefrom, and to study the conservation, development, and the use of land and water resources for agricultural purposes. Nine laboratories, which co-operate closely with certain states or with groups of states, have been established under this act:

A vegetable breeding laboratory at Charleston, South Carolina.

A pasture-improvement laboratory at State College, Pennsylvania.

A laboratory working on soybean breeding for industrial use at Urbana, Illinois.

A swine-improvement laboratory at Ames, Iowa.

A range-sheep–breeding laboratory at Dubois, Idaho.

A laboratory working on the communicable diseases of domestic animals at Auburn, Alabama.

A laboratory seeking to improve poultry viability at East Lansing, Michigan.

A laboratory investigating the relationship between the salinity of irrigation waters and plant growth at Riverside, California.

A laboratory studying nutrition from soil to plant, to animal, to human being at Ithaca, New York.

The Agricultural Adjustment Act of 1938 provided for the establishment of four large regional research laboratories for fundamental research in the utilization of farm products and by-products. These laboratories are located at Peoria, Illinois, New Orleans, Louisiana, Wyndmoore, Pennsylvania, and Albany, California. Their primary job is to bring chemical and engineering research into joint play to develop new uses for or to expand existing uses of agricultural products. They now essentially constitute the Bureau of Agricultural and Industrial Chemistry.

The agricultural Research and Marketing Act of 1946, which became law on August 14, 1946, authorized very generously increased appropriations for additional research into the basic laws and principles relating to agriculture, and to improve and facilitate the marketing and distribution of agricultural products. One of its basic objectives was "to assure agriculture a position in research equal to that of industry."

Basic agricultural research already carried out under various grants of Congress was thus greatly expanded in scope. The Bankhead-Jones Act of 1935 was broadened. As far as possible the research must be carried on in already existing federal and state laboratories, the state experiment stations securing considerable benefits as well as the Department, but co-operative research with other institutions was also provided. Investigation was authorized of and on production methods, human nutrition problems, new and useful crops, expanded use of farm products, and the conservation and development of land, forest, and water resources for agricultural purposes.

Finally, before we go ahead to consider the Department's research achievements in the different scientific categories, it may be worth while to pick up two or three problems which agitated the Department or Patent Office staff in early days and see what became of them. For instance, the ravages of the Hessian fly agitated Henry L. Ellsworth, and he thought something should be done about it. Something finally was.

However, the accomplishment took nearly forty years, and the list of federal and state investigators who contributed materially to the progress of the investigations is too long to insert here. The fly has been the most injurious insect enemy of our wheat since Revolutionary times and in single rather recent years has caused losses in yields of winter wheat amounting to at least a hundred million dollars.

From 1904 through 1942 many state experiment-station and Department entomologists conducted co-operative time-of-sowing experiments in our principal wheat-growing states. It was found that delaying the seeding of winter wheat sufficiently to avoid the fall egg-laying period of the Hessian fly would prevent or reduce spring infestations. Farmers now have ready access to bulletins which tell them just when to plant wherever they may be located. The dates are approximate and subject to correction for local weather and other conditions.

But the plan works. The recommendations are generally observed throughout the winter-wheat–growing region, particularly in years of high infestation hazard. The investigation was successful and has been closed.

Next we shall look into the long-popular idea that we could produce our own silk. This bewitched many American farmers, but the tale ended differently from that of the Hessian fly.

In 1865, Townend Glover carefully brought some silkworms back from that convention of entomologists he attended in Paris. In 1884 Congress made the appropriation of $15,000 for the promotion of silk culture. With that money silkworms and mulberry trees were distributed. The main objective of these investigations was to reduce the cost of silk production sufficiently to make the industry commercially feasible in the United States. The principal problem was to find a machine that could be used to reel silk from cocoons, a problem only now approaching solution.

Boys raised batches of silkworms as adjuncts to the Department's silk-culture project. Some of them devoted whole summers to collecting mulberry leaves to feed the worms. Many of them were quite abashed when they received checks for sums in the neighborhood of 90 cents to repay them for their summer's work! But around 1891 the work terminated, though it was undertaken again in 1902.

It was then shown that, with reasonable care, silkworm cocoons could be produced almost anywhere in the United States. Mulberry trees also grew well almost anywhere in the country. But the costs of raising the cocoons and reeling the raw silk remained so prohibitive that we could not compete with the Far East. Therefore, distribution of mulberry cuttings and silkworm eggs was discontinued, and the project was terminated. By 1908 the Department had neither funds nor authorization to continue it.

However when ill feeling developed towards Japan in the late nineteen thirties and Japanese products began to be boycotted, many Americans again thought we could make our own silk, and they appealed to the Department of Agriculture in all confidence, just as they have for many years, to assist them. It became necessary for the Chief of the Bureau of Entomology and Plant Quarantine to issue a mimeographed letter to all and sundry explaining that silk production simply was not economically practicable in this country.

In this letter, dated August 19, 1941, the silk project was reviewed. It was explained how appropriations for it had been discontinued thirty-three years earlier and that bulletins and reports hitherto issued on the subject were out of print. No information could be sent out. This project might be regarded as a failure, but remember that carefully ascertained negative findings have distinct value, even monetary value. For, if heeded, they will prevent people from losing their money unnecessarily. Furthermore, the American public was long interested in this project and induced Congress to support it.

Finally let us consider the sugar-from-cornstalks project about which there was much talk earlier. It will be remembered that Henry L. Ellsworth was impressed with the idea and declared that one thousand pounds of good table sugar per acre had been produced from cornstalks in Delaware by the simple expedient of not permitting the ears to ripen. He returned to this subject repeatedly, yet nothing eventually came of the project. Was it wholly absurd? By no means.

Great Britain abolished slavery in 1838, its colonial cane-sugar production declined, and the world seemed to face a sugar famine. Just a little later than this the French botanist Pallas announced that if undeveloped ears of corn were removed from the stalk before maturing, the quantity of sugar in the stalks multiplied several times over. When Ellsworth was commissioner of patents from 1836 until 1844, it was only intelligent that he should call attention to this matter and seek to follow the lead.

Naturally Americans felt that the United States should, in this ominous situation, begin to produce its own sugar. What was more natural than to fall back on a native plant, Indian corn, or a plant related to it? Therefore, the Patent Office began to investigate the matter and reported initial success. Then in 1850 "Chinese sugar cane," or sorgo, was introduced in France. In 1854 the Patent Office, well on the alert, had seeds brought from Paris, and the sorghum project began to submerge the cornstalk-sugar project.

Sorgo became a craze. Plots of it were grown all over the country wherever it would thrive. Samples of the cane and juice were analyzed by many well-known chemists, including those of the Patent Office. For instance, in 1856, C. T. Jackson of Boston made an extensive report on sorgo to the Patent Office. He, incidentally, was one of the discoverers of the anesthetic properties of ether. In 1858 about a hundred thousand acres of sorgo were planted. Antisell, McMurtrie, Collier, and Wiley all worked on the plant.

It was Peter Collier who, in 1881, however, conducted the Department's first extensive work on cornstalk sugar, for the trend had again turned in that direction after the initial sorgo craze. This sugar was exhibited at the St. Louis Exposition in 1903. But the low purity of cornstalk juice became the main obstacle to economical production.

When Harvey W. Wiley took over Collier's work, he reverted to sorgo. (He also did masterful work on sugar beets to be described later.) He had sixty acres of sorgo planted near Eckington, which is now part of Washington, D. C. This was probably the greatest crop of sugar-producing plants ever raised in the District of Columbia. Yet we should remember that, in 1839, the District of Columbia had produced more rye than Wisconsin, more hay than Mississippi, more tobacco than South Carolina and Wisconsin combined, and the value of its orchard and market-garden produce was three times that of Florida! Times do change.

Still the cornstalk-sugar project lagged. Then in 1912 the Department again began work on it. Crystalline sugar was obtained, but the process simply was infeasible commercially. The outstanding patent for processing maize to make sugar was taken out by F. L. Stewart in 1906. It resembled the process for making sorgo sugar and there was an average of 12 per cent sugar in the cornstalks used. Sirup of satisfactory cooking quality was also made.

The final Department publication on the subject was entitled "Preliminary Report on Sugar Production from Maize," by C. F. Clerk, an agronomist in the Bureau of Plant Industry. The work was carried out under the supervision of William A. Orton, a great Department scientist whose work will be discussed at length later. Thus ended the chapter, but again negative results proved valuable and the problem was solved: Scientifically possible but commercially impractical was the answer.

Before we turn to the interesting and extraordinary discoveries made by Department scientists in various fields of endeavor, a further word should be said about research in general. Originally, of course, research was the work of gifted amateurs, usually of independent means, who adopted science as their vocation or avocation. The practice of paying scientists salaries to perform research was just beginning about the time the Department of Agriculture got under way in embryo in the old Patent Office. But the payment was almost always made by state agencies or academic institutions, because paid industrial research workers were not yet in fashion.

Therefore, when the Department was created, it was natural for it to hire a chemist, an entomologist, a botanist, a statistician, and an expert gardener to do research on salary. For many years the book containing the Department's annual reports contained likewise a report from The Chemist, The Entomologist, The Botanist, and so on. This also was the day of lone wolves, and that lasted well into the beginning of the next century. It was definitely known that this or that scientific worker had, as an individual, discovered this or that. The credit was all his.

If there was a scientific team, he was the head of it, suggested all the worthwhile ideas, signed all the papers, and took all the credit. Later science became very much more complex, a dozen, then a score or more different kinds of chemistry alone became compartmentalized, and groups of scientists, sometimes trained in quite different sciences, began to work together and to solve problems as teams. It therefore became increasingly difficult to apportion the credit or to identify the individual who had made the specific discovery.

As time passed, Department agencies, first sections or divisions, then bureaus, had to be organized. Soon it became apparent that two or more sciences might become necessary for the solution of a problem, and specialists from several different scientific disciplines might team together. In time, also, some sciences that had once been looked upon as distinctive specialties finally became tools used by scientists of every kind. This proved true of statistics; it also proved true of microscopy.

In 1870, when Thomas Taylor came into the Department, microscopy was regarded as a separate science like chemistry or botany. Hired originally to study rusts, mildew, molds, and various fruit and vegetable diseases with the microscope, Taylor ulti-

43

mately branched out into widespread fields. Soon he was studying oleomargarine, butter, Demarara sugar, edible and nonedible mushrooms, and a sulfuric acid treatment which he found to heighten the germinating power of seeds. Then he turned to food adulterants; he also had a look at swine trichinæ.

The passage of the Oleomargarine Act in 1884 led him to perfect tests for the detection of butterfat substitutes, such as cottonseed oil, benne oil, and "ground-nut" oil, and he issued a bulletin on the subject. By 1888 he had turned his attention to foodstuffs in general, including spices, condiments, and tea; and, in 1890, he reported on the tensile strength of vegetable fibers. Obviously he was showing that microscopy was an adjunct to scientific studies in many fields rather than a separate science itself.

In his annual report the Secretary remarked in 1893 that Taylor's work should be assigned elsewhere. In 1895 the report remarked that there were now microscopes in all laboratories and that a Division of Microscopy was an anachronism. If all who used microscopes were microscopists, then the Department had about five hundred of them in addition to Taylor. Thus it was that Taylor's work was dispersed after he had introduced the use of the microscope throughout the Department.

In time also less emphasis began to be paid to the particular science in which an expert was trained. Emphasis was placed upon the problem, the project, the objective. It was placed upon broad lines of work, each specialist helping where and as needed. However, we shall for convenience use certain broad categorical heads for the following chapters in which the accomplishments of Department scientists in various fields will be discussed.

PART II : ACHIEVEMENTS

CHAPTER 5

Test Tube Magic

As was indicated earlier, the Department of Agriculture had "a chemist" in 1883, when Harvey W. Wiley succeeded Peter Collier. In 1884 Wiley became chief of the newly organized Division of Chemistry, which, in 1901, became the Bureau of Chemistry with Wiley still at its head. Wiley was an extraordinary character, a scientist-publicist-statesman all combined. He was in many respects a great man, as great in personality as in stature. Naturally his bureau assumed the coloration of his character, and for years it had a sort of independent personality of its own.

Because Wiley was early interested in misbranded and adulterated food and because he had the force of character to influence others, the work of enforcing the first Food and Drug Act (1906) naturally found place in his bureau, which doubled in size to accommodate the job. No one protested more when, in 1927, the regulatory work was split from research in the old Bureau of Chemistry, than Wiley himself, though he had resigned as the bureau chief fifteen years earlier.

This was a necessary administrative action. At this time the Food, Drug, and Insecticide (later just Food and Drug) Administration and the Bureau of Chemistry and Soils were organized. In 1938 all research work on soils was transferred to the Bureau of Plant Industry, while soil reclamation and maintenance work went to the Soil Conservation Service. The Bureau of Agricultural Engineering was then combined with what was left of Wiley's old bureau, and it became the Bureau of Agricultural Chemistry and Engineering.

On February 21, 1943, the Division of Protein and Nutrition Research was transferred from this bureau to the newly renamed

45

Bureau of Human Nutrition and Home Economics. Two days later the agricultural engineering research and research on effluent contaminants was transferred to the newly organized Bureau of Plant Industry, Soils, and Agricultural Engineering. Then the Bureau of Agricultural Chemistry and Engineering became the present Bureau of Agricultural and Industrial Chemistry, its essential subdivisions being the aforementioned four regional research laboratories. Certainly Wiley would be hard put to it to recognize his old bureau today, but the changes were necessary nonetheless.

Wiley was born on October 18, 1844, and died in 1930. During the Civil War he was a corporal in the Union Army. He attained degrees in both chemistry and medicine, and from 1874 to 1883 he taught chemistry at Purdue University and was also state chemist for Indiana. In 1883 bland Commissioner Loring, who also had been educated as a physician, made him Department chemist.

He is best known to the general public—and at one time he was in the newspapers every day—as the father of the first Food and Drug Law, which was finally passed largely as a result of his inexhaustible pertinacity. In addition, he was the author of several volumes on chemistry, of some 60 government bulletins published from his own bureau, and of at least 225 scientific papers. Finally, he has been called the father of the beet-sugar industry in the United States by reason of his comprehensive and definitive work on the influence of environment upon the composition of the sugar beet.

Wiley was a big, hulking fellow, some said homely, but always most interesting in appearance and personality. As I remember him from 1910 on, the year in which I became an underling assistant chemist in the old Bureau of Chemistry, Wiley's face was ever interesting and usually quite genial. He was lively, vivacious, and had an enchanting sense of humor. He made news almost unconsciously. He could hardly say that it was a clear day without getting into the headlines. He was also a great fighter; he gave no quarter and he expected none. When he resigned, we filed through his office and wept. It seemed impossible that his old bureau could exist without him on the bridge.

It was about 1885 that Wiley began to pour forth publications which rose to a flood of far-reaching influence and importance. Many of these were veritable classics. They were widely used in colleges and universities, and students of chemistry met them early in their careers. The bulletins described methods for the analysis of food, drug, and agricultural products and were the guidebooks in every laboratory in the country which engaged in such work. They represented pioneering on Wiley's part, the actual creation of methods where none existed before.

Finally, this work on foods and food adulterants appeared in ten parts, published at intervals between the beginning of the work and 1902. The publications were in such great demand that they often became unobtainable. They appeared in days when the grossest sort of adulterants commonly were found in foods and drugs. It was almost wholly as a result of disclosures made by Wiley that the so-called Pure Food Bill attracted the favorable attention of President Theodore Roosevelt and was passed in 1906.

Although food and drug research will be treated in a later chapter, it is pertinent here that Wiley's work gave impetus to the examination of foods and drugs by other investigators. It formed the technical foundation for the later evolution of more refined methods of analysis. Yet Wiley had time also not only to work on beet sugar but in addition to perform the necessary research and issue a publication on the manufacture of industrial alcohol from agricultural commodities. This appeared in 1910, in the expectation that tax-free denatured alcohol could be made on farms and in rural communities by many small plants. While these expectations were not realized, the basic idea was sound and the method well worked out.

Also famous was Dr. Wiley's "Poison Squad," a group of employees of his bureau who ate their meals at their place of business for many months in order to find out whether common food preservatives ordinarily used in the processing of commercial foods were harmful to human beings. The slogan of the squad was: "Only the brave can eat the fare." Dr. Fred C. Weber was in charge of this squad, and William Carter, a Negro who came in as its waiter, stayed on to complete a course in pharmacy and to become a faithful employee of the Food and Drug Administration.

While the results of this experiment indicated that the preservatives then used in the commercial processing of foods were not harmful to human beings, Wiley could not accept this point of view. A furious controversy arose—controversy and Wiley constantly kept company—so a special board under the chairmanship of President Ira Remsen of Johns Hopkins University had to be appointed to adjudicate. The board upheld the results of the test as recorded. Possibly the most notable result of this experiment was the impetus it gave to similar and better controlled nutrition work of the kind.

Wiley's study on beets clearly pointed out the sections of this country in which sugar beets could be grown commercially. Though published in 1901, its results still stand. Wiley studied the effects of latitude, altitude, sunshine, rainfall, and other environmental factors on the growth and sugar content of the beets. Before his work, efforts to grow sugar beets here had been sporadic and ill planned. It was he who showed that producing beet sugar could become a commercially successful industry in the United States.

Wiley's work, as broad in scope as his own magnificent personality, and systematically carried out over the period from 1883 until 1912 in a wide variety of localities and on many subjects, put an end to speculation and placed a solid foundation upon which others might build. The basic facts he discovered and the general conclusions he drew from his data still are valid. Nor did he leave the sugar-beet work until he had greatly improved the process of extracting sugar from beets and stimulated improvement also in cane-milling methods.

Certainly Wiley, who, more than forty years ago, wrote: "Chemistry has done much to promote the progress of agriculture in the line of chemical technology" and who declared it would do a great deal more in the future, justified Isaac Newton's faith in what this science could perform for the American public. He also built a great research institution behind him, which down through the years has likewise justified his faith in it and in the science of chemistry.

Dr. Carl L. Alsberg, who succeeded Wiley, was a firm believer in the value of fundamental chemical research to the agricultural industry. He surrounded himself with scientists of outstanding

Staff of Division of Chemistry, 1883–84. Dr. Wiley is third from the right

Dr. Harvey W. Wiley, "father of the Pure Food Law," in a laboratory of the old Bureau of Chemistry, about 1900

ability. Dr. Frederick Belding Power, long director of the Wellcome Research Laboratory of London and already an internationally known phytochemist, was one of them. He proved the effectiveness of chaulmoogra oil in the treatment of leprosy. In the Bureau of Chemistry he and his colleague, V. K. Chesnut, made important contributions on the odorous constituents of fruits and plants. In doing so, they identified the chemical which, given off by the cotton plant, attracts the boll weevil.

Dr. Claude Silbert Hudson (to whom the writer was a humble and blundering assistant) did important work during the same time on methods of preparing pure sugars and rare carbohydrates from many agricultural raw materials, and in making derivatives of these. He also did important fundamental research on certain enzymes, on the optical properties of sugars, and on the esoteric theory of mutarotation. As a result he formulated rules and generalizations which have been of great value in clearing up the basic chemical structure of many carbohydrates.

The determination of the constitution and the subsequent synthesis of vitamin B_1 was the important contribution of R. R. Williams. This work had begun years before when Williams was connected with the Philippine Bureau of Science; he continued it in the Bureau of Chemistry, and finally completed it after he joined the research staff of the Bell Telephone Company.

Dr. H. D. Gibbs's most outstanding contribution while in the Bureau of Chemistry was his discovery and development of the catalytic process for making phthalic anhydride by the oxidation of naphthalene. This sounds obscure, but its industrial use is basic to the modern dye industry, phthalic anhydride being an important intermediate used in the preparation of lacquers, plastics, synthetic indigo, alizarine, indanthrene, and so on.

Dr. Alsberg's successor, Dr. C. A. Browne, was a leading authority in the broad field of agricultural chemistry, as well as on the history of chemistry. Moreover he was an internationally recognized specialist in the field of sugar analysis, his book (later revised with Dr. F. W. Zerban), *Physical and Chemical Methods of Sugar Analysis*, being the classic in this field. He is still a collaborator of the bureau at this writing. Browne's successor, Dr. Henry G. Knight, was most notable for the important part he played in organizing and establishing the four regional research laboratories for which Congress made provision in 1938.

In May, 1941, Dr. Knight received the medal of the American Institute of Chemists, presented annually for "noteworthy and outstanding service to the science of chemistry or the profession of the chemist in America." At last great impetus was given to the industrial utilization of farm crops, and the prescience of Newton and Wiley became visible in reality and in practice. Agricultural chemistry and engineering really came into their own in these great laboratories, which will be described later on.

Some work that was done in this bureau, such as that of Dr. D. Breese Jones and associates over a period of many years on vegetable proteins, will be considered under other subject-matter headings as more appropriate. Fundamental investigation on fatty oils of vegetable origin was also long a project of this bureau, carried on by Dr. G. S. Jamieson, almost certainly the foremost American authority in this field. His book, *Vegetable Fats and Oils*, is the standard book of reference on the subject.

He has accumulated vast information on oils of both foreign and domestic origin and can talk illuminatingly and fascinatingly on the subject as long as one cares to listen. He has also developed and improved methods of analysis. His work on the oils and waxes has been of basic importance to the industries producing, refining, and using these commodities.

Years ago assistance began to be rendered to the citrus fruit industry, plagued with periodic gluts of a highly seasonal crop. Work on the marketing of canned and otherwise processed citrus products and by-products began with the establishment of a citrus by-products laboratory in Los Angeles in 1911. Dr. E. M. Chace—distinguished also for his work on the dehydration of food in both world wars—took charge, and other laboratories were set up later in Texas and Florida. As a result citrus products began to reach consumers in a variety of new forms, and culls and by-products ceased to be waste material.

In fact, before plants for cull disposal were built, it cost handlers a dollar or two per ton merely to get rid of the culls. The existence of by-product plants now makes these culls worth eight or ten times that much a ton. The public not only gets large quantities of canned citrus products, but citric acid, pectin, lemon oil, orange oil, and other valuable by-products are manufactured. As a result the by-product industry soon began to yield the California citrus industry an additional ten million dollars a year, while by-product processors made an additional million annually themselves.

Similar results were secured in Florida and Texas. Large percentages of the yields went out in the form of canned products, while in Florida alone citrus by-products used for cattle feed assumed a value of two million dollars a year, instead of requiring large expenditures for their disposal. The research paved the way also to meet wartime needs for citrus concentrates containing much-needed vitamins, as well as for citrus pectin—made from the white part of lemon and orange peel, and in common use in jams and jellies and as a stabilizer for emulsions in surgery and industry. Even the formerly wasted press juice, which used to cause stream pollution, is now used for making alcohol.

For many years Fletcher P. Veitch, Ralph W. Frey, and others did important research in this bureau on hides, tanning, the care of leather, the factors promoting deterioration of book-binding leather, and so on. It was shown that chrome- or combination vegetable-chrome–tanned leathers resisted atmospheric pollution causing the breakdown of leather bindings better than did vegetable-tanned leather. It was also shown that the waste bark from western hemlock could be used to manufacture tanning extract.

In 1942 Frey received the W. K. Alsop Award for outstanding work in the field of leather manufacture. Veitch also performed research which resulted in greatly increased profits for the naval-stores industry. A large part of these profits go to persons who produce gum from which rosin and turpentine are made. Largely as a result of Veitch's efforts the Naval Stores Act was passed, from which the producers, handlers, and utilizers of these products benefited. Thus the work of Veitch and C. F. Speh has proved of enormous value.

The bureau discovered that ethylene gas would aid in removing the hulls of sticktight California walnuts. It has also been shown that this gas hastens and renders more uniform the ripening of pears and imparts a pleasing yellow color to the skins of mature, edible oranges which have remained green externally and are therefore less salable. Some of these items seem small, but each one benefits some industry, some group of producers, or some large class of growers.

A method developed in 1927 for the production of gluconic acid through the mold fermentation of glucose reduced the cost of this chemical, valuable in making the important medicine, calcium gluconate, to one-sixth of what it was originally. The production of furfural from corncobs by F. B. LaForge and associates resulted in efficient commercial processes for producing this chemical from oat hulls; furfural is used in the purification of rosins, gasoline, and lubricating oils, and is a basic material in the manufacture of synthetic resins. This research has enabled farmers to dispose profitably of what was formerly waste.

Dye research performed in this bureau has resulted in the making of bright, permanent colors which have assisted vitally in the expansion of the cotton market. Its scientists succeeded in preparing and making commercially a high grade of starch from sweet potatoes, a product useful in many industries for a number of different purposes, including the sizing of cloth and paper, the making of adhesives, as laundry starch, and as an ingredient of bakery goods and confectionery. The starch can here replace a type of special starch that was formerly imported. Cattle feed can be made from the sweet-potato residue after the starch is extracted.

The effect of phenothiazine on human beings and animals was studied by scientists in this bureau, in co-operation with those in Stanford University Medical School. It was ultimately found to be one of the most versatile chemicals brought to light in recent years. A public patent was granted the Department workers covering its medical use, while other Department scientists determined that it was also an excellent vermifuge for sheep, swine, and horses, and a good fungicide as well.

Dr. R. C. Roark and L. E. Smith synthesized phenothiazine for use as an insecticide and proved it to be more effective against some insects than nicotine or lead arsenate, yet harmless to foliage and relatively inexpensive. Later it was shown to be highly toxic to mosquito larvæ. This was a long-drawn-out job which took years of work, but was well worth the time expended on it.

The chemists have also done work on sugar plants throughout the years, their efforts directly descending from those of the early chemists on sugar beets, sugar cane, and sorgo. New methods of crystallizing the sugar out of sorghum sirup and of making lighter, higher-quality cane sirup have resulted. Not even the possibility of recovering some six or seven million pounds of useful wax from the sugar cane "mud," which appears during the clarification of cane juice, was overlooked. Hitherto discarded as waste, the mud was found to contain 5 to 17 per cent of valuable wax.

The reorganization of the chemical work which accompanied the establishment of the four regional research laboratories essentially made the laboratories constitute the bureau. The creation of the laboratories was characterized by a high degree of fortuity, yet had we not had them at hand when war broke out, we should have lacked facilities to carry on a great deal of valuable and highly essential emergency research.

A senator from a cotton state became convinced that the cotton industry, which had worried over surpluses for a century, could probably be helped most by the establishment of a big laboratory wherein chemists and engineers would seek to find new uses for cotton and its by-products. Other senators contended that this would essentially be a regional laboratory and that if one were established for the South, the other regions should not be neglected. Each had its farm problems that might be solved by research in institutions of this kind.

Ultimately a decision was made to appropriate about one hundred thousand dollars to finance a survey of the possibilities of such laboratories. Then, in the high-pressure moments towards the end of a session of Congress, not only this sum but also four million dollars, one million per laboratory, was appropriated to get the scheme underway at once. This action came about largely by accident, taking the scientific administrators of the Department by surprise.

The laboratories are impressive U-shaped buildings, usually air-conditioned, each containing about eighty fully-equipped individual laboratories, a full complement of necessary offices, and one wing, reaching up through all four stories, capable of being used for large equipment and tests on pilot-plant and semicommercial scale.

Hence processes which start in laboratory glass undergo manufacturing tests before they are released; and they are then released for specific localities only, where raw material, labor, and other conditions make them economically feasible, for the economic considerations are carefully investigated and the design of any special machinery required is finished in the regional laboratory.

To the Northern Laboratory have been assigned problems in the industrial utilization of corn, wheat, soybeans, and farm residues such as stalks, straw, and hulls. The Eastern Laboratory undertakes problems concerned with the utilization of milk, potatoes, vegetables, apples and other fruits, tobacco, animal fats and oils, and hides and tanning materials. The Southern Laboratory works on cotton, peanuts, and sweet potatoes; the Western on the utilization of fruits, vegetables, poultry products and by-products, potatoes, and wheat. Each must stay in its legal category, too.

Since the Northern Laboratory had on hand the largest collection of nonpathogenic but industrially valuable yeasts, molds, bacteria, and other micro-organisms anywhere in the United States, it was here in its Fermentation Division that the drama of penicillin unfolded. Here also scientists discovered how to increase the yield of penicillin a hundredfold. Dr. Charles Thom, foremost American mycologist and long a Department employee, and Drs. Robert D. Coghill and A. J. Moyer of the division, soon had penicillin pouring forth as it had never done before.

Penicillin is the product of a mold called *Penicillium notatum*. The scientists at the Northern Regional Research Laboratory found that the mold grew better on corn steep liquor, a by-product of the corn wet-milling process than on any other substance hitherto tested. Then selection among the strains of the mold helped the process also. Manufacturers were instructed in the new methods and processes, and the tremendous increase in penicillin production resulted. As yields increased, production increased and prices declined. At this writing more than two hundred new strains of the mold have also been isolated and tested.

The United States was fortunate indeed to have had the Northern Laboratory established and manned when the war broke out. Our pool of scientific knowledge, equipment, and personnel here proved tremendously valuable in the emergency. The work on penicillin alone has justified the establishment of the laboratories even if other important research were not being carried on.

However, the Northern Laboratory has also done excellent work on the production of rubber substitutes, like Norepol, made from farm products. It has shown how ground corncobs and other milled farm wastes could be used to replace hominy in "sandblasting" the carbon from airplane engines. It has produced an excellent film-coating resin named "Norelac," superb for moisture-proofing packaging materials.

Meanwhile, the Eastern Laboratory has made rubber from Russian dandelions and has turned out the apple sirup used to replace glycerine in making certain brands of cigarettes. Its James F. Couch produced from tobacco and buckwheat plants a drug (rutin) effective in treating high blood pressure, because it reduces capillary fragility and, hence, liability to hemorrhage. Its E. Yanovsky developed an amazing new lacquer from starch, resistant to heat, water, acid, alkali, and other agents which damage wood.

Here, too, it was found that we have been discarding from vegetables, before shipping, processing, or eating, the parts which contain the most vitamin B and by far the best protein. From this discarded vegetable waste scientists have produced high-quality, high-protein cattle and poultry feeds, the outer broccoli leaves and the tops of beets, carrots, and rutabaga being first rate. They have made interesting wool-like fabrics and extraordinary plastics from milk proteins. They have worked successfully on the tannin-replacement program, studying the roots of canaigre, a plant of the dock family, domestic sumac, and a Peruvian plant called "tara," all of which offer excellent possibilities.

The Southern Laboratory on the outskirts of New Orleans has been performing miracles with cotton, turning out better-wearing tire cord for heavy trucks, producing better bandages for surgical use, designing machinery to cut lint cotton into suitable lengths for processing into smokeless powder, and discovering improved substitutes for binder twine. Fabrics used by the armed forces have had their resistance to weather, fire, and micro-organisms enhanced. All this work has been carried on in close collaboration with the armed services.

Scientists here have also further perfected the method of making high-grade root starch from sweet potatoes. They have produced excellent rubber from goldenrod. They are tailoring cottonseed and peanut oils to fit new uses, making from the former a product closely resembling cocoa butter, and from the latter an excellent substitute for olive oil used as a textile lubricant. Processes are also being worked out for new industrial uses of cottonseed and peanut proteins.

The Western Laboratory, standing on the east shore of San Francisco Bay, caught the bulk of the work on fruit and vegetable dehydration. The dehydration project was one engaged in by several of the agencies in the Agricultural Research Administration, and remarkably fine work was done in perfecting processes with great rapidity, under the whip of wartime emergency.

Dr. E. M. Chace, whose work on establishing maturity standards for oranges had profited the California citrus industry four million dollars during the first seven years it was used, had active charge of the West Coast vegetable-dehydration project; W. B. Van Arsdel and L. B. Howard of the laboratory were active in engineering and technological studies. Approximately one-third of the Laboratory staff was engaged on this work, and as a result a complete wartime dehydrated-food technology was developed and given to the trade. Advances were also made in the compression of dried food products to save shipping space.

Here the preservation of fruits and vegetables by freezing is under close scientific investigation. The objectives are better products through improved freezing technology, less waste, lower costs, and altogether new products—such as Velva Fruit, a new smooth-textured dessert that may be frozen commercially or in the home refrigerator. Data are also being obtained on the growth of yeasts for human food upon fruit waste, and on methods of producing tartrates from grape wastes. The freezing and drying of eggs and the freezing of poultry are likewise under study.

Some 500,000,000 pounds of food were dehydrated in 1943, much of it by methods worked out in the Western Laboratory. War accelerated the growth of the dehydration industry to major proportions. The value of the Western Laboratory in this connection was enormous.

When these four laboratories were founded certain congressmen declared that unless they paid for themselves within a decade, they should be abolished. It could undoubtedly be proved that any one of the laboratories has, during its existence of less than a decade, fully paid the costs of building, equipping, and operating all four of them. This has been done in terms of the actual monetary value of improved methods, discoveries made, and practical applications put into effect in industry.

Agricultural chemistry has come far since the days in which Isaac Newton expressed profound faith in its infinite possibilities to aid the agricultural industry. The single scientific paper issued by Charles Wetherill in 1862 has fructified into between eight and ten thousand scientific papers in the field of agricultural chemistry alone, representing research by Department of Agriculture scientists. Newton's initial faith has been fully justified, for agricultural chemistry has made good.

CHAPTER 6

The Bugs Crawl Out

WORK IN THE FIELD OF ECONOMIC ENTOMOLOGY began in the old Agricultural Division of the Patent Office, where, in 1854, Townend Glover was appointed "expert for collecting statistics and other information on seeds, fruits, and insects in the United States." Published with the annual report of the Commissioner of Patents for that year, which appeared in 1855, was an article by Glover on insects injurious and beneficial to vegetation.

When the Department of Agriculture was created, Glover immediately became the first of its entomologists. With the exception of a two-year interval, Glover served until his health failed in 1878. Then the already illustrious C. V. Riley, state entomologist of Missouri, succeeded him. Riley served as head of the entomological work until 1894, except for the two years between May, 1879, and March, 1881, during which time the equally famous John H. Comstock served.

Charles V. Riley was already well known when he entered the Department. His reports from Missouri were different in kind from anything so far published in the field. They were sound, admirably illustrated, and based squarely on observation. To him goes the credit for founding the United States Entomological Commission, which prepared classical works on many destructive insects. Riley's investigations of the grapevine phylloxera was a boon to the wine industry in both France and the United States. He conceived and directed the first notable and successful introduction of parasites to control destructive insects by bringing the Australian Vedalia or ladybird to this country, which saved the California citrus industry from destruction by fluted scale.

Riley was born in London, educated at Dieppe and Bonn, and

came to the United States in 1860, where he spent three years studying practical agriculture and doing newspaper work. He then entered the Union Army. He became Missouri state entomologist in 1868, and assisted in founding the *American Entomologist*. After he came to the Department, he aided in the invention of the cyclone or eddy chamber in nozzles used for spraying and made many discoveries in the field of pest control. It was Riley also who originated the use of kerosene emulsions in spraying. He has been described as a naturalist, a linguist, an artist, a soldier, a delightful companion, and a devoted friend.

The man who filled the interim of two years while Riley was not chief, was also a remarkable character, although he did his most important work elsewhere. Comstock had been a sailor in youth. Later he went to Cornell, graduating in 1874. While he was attending the university, his interest in insects had led him to find out so much about them that his fellow students petitioned the faculty to permit him to teach them entomology. This was arranged, and he became a member of the faculty while still a student. After leaving the Department of Agriculture, he returned to Cornell as professor of entomology. His most notable research was in the field of insect wing venation and was basic to the elucidation of the phylogenetic relationship between different groups of insects.

In 1878 there joined the staff of the Department a young man who had graduated from Cornell two years earlier. He was destined to become head of the Division of Entomology in June, 1894, chief of the Bureau of Entomology when it was created, on July 1, 1904, and so to serve until he gave up administrative duties on October 15, 1927, finally retiring in 1930. He was L. O. Howard, known widely for his work and his book on the housefly, which started a world-wide crusade against that insect; for his investigations on the malaria mosquito; and for his widely read book, *The Insect Menace*.

As early as 1888 Howard had achieved an international reputation for his studies of certain parasitic hymenoptera; his mosquito investigations began in 1892. When these insects were found to transmit disease, he was ready to suggest control methods which rendered the work of Walter Reed and W. C. Gorgas more effective. His *History of Applied Entomology* presents a fascinating account of insect-control work in this country.

After Howard's retirement C. L. Marlatt became chief of the Bureau of Entomology. Marlatt headed the Federal Horticultural Board from its creation on June 29, 1912, until October, 1927, when it was replaced by the Plant Quarantine and Control Administration, headed by Lee A. Strong from then until 1934. During that time the agency's name was changed to the Bureau of Plant Quarantine, which was combined with the Bureau of Entomology on July 1, 1934, to become the Bureau of Entomology and Plant Quarantine. Strong headed the combined bureau until his death, June 2, 1941.

Great numbers of Department entomologists did notable work. D. W. Coquillett developed cyanide fumigation to control insect pests. W. E. Dove, the medical entomologist, discovered that endemic typhus may be transmitted by the tropical rat mite. This led to work of the Public Health Service which disclosed that fleas were also important vectors of the disease. Dove also had overall supervision of the remarkable work on DDT and other insecticides and repellents carried on at Orlando, Florida, during World War II. G. F. White, investigator of many bee diseases, developed sterile-maggot therapy for osteomyelitis.

The early work of the bureau was published in the main in its annual reports. Its workers soon developed most modern methods of insect control. They did fundamental work in the field of fumigants and insecticides generally. They literally founded the liquid-soap and oil-emulsion industries. Their work on the introduction of natural insect enemies to eradicate domestic insects dangerous to various crops and fruits was ingenious and effective.

In 1868 fluted scale smuggled its way from Australia to the citrus-fruit orchards of California. It spread rapidly, attacking citrus and other plants, so weakening many orchards that they had to be destroyed. The female secreted a dense, fluted, cottony mass that made the eggs practically impervious to insecticides of the day.

In 1886 Riley decided that an organism so obnoxious must have enemies somewhere, and he determined to find them. As Australia was believed to be the home of the pest, he sent Albert Koebele there to investigate. Later Koebele brought back thousands of living parasitic enemies of the scale, among them *Vedalia (Novius) cardinalis*. The Vedalia beetle propagated and spread with amazing rapidity, stripping the scale from the trees. It saved the citrus-fruit industry of California and has, for the past fifty years, kept the scale well under control.

Between 1885 and 1895 Department entomologists first used arsenic and other poison sprays to destroy insects. Explorers went to many foreign countries to bring back natural predators of our own destructive insects, and thus many agricultural crops were spared annihilation. Ultimately it was found possible to breed strains and varieties of plants of economic value which were not relished by insects. Entomologists even learned how to prevent insects from damaging our crops by coping with them before they entered this country. Thus the citrus black fly was fought in Cuba by importing into that country a predator which kept it under control and prevented it from entering Florida to attack the citrus crop there.

Many wholly new types of insecticides, harmless to human beings, have been developed by Department chemists and entomologists working together, but only relatively few of this bureau's many specific projects can be mentioned here. The use of poisoned bait for the control of grasshoppers and Mormon crickets is a conspicuous example of the development of insect-control measures of noteworthy economic value. When D. W. Coquillett, in 1884, observed crude attempts by California farmers to apply this method, he promptly brought it to general attention. The first practical large-scale use of such bait was initiated by entomologists of the Kansas Agricultural Experiment Station in 1913.

Since then great improvements have been made in methods of application, and the cost of the bait has been much reduced by further investigation. Federal and state entomologists now engage in co-operative campaigns against grasshoppers, largely preventing the enormous loss of staple crops that could otherwise occur in the twenty-four states which must be protected from the ravages of these insects. Dr. Claude Wakeland has his headquarters as head of the Division of Grasshopper Control in Denver. Here the probable prevalence of grasshoppers and Mormon crickets is forecast and the strategy of campaigns is mapped.

The Hessian fly and the breeding of varieties of economic plants which prove resistant to insect damage are, as mentioned earlier, of interest to this bureau. As early as 1781 a yellow-bearded wheat variety was imported into this country and grown in the vicinity of New York City because it was resistant to the Hessian fly. The first systematic attempt to learn the comparative fly resistance of different wheat varieties was made by C. W. Wentworth of the California Agricultural Experiment Station and was reported in 1890. Similar observations by J. W. McColloch and S. C. Salmon in Kansas, about 1916, gave impetus to the project.

By 1942 this investigation began to culminate in the development of wheat varieties that are almost immune to the Hessian fly and which also have high resistance to stem rust, leaf rust, and bunt. In addition they give high yields of good quality. They represent an excellent but typical example of fruitful co-operative work on the part of state and federal entomologists, plant breeders, and plant pathologists. Their development makes possible an annual saving of $13,000,000.

Annual losses caused by the corn-ear worm are estimated at $96,000,000, by the chinch bug at $15,000,000, and by the European corn borer at $5,000,000. Feeding insects is indeed expensive business. At the present time progress is being made in the development of corn varieties which are resistant to the corn-ear worm, the chinch bug, and the borer. Fortunately corn resistance to insects proves heritable, and a few insect-resistant lines are already being used in the production of commercial corn hybrids.

Other bureau workers have shown that the destructive pea aphid is unable to survive and breed on certain individual alfalfa plants. Their findings were followed by federal-state work which demonstrated that the Ladak variety and individual plants of Kansas Common and of other varieties possess a highly transmissible resistance.

If only one-fourth of the insect losses to the plants mentioned above could be prevented by this sort of research, the savings realized in a single year would pay for all the investigations many times over. The practical use of insect-resistant varieties of plants would involve little if any increased cost to the grower. They would free him from the restrictions and expense imposed by the more or less satisfactory cultural and other control measures which he now uses. For these reasons varieties and lines of sorghums, oats, barley, and other grains that are resistant to one or more insects are currently being developed.

From the beginning of cotton production in Colonial days, the bollworm and the cotton-leaf worm have caused great damage. Control of these insects was among the first important problems to engage the attention of Department entomologists. The "Report Upon Cotton Insects," prepared by J. H. Comstock in 1879, while he served the Department, was epoch-making. Up to that time it was the most comprehensive document on economic entomology published in the United States. It was followed by the publication in 1880 of the large illustrated *Bulletin No. 3*, from the United States Entomological Commission, on the cotton worm, by C. V. Riley. In 1885 the *Fourth Report* of the same commission devoted more than six hundred pages to the cotton worm and the bollworm.

The spread of the boll weevil from Mexico to Texas in 1892 and its establishment in that state during the next decade directly caused great expansion of Department entomological research. Indirectly it also expanded the Department's activities; for instance, the far-flung Extension Service grew out of farm-demonstration work begun by the Department in its campaign against the boll weevil.

No other insect ever caused such widespread devastation and economic depression in this country as the boll weevil after it really got underway. The first cultural practices used to combat it followed early investigations by Townsend, Howard, and Mally, from 1895 until 1900. Many others continued these studies until they comprised the most extensive series of investigations ever made of one insect. The discoveries made in this connection had world-wide influence on insect control, and new industries were established as a result thereof.

During World War I calcium arsenate was developed as an insecticide for boll-weevil control. The manufacture and use of this material expanded so much that in 1941 and 1942 something like seventy million pounds of it were used for the control of cotton insects in this country.

As early as 1919 airplanes were used under the direction of W. D. Hunter, of this bureau, for locating both cotton fields that had become infested with the pink bollworm and mosquito-breeding areas concealed from view by woodlands. An airplane was first used for the application of an insecticide on August 3, 1921, when six acres of catalpa trees at Troy, Ohio, were dusted with lead arsenate for control of catalpa sphinx. This experiment, conducted by entomologists of the Ohio Agricultural Experiment Station, set a trend.

Airplanes were soon used extensively for the application of insecticides to control cotton insects. At the bureau's Tallulah, Louisiana, laboratory, investigations were conducted in co-operation with the Bureau of Public Roads and the United States Army Air Service from 1922 until 1931. A staff of entomologists, engineers, chemists, airplane pilots, mechanics, and others was engaged on this project. Much progress was made in designing hoppers and testing airplanes and methods of application.

The second successful tests of the use of airplanes in the control of an important insect came during July and August, 1922, when the method was used to apply calcium arsenate to several fields in the Delta section of Louisiana and Mississippi for the control of the cotton-leaf worm. These experiments proved the value of airplanes in work of this sort. Effective control of the boll weevil was also gained by the method. Almost immediately the airplane dusting of cotton was adopted as a commercial practice. By 1926 a number of commercial companies were engaged in airplane dusting of cotton, chiefly in Texas and Louisiana, and the business grew.

Many new methods and principles of insect control have stemmed from this bureau. Some of them seemed small but were large in accomplishment. Until 1937 there was no known way of protecting sweet corn from the ravages of the corn-ear worm. During the summer of 1936, however, George W. Barber, one of the Department's investigators who had been working on the problem for several years, made a momentous discovery.

He found that if about one-quarter of a teaspoonful of refined odorless and tasteless mineral oil were injected into the silk mass at the tip of the ear—after pollination was complete—fair protection from the corn-ear worm could be obtained without preventing normal kernel development. The treatment can be applied safely as soon as the silks begin to wilt and turn brown. The oil makes its

Henry L. Ellsworth

Gifford Pinchot

A. C. True

W. O. Atwater

way down and forms a barrier the worms cannot pass. Protection was not satisfactory, however, for ears having long, tight husks.

A low-priced oiler was next designed, attached by a short hose to a portable container. This piston-type equipment was effective for injecting doses of accurate size on commercial areas, an ordinary eyedropper being satisfactory for home-garden plantings. Further studies showed that the addition of a little pyrethrum extract to the oil made it fully effective in all cases.

The method was highly acceptable to commercial corn growers, and its use has proved very profitable to them. It has also been demonstrated that the same means can be used effectively to prevent infestation of valuable hybrid sweet corn in the Idaho seed-producing areas.

Another instance involving the use of a new principle concerned the leaf hopper *Empoasca fabæ* (Harr.), recognized in 1896 as a potato pest by Herbert Osborn, who described "hopper-burn" injury. Later workers found that this insect also destroyed alfalfa, clover, apples, beans, and other crops, though the nature of the injury remained mysterious. Work by F. F. Smith and F. W. Poos in 1931 showed that overaccumulation of carbohydrates, above the point of injury by the insect, caused the symptoms noted.

Detailed life-history studies of the insect followed. Control of the pest on crops such as alfalfa was effected by delaying the time of cutting the first crops until most of the eggs had been laid by spring migrants. The application of Bordeaux mixture and pyrethrum dust provided control for bean, potato, and peanut plants.

Then in 1929 D. M. De Long showed that if bean leaves were sprayed with Bordeaux mixture, they absorbed sufficient copper to be toxic to leaf hoppers feeding on the cell contents. This established a new principle of insect control that has been used increasingly since that time; get the insecticide into the plant and then let it act as its own insect killer. The method often works. Meanwhile, it has also been found that the hoppers damage highly hairy strains of clover, apples, and soybeans less than they do smooth, ones.

Vacuum fumigation—achieved by reducing the air pressure in a chamber containing a commodity, by removing most of the air in and around the commodity, and then applying the fumigant in that partial vacuum—also originated in the Department. The first work was done by E. R. Sasscer and L. A. Hawkins in 1915, when they tested this method in fumigating seed. It was successful. The insects were killed with much shorter exposure to hydrocyanic acid than usual.

The first large-scale application of the new process was in fumigating baled cotton, authorized the following year as a quarantine measure for cotton imported from areas infested with the pink bollworm. The process was later adapted to the fumigation of domestic cotton in areas infested in this country and, before long, half a million bales were being fumigated annually.

Since then the process has been adapted to the fumigation of rice, wheat, corn, and cereal products, nut meats, dried fruits, tobacco, potatoes, and many other commodities. Its use has spread outside the confines of this country, too, and it has become a standard method of insect control everywhere.

The vapor-heat treatment for citrus fruit was developed on a commercial scale in Florida during 1928-29. It was adopted by Department workers as a means by which fruits infested with the Mediterranean fruit fly could be treated and then shipped to market without danger of disseminating this pest. Initial laboratory studies had already been made, hence practical application did not lag. The fruit is simply heated to 110 degrees Fahrenheit and held at that temperature for eight hours.

This process requires an insulated room, usually having a capacity of about a carload of fruit stacked in shallow boxes. The air is withdrawn at the floor level and conditioned outside the room, large blowers providing forced circulation. The conditioned air is reintroduced near the ceiling of the room. Hundreds of carloads of fruit have been treated in this way. The practice was discontinued when the fruit fly was eradicated, but in 1938 the method again came in handy for treating citrus fruit from areas of Texas infested with the Mexican fruit fly. It was also used that year on Hawaiian fruit and vegetable hosts of the Mediterranean fruit fly and the melon fly, to permit shipment into the United States.

Extremely fortunate was the development of the aerosol method in April, 1941, just before the war emergency broke. It is a fine-fog process of dividing and spreading insecticides devised by bureau scientists. It was primarily the result of an idea of Lyle D.

Goodhue, who was aided in its perfecting by W. N. Sullivan. The method went into practical use early in 1943.

By this method the insecticide to be used is dissolved in a highly volatile, noninflammable, nontoxic solvent, along with an activator. The mixture is kept in a container under high pressure. On its release the insecticide is propelled forth atomized into a fog. It not only makes a little insecticide go a long way but it is more effective than any method previously used. Military authorities immediately seized upon the discovery to protect men in the armed services from various insects.

The principle here involved is so fundamental that it will revolutionize many current pest-control practices. Its value will prove incalculable in peacetime. Quite as extraordinary has been the development and widespread use of dichloro-diphenyl-trichloroethane (DDT) as an insecticide. Work on it was done mainly in an emergency laboratory at Orlando, Florida, set up at the express wish of the armed forces and under the overall direction of W. E. Dove.

All too brief reference can be made here to the revolutionary accomplishments of E. F. Knipling, and his associates, at Orlando, where, under the forced draft of war, research fires burned brightly, discoveries came quickly, and the entire tempo of scientific investigation and practical application was immensely accelerated.

DDT was first made in a laboratory by Othman Zeidler, a German chemist, in 1874. Many years later a Swiss corporation began to sell the substance as an insecticide because it seemed to be effective against some agricultural pests. A representative of this company brought samples to the Orlando laboratory on October 16, 1942. It was but one of thousands of highly recommended materials to come there for test, for samples such as this came from all over the world at a rate of six to eight hundred a month. Rapid methods of preliminary testing were devised which readily screened out and eliminated substances which were inferior to those already developed. However, DDT showed great promise at once.

The rest is history. The substance can be used to completely eradicate body lice and to control the diseases they spread. Wholly new methods of insect control, accomplished by impregnating fabrics or spraying walls with the insecticide for semipermanent effect, have been developed and utilized. American authorities obtained spectacular results when they first used the material in North Africa in 1943; later it stopped the typhus epidemic in its tracks at Naples during the winter of 1943–44.

However, many matters which required conscientious and meticulous research had to be set aside for later study. DDT is in some ways so good an insecticide that it can be harmful. Many insects are beneficial to man and must be protected, yet when applied from an airplane, this material can kill practically every insect in large areas. There is talk also of its upsetting the biological balance and killing valuable fish and wild birds and animals.

While the material has the greatest possibilities of any yet developed or tried for forest insects, much investigation still must be painstakingly carried through before it can be used scientifically and with complete confidence. Entomologists must still find out how to formulate DDT, how to use it, and, above all, when and where *not* to use it, and they are going ahead with this job now. In time it will undoubtedly occupy an even more important place in pest-control programs, but that period is as yet in the future.

Small sprayers working on the same principle as the aerosol bombs have been developed which finely atomize concentrated solutions of DDT. Seven strokes of the handle of one of these sprayers will atomize about seven drops of the solution it contains, which is sufficient to kill all the flies and mosquitoes in a space of one thousand cubic feet.

If properly used, DDT is not dangerous to human beings, but even in that connection further details must be worked out. Finally, since the substance is not effective for a number of insect species, it is no universal panacea.

An entire book could be written about the accomplishments of this Orlando laboratory alone; yet it merely forms an emergency part of a single division of one Department bureau. With its scientifically managed louse and mosquito factories and its patient human pastures for feeding them, its development and achievements form an exciting and dramatic story in themselves. It has shown how to use airplanes to treat more than five hundred acres with eight hundred gallons of DDT spray in thirty minutes, killing all larvæ and adults of the malaria mosquito.

It is developing and has developed many methods of pest and insect control which will serve mankind well. Its study of mosquito repellents, material to eradicate blowflies, scabies mites, ticks, bedbugs, cockroaches, fleas, and houseflies will all stand us in good stead. Here, as elsewhere, the scientist's leisurely peacetime routine was interrupted during the war; stimulated by the wartime emergency, research projects were completed quickly and well. Now reduced pressure will give time for further study of details that were deliberately ignored, and the gain to the American public will be tremendous.

Insecticide investigation has also long been underway in a division which was put on an organized basis as a result of the passage of the Insecticide Act of 1910. For years the work was directed mainly towards the enforcement of that act. But on July 1, 1927, a division wholly devoted to research work on insecticidal materials was created in the Bureau of Chemistry and Soils and was transferred to the Bureau of Entomology and Plant Quarantine on September 1, 1934. It has been under the leadership of R. C. Roark since 1927.

It started with the premise that any plant used by savages to kill fish might logically be expected to yield some constituent toxic to at least some insects. Plants were collected from all over the world and studied. It soon became evident that some of these, containing a chemical called "rotenone," took front rank. Considerable chemical work had been done previously on one of these, derris from the East Indies, and certain restricted insecticidal uses had been found for its powdered roots. Intensive investigation in the Division now elucidated its chemical structure.

This achievement was recognized in 1933 by the award of the Hillebrand Prize to F. B. LaForge and H. L. Haller, who, with the assistance of L. E. Smith, solved this difficult problem. Publicity resulting from this chemical research so spurred collateral insect-testing that rotenone rapidly took its place as the best insecticide for control of the pea aphid, the Mexican bean beetle, and other pests. In 1929 the late E. P. Clark of the division discovered rotenone in a wild plant known as "cube" and used to poison fish in Peru. Today growers can market worm-free raspberries, loganberries, and youngberries merely by dusting with derris or cube powder.

The value of the work on rotenone is shown by the fact that nine million pounds of rotenone-bearing roots were imported in 1941, enough to make ninety million pounds of insecticidal dust.

The demand for this type of insecticide was built up in the main through work in the Department. Rapid expansion occurred. Next a search started for other plants that might contain rotenone or something like it, when the war had cut off our supply of derris from the East Indies. The substance was found in devil's shoestring, a plant previously shown by a Texas worker to have insecticidal activity.

About ninety patents have been granted to workers in the Division of Insecticide Investigations on their discoveries and inventions. These concern a wide variety of new substances, mixtures, methods, and processes. For instance, among them is an apparatus for determining the particle size of powders which is now in wide use not only among the manufacturers of insecticides, but among concerns which make cement, paint, and many other products. That may be regarded as a sort of unearned increment on the original work.

The first use of methyl bromide as a fumigant for insect control in this country was by D. B. Mackie of the California State Department of Agriculture in 1937. While the first tests were on potatoes, the bureau soon tested and approved the method for the treatment of fruits and vegetables infested with Japanese beetles. The material is now used in fumigating mills, warehouses, and seed houses for control of insects which attack grains and cereal products and also in special gas-tight chambers or vaults for these products, as well as potted and balled-and-burlapped plants. Finally, it has been shown that methyl bromide diluted with water makes an excellent soil fumigant. Many other nonexplosive fumigants now in general use were developed by workers in this bureau.

The "white fly," or beet leaf hopper, not only infests many crops, but also carries and transmits the virus of the destructive sugar-beet disease known as "curly top." The same disease adopts the pseudonym "western yellow blight" when it attacks tomatoes. A single leaf hopper can do a masterful and thorough job of spreading the virus, too. A few can cause very severe damage to a crop. For years curly-top disease was a limiting factor in sugar-beet production, and many sugar factories had to close because of its presence.

The development and distribution of sugar-beet strains resistant to curly top, a service performed by Department plant scientists, reduced the magnitude of the losses and helped stabilize the industry. Knowledge of the leaf hopper's life history, painstakingly assembled by entomologists, proved of great assistance. V. E. Romney then discovered that damage to beets grown for seed could be materially reduced by use of a pyrethrum-oil spray.

A discovery that was important to the related cane-sugar industry was the demonstration by E. V. Abbott and J. W. Ingram of the Department, in 1941, that a serious sugar-cane ailment called "chlorotic streak" (new to this country) was spread by a leaf hopper commonly found feeding on Louisiana cane. Discovery by other Department members, E. W. Brandes and E. M. Summers, working with Ingram, that destructive sugar-cane mosaic disease can be transmitted both by the rusty plum aphid and the green bug, as well as the corn-leaf aphid, was also most helpful in control work.

Until control measures were devised, the peach-tree borer, a native American pest, was very destructive to peach orchards, because a single borer could girdle a tree and cause its death. Until 1919 the borers had to be dug out by hand, a laborious, time-consuming process. Then E. B. Blakeslee, a Department entomologist, discovered that the borers could be controlled at a cost of a few cents per tree by the use of paradichlorobenzene. Later Oliver I. Snapp and J. R. Thomson improved the control achieved by changing to an ethylene dichloride emulsion which did not injure young trees. Their method was generally applied. Now at a cost of about ten cents a tree, fruit growers are saved over one and one-half million dollars annually.

Since the earliest days of forest-insect investigations there has been real need for sprays that could be applied to the bark of trees or logs to prevent attack by bark beetles and wood borers and to kill other insects with similar objectionable habits. R. S. St. George supplied the need in 1919 by discovering a chemical called "ortho-dichlorobenzene," which had the required insecticidal properties, and its use became widespread. Since then methods and sprays have improved rapidly, providing great savings for the lumber industry.

The work of the entomologists has been helpful to cattle growers as well as to growers of cereals, vegetables, fruits, and lumber. The development of "Smear MS 62" is a case in point. It is a combination screwworm larvicide and protector of wounds. It resulted from tests of hundreds of compounds and comprised a combination of two treatments that had previously been developed for separate use.

The discovery that sodium fluoride would control poultry lice, and the development of simple, practical methods of employing the material, we owe to work by F. C. Bishopp and H. P. Wood about 1927. It was an outstanding accomplishment as viewed by poultry raisers and farmers generally. It is a simple, standard, effective treatment, and the bulletin describing it went through twenty editions for a total of more than one and one-quarter million copies.

The cattle grub or heel fly is capable of doing $350,000,000 worth of damage to the cattle industry per year. In Dallas Dr. Ernest W. Laake is at the forefront of the fight on what he regards as menace No. 1 to the livestock growers. The grubs injure enough hides yearly to make shoes for a million persons. They lower the value of steers considerably and prevent animals from putting on flesh at a normal rate. They cut the milk yields of dairy cattle, reduce the production of baby beef, and have affected 35 per cent of the cattle slaughtered.

A special campaign was waged against the pest when war made meat production at a high level most urgent. Fortunately entomologists had found that rotenone, properly used, would effect excellent control. Yet the ill effects of heel flies had been known since the time of Virgil and possibly earlier, and in more recent times many and often contradictory articles had been published on the subject in Europe.

C. V. Riley first directed attention to the pest in this country, and in 1890 Cooper Curtice, famous Bureau of Animal Industry scientist, reported finding the larvæ of the insects in the bodies of animals. He assumed that cattle became infested by licking the eggs or larvæ from their own coats. Riley accepted this theory of trans-

Old frame plant-inspection house at Fourteenth and C streets, where
samples from foreign lands were "stored" on the sidewalk

Hoboken Inspection House, a finely equipped institution used in
plant-quarantine work today

mission via mouth. But systematic research between 1917 and 1926 by F. C. Bishopp and others disproved this theory.

It was then shown that the newly hatched larvæ could penetrate the skin directly from the point at which the eggs were attached to the animal's hair. No grubs developed in animals fed heel fly eggs or newly hatched larvæ. The findings were confirmed by others. Once these facts were established, control by use of rotenone-bearing powders followed as does the night the day.

It is refreshing and revealing to travel over the country and to find entomologists and plant-quarantine experts at work everywhere protecting plants and animals of economic importance from insect pests, and thereby protecting the American public. For instance, there is the white fringe beetle, an omnivorously destructive dark gray or blackish bug which has a fringe of somewhat dirty white about its body. Its native heath is the southern part of South America, but around 1936 it entered this country. It soon proved extraordinarily destructive and a call for help went to the government.

L. J. Padget, working under B. M. Gaddis of the bureau's Division of Domestic Plant Quarantine, thereupon mapped out and put into effect an amazingly fine campaign against the new insect, working from Gulfport, Mississippi. While only small areas of some five states became infested, the bug relishes 80 species of plants and its larvæ hover near and eat the roots of 236 more, so that it was a deadly potential menace to crops. Study of its native habitat indicated that it could infest about one-half of the United States if given a chance.

Five species of the beetle have been identified here, but they all like cover. Lacking vegetation for shelter, they die. Therefore, special herbicides were developed to kill weeds. It was found that the beetles spread via railroad lines, lumber yards, and nurseries. Highly effective methods of divesting the first two of weeds and fumigating the soil of nurseries were developed. All these measures were taken with the utmost economy and efficiency, wholly new machines being designed when necessary and costs of the treatment being lowered constantly.

The adults, all females, reproducing parthenogenetically, are prevalent only from June 15 to September 15, but they are fought with deadly weapons during that time. Changed cropping practices have been widely introduced, which, interestingly enough, enable farmers to make more money than they did before, while growing crops the beetles do not relish, and growing those they do relish at times when the adult is not prevalent. Wholly new and ingenious spray machines and methods of applying very concentrated sprays have been designed which eradicate the beetles in large agricultural areas at once, the actual poundage of insecticide used being less than when more dilute sprays were utilized far less effectively. This is a tremendously effective and many-sided campaign.

Meanwhile, H. T. Rainwater and his assistants of the same bureau are pressing the sweet-potato beetle back from headquarters at the same town of Gulfport. The sweet potato is in reality a morning-glory plant, and those in charge of the fight on the destructive sweet-potato beetle are slowly pushing the insect back to the wild morning glories, greatly to the financial enrichment of growers in several southern states.

How many of us know that much of this sort of work goes on constantly? Go to any port and you will find the inspectors right on the spot, sometimes fumigating whole freight-car loads of material and commodities, six at a time, at other times examining the produce bought by citizens of a border town in the markets of old Mexico. Day in and day out the work continues, and every one of us profits from it, though often unknowingly, because only a rare few can know about it, while fewer still understand its import and value.

When a new pest, such as the Japanese beetle, appears, everyone wants immediate action for its eradication, including the Bureau of Entomology and Plant Quarantine. Unfortunately DDT is only fairly effective on the Japanese beetle, and work must be pressed in other directions, where results may be slow to appear.

This beetle was first found in New Jersey in 1916. One of the first acts of entomologists when its spread menaced the entire Atlantic seaboard was to devise a trap containing chemicals, used in the perfume industry, which they had discovered were especially attractive to the pest. The traps do not control and are not intended to control the beetle, but they do reveal its presence and relative prevalence.

The Department first began intensive study of biological control methods for this beetle in 1920, when trained entomologists were sent to study the insect in Japan, where it is kept below pest proportions by natural enemies. Some twenty-six species of insect parasites and predators of the beetle were sent to the United States for study, and individual parasites of at least sixteen species were liberated in this country. Several species became well established and will prove of ultimate value in keeping the Japanese beetle population in bounds.

Next, a group of bureau workers developed the use of lead arsenate in the soil as a control measure against Japanese beetle grubs. Over a million and a half pounds of this chemical were successfully used for the purpose of protecting lawns, golf courses, and park turf areas in 1941-42. In 1940 other bureau workers discovered new spore-forming bacteria which caused among Japanese beetle larvæ a fatal milky disease, so called because the affected grubs became milky white and died.

Somewhat earlier still, other milky-disease organisms had been found. The Department, in co-operation with several state agencies, undertook control measures by this means. The program got underway in 1939, and by the end of 1942 nearly thirty thousand acres of land had been treated by the implantation of more than forty thousand colonies of the bacteria. These spread naturally and greatly decrease the number of beetles in the locality by destroying the grubs. A method has now been developed to effect mass production of the spores of the milky disease, and they are available commercially. Japanese beetles themselves can be dusted with the spores and then liberated to spread milky disease!

Entomologists seek not only to destroy harmful insects but also to encourage beneficial ones. That is why the bureau intends to study DDT well before making final recommendations for its use. The bureau has also for a long time employed specialists to study the honeybee, to improve its production of honey and, if possible, to eradicate diseases which destroy the insect. Since at least fifty important crops depend entirely upon benign insects to effect their pollination, and would not otherwise produce seed or fruit, a plentiful supply of honeybees helps greatly to increase crop yields. Among them are red clover, deciduous fruits, melons, cu-

cumbers, onions, cabbage, cauliflower, brussels sprouts, turnips, carrots, and alfalfa.

Modern insecticides menace the useful as well as the harmful insects; that is why special protective measures must be adopted for the former. This is also why the bureau feels that something has been accomplished when one of its scientists unravels the mystery of a bee disease, as C. E. Burnside recently did of honeybee paralysis.

Hitherto growers had been inclined to diagnose this disease every time their bees began to grow bald, but Burnside found that bees could become hairless for a number of other reasons, among them being the fact that they sometimes engage in hair-pulling contests quite as human beings do. Healthy bees "pick" on the sick ones in that way. Burnside also showed that bee paralysis was caused by a virus, and now a preventive or cure may be sought intelligently.

There are several different races of honeybees, some much to be preferred to others. For example, some strains differ from others by as much as one hundred pounds per colony per year of honey produced. But until a few years ago it was impossible to control matings so as to breed pure races. Hence honeybees had failed to keep pace with improvements in other fields of agriculture. Mating took place on the wing, and any old drone would do for the finest queen.

In 1923 C. W. Quinn and H. H. Laidlaw began efforts to effect matings by hand manipulation. Much interest was aroused. Next, in 1926, L. R. Watson of Cornell University demonstrated the successful artificial insemination of honeybees. The methods have been improved by workers both inside and outside the Department.

The Department has also made extensive study of the existing races and strains of honeybees. It investigates their genetic make-up and catalogs their characteristics—resistance to disease, propensity to sting, capacity to gather honey, pollinating ability, hardiness, and longevity. It will be possible in time to combine the qualities most desired and tailor honeybees to special needs.

Co-operative research is being carried on with several agricultural experiment stations on strains capable of resisting foul brood, a contagious disease of young bees which results in the loss of thousands of colonies annually. The work on disease resistance shows great promise. These biological investigations, coupled with extensive research on the economics of honey production, have been welcomed by American apiarists.

Mention was made earlier that scientists connected with this bureau are found at many outposts. Some of them, like those at New Haven, Connecticut, are engaged in research; there the study is upon airplane methods of using insecticides to destroy harmful forest insects, a project being carried out in several states from the New Haven headquarters. In other instances the workers are engaged in plant quarantine and are usually trained plant pathologists or entomologists. They are seeking to prevent the spread into and around this country of harmful, disease-carrying insects, and of plant diseases generally.

The United States was the last of the economically important countries to establish service of this nature. It has been estimated that the losses caused in this country by insects introduced from elsewhere—without considering plant diseases—approximate an undesirable tax of one and one-half billion dollars annually. It was only after several years of agitation and consideration that the Plant Quarantine Act of August 20, 1912, became law, and restrictions were placed upon the entry of plants and plant products. Before that date injurious pests such as the San Jose scale, the coddling moth, the Hessian fly, the cotton boll weevil, the oriental fruit moth, the potato wart, and the chestnut blight became firmly established to flourish and destroy. The history of these pests is a depressing tale of crop destruction, economic loss, increased production costs, expensive control measures, and troublesome agricultural readjustments.

In enforcing the act, an effort has been made to use the most efficient and economical control methods which will least disturb normal commerce and the essential needs of horticulture. Prohibitory and restrictive quarantines have been established, a permit system has been developed, plant-quarantine inspectors have been placed at ports of entry, and methods of treatment have been perfected.

Persons familiar with Washington, D. C. some years ago will undoubtedly remember tripping over foreign-looking boxes, crates, and nondescript packages as they tried to pass some dilapidated frame buildings which stood at the corner of what is now Twelfth Street and Constitution Avenue. The foreign plant shipments then had to be stored on the sidewalk because storage facilities were lacking, and facilities in general were crude.

Yet 80 to 85 per cent of all special-permit importations were inspected here at the time. Peak volume was attained on June 30, 1927, when 46,625,648 plants, bulbs, and other materials were imported and had to be examined. Today this work is done at the Hoboken plant-inspection house, a fully equipped $400,000 building occupied on June 28, 1940. It is four stories high, 144 by 52½ feet, and has every modern facility, including cold-storage rooms, service equipment, storage space, and vacuum fumigation apparatus. Thus the work progresses and is appreciated by those who know what it accomplishes.

But the inspection of products which enter under permit is not enough. Close watch must be kept on vessels, freight cars, railway coaches, airplanes, automobiles, parcel post packages, baggage, and everything else that enters the country from abroad. That is why we have places on the Mexican border where several freight cars can be fumigated at once to prevent the entry of pink bollworm of cotton. Interception of hundreds of thousands of insects at American ports of entry is commonplace.

This plant-quarantine system is squarely based on science and research. It must keep alert to every new development in both the insect- and the plant-disease fields. While entomology is basic, the widest possible knowledge of plant species is also required. Likewise, there must be sound information on which plants do or can act as hosts to which insects. The entomologist must therefore try also to be a botanist, while knowing the habits and life histories of a vast variety of insects and devising methods for their eradication or control. If insects enter this country, their domestic spread must be prevented as much as possible, and here our domestic plant-quarantine system takes over.

Those who engage in this work must also be well trained in plant pathology. They must be able to identify a vast number of pathogenic fungi, bacteria, and nematodes and to understand their life histories, habits, and the symptoms they are capable of producing in various plants. Finally, they must develop treatments and procedures which will permit the safe entry of plants from abroad as well as their domestic movement. To say that this work is specialized and complex is an understatement.

The Bureau of Entomology and Plant Quarantine constantly carries on research to develop the information it needs. It also depends heavily on the Bureau of Plant Industry, Soils, and Agricultural Engineering and on a host of state agencies for research background, both in entomology and in botany and plant pathology. Department entomologists are always busy identifying and classifying insects, maintaining records of their habitats and occurrence, investigating their foods and life habits, determining their host and climatic relationships, and working out treatment, eradication, or control measures as are practicable.

This country is so large, and it offers so many climatic and nutritive opportunities, that the raising of fruits, vegetables, cereals, fiber crops, and animals requires unrelenting warfare against insects. Modern means of rapid transport complicate the problem. The slightest relaxation of entomological control measures would result in enormous losses and often the utter destruction of entire crops and industries. The very success of the system tends to make it less noticeable to us. Nevertheless, the work goes on constantly by a large force of highly trained persons, with so little publicity that most citizens are entirely unaware of it, except occasionally when they return to a port of entry or pass a line of domestic quarantine. Then they are likely to be irritated rather than appreciative.

Moreover, insect and disease problems change constantly. About 1870 the San Jose scale was introduced into California from Asia. In 1880 the gypsy moth was first found here. In 1892 the boll weevil was an important visitor from Mexico, and in 1917 the European corn borer was found to have emigrated here from Hungary. In 1916 came the Japanese beetle, and so on, as we have seen.

Then when the Graf Zeppelin made its second trip to this country in 1929, plant-quarantine inspectors found on the material it carried twenty insect species, six of which did not occur in this country. Fast and constant airplane transportation makes the control problem extremely difficult, as insects are quick to adopt new modes of long-distance transportation.

Meanwhile there is urgent necessity for continuous research on methods of coping with domestic insects already here. Mites, ticks, and insects levy on us an annual tax of three billion dollars, taken in the form of commodities and crops destroyed. Therefore, the bureau has also to do extensive research on insects destructive to stored commodities and products as well as to growing crops.

According to records of the Insect Pest Survey there are at least twenty thousand potentially destructive insects, mites, and ticks among us, half of which constitute pests of importance. Much of the loss occasioned is preventable. A great deal of it has been and is being prevented as a result of research and quarantine work carried on by faithful Department and state workers who are at their job constantly all over the United States.

CHAPTER 7

All Flesh Is Grass

SCRIPTURE IS PROFOUNDLY CORRECT in stating that all flesh is grass. Animals lack the ability to subsist on the simple elements in air, water, sunshine, and soil. To perpetuate themselves, they must eat grass or one another. Without that silent, cool, continuous manufacturing process which goes on in the green leaf under the influence of sunshine, air, moisture, and chlorophyl, animals would be entirely out of luck. Consequently we owe a great debt to the scientists who have worked in the field of plant science.

In February, 1945, one of them, Leonard L. Harter by name, retired after over forty years of service. Persons who have probably never even heard his name owe him much. Not long before his retirement he spoke with great enthusiasm about one of his major problems, which was now of very minor importance—the development of effective control measures for sweet-potato diseases, black rot in particular, which had been taking a toll of over one-third of this important food crop per year.

These control measures, developed in close co-operation with the state agricultural experiment stations, resulted in an annual saving of five million dollars. They made a year-round supply of good sweet potatoes possible. Since losses had been cut to only one-tenth of the crop, Harter regarded the project as of minor importance now. However, that was only one of his projects, for he was an international authority on plant diseases and the author of more than one hundred publications in the field. He also worked out a method of telling accurately when apples of various varieties were ready to pick, which is of great practical use to growers. Like many other plant scientists, he built up a huge annuity—which, however, accrued to the general public.

Mark H. Haller was another notable plant scientist. He worked with strawberries, developing a method by which dormant strawberry plants could be held through the winter in storage. Thus removed from winter hazards in the field, the plants were ready to fill spring orders. Big strawberry-plant shippers adopted the method readily because it saved labor when labor was in peak demand. Haller pointed the way to an annual saving by strawberry growers and handlers equivalent to the total of his modest salary for about thirty years.

When you read the formidable title of a research paper by two scientists from the Bureau of Plant Industry, Soils, and Agricultural Engineering—say, "Inheritance of Male Sterility in the Onion and Production of Hybrid Seed," by Henry A. Jones and Alfred E. Clarke—glance also into the future. The paper means that onion production can be increased from 20 to 50 per cent by the authors' development of a sort of confused male-sterile onion, which, for breeding purposes, acts entirely female. It can bear seed but cannot supply pollen. Crossed in the field with normal onions naturally supplying the pollen, it will bear highly prized hybrid seed.

Such research reaches back into the dim past of Patent Office days, when the government employed its first botanist. A Division of Botany was established in the Department of Agriculture in 1869, the Division of Gardens and Grounds having been organized under William Saunders soon after the Department's creation. The Division of Botany maintained the United States National Herbarium until the Smithsonian Institution took it over on July 1, 1896.

Charles Christopher Barry, born in England, was the first Department botanist. He graduated from Union College, took a medical degree at the New York College of Physicians and Surgeons, entered medical practice in Iowa, and then abandoned this career for botany. Largely self-taught, he became botanist of the Mexican Boundary Commission in 1849, serving until 1853, and then for a long time collected plants privately. While with the Department his work was mainly in the herbarium, though he visited Europe and Kew Gardens the while. He retired from government service largely because critics claimed that his work had an insufficiently agricultural outlook.

George Vasey, also English-born, succeeded him. He also took a medical degree, but he specialized in botany early in life at the instance of a botanist. He systematically classified and enlarged the National Herbarium and began the collection of sections and botanical specimens of forest trees. He issued a comprehensive publication on the subject of forestry which led Congress to appropriate $2,000 to compensate a properly qualified man to report still more in detail in this subject—Franklin B. Hough, whom we shall meet in the forestry chapter, was appointed. Vasey served as Department botanist from 1872 until 1893, when F. V. Coville, who, with G. M. Darrow, so improved the wild blueberry over Nature's creation as to make it a two-million-dollar annual crop, succeeded him.

A Division of Pomology (fruit investigations) was established in 1886. A Section of Mycology was created in the Division of Botany the same year; it was renamed the Section of Vegetable Pathology in 1887 and became a division in 1891. Fiber investigations began in the Department's Division of Statistics in 1889, the Office of Fiber Investigations being established the next year. The Division of Agrostology, later Division of Grass and Forage Plant Investigations, also originated in the Division of Botany, becoming independent on July 1, 1895. Plant exploration became an officially recognized activity of the Department in 1897, when David Fairchild persuaded Secretary Wilson to regard it in that light.

An order grouping some of the above-named agencies into an Office of Plant Industry was issued by Secretary James Wilson in October, 1900. The Agricultural Appropriation Act of July 1, 1901, added the Division of Botany to the group and renamed the agency the Bureau of Plant Industry. Later, by Executive Order, the Arlington Experiment Farm (started in 1901), tea investigations (dating back to Patent Office days), Foreign Seed and Plant Introduction (created in 1898), and the Congressional Seed Distribution were added to the new bureau. Ultimately other lines of investigation were added; and, in 1943, the agency assumed its present title, Bureau of Plant Industry, Soils, and Agricultural Engineering, but we are here concerned with plant investigation only.

It was largely through the efforts of Frank Lamson-Scribner (born Lamson, and Scribner by adoption) that the Section of Mycology was established in the Division of Botany with himself at its head. He had become an assistant botanist in the Division in 1885, after graduating from Maine Agricultural College. In 1888 he resigned to take the chair of botany at the University of Tennessee; and Beverly T. Galloway came in as chief of the Section of Vegetable Pathology, as it was now called.

Lamson-Scribner returned to the Department in 1894, after having been Director of the Tennessee Agricultural Experiment Station since 1889. He now organized the Division of Agrostology and served as its chief until 1901, when he resigned to go to the Philippine Islands to organize the Insular Bureau. He remained there until 1904, when he returned to take over the Department's work on exhibits, which he handled for two decades. His publications in the field of American grasses are classics.

Galloway was a Missouri-born failure in the drug business, which he had to give up on account of ill health. Graduating from Missouri University in 1884, he had done much horticultural work on the college farm and had become superintendent of greenhouses and gardens while still a student. He was appointed an assistant in the Department's Section of Mycology in 1887 and became its chief a little later. Later chief of the Division of Vegetable Physiology and Pathology, he was the first chief of the Bureau of Plant Industry, serving from its creation until 1913. He was later still Dean of Agriculture at Cornell and also an assistant secretary of agriculture.

Galloway's own researches were mainly on grapes, nursery crops, and nursery-crop diseases. He is most notable perhaps for having assembled around him a galaxy of brilliant plant scientists who built the foundation for the science of phytopathology and became internationally known. At William Saunders' death the work connected with Gardens and Grounds was also turned over to Galloway.

Among those who joined the staff of Galloway's division was Erwin F. Smith, already hard at work on peach yellows, in the fall of 1886. Effie A. Southworth, the first woman pathologist, came in shortly after Galloway. M. B. Waite joined in 1888, Newton Pierce in 1889, David Fairchild in 1890, Palemon H. Dorsett and Walter T. Swingle in 1891, and Herbert Webber in 1893. Albert F. Woods, then assistant botanist at the University of Nebraska, was brought into the division in 1893, and soon became assistant chief of the section. He was later president of Maryland University, director of research for the Department, and director of the Department of Agriculture Graduate School. These workers largely established plant pathology as a new science.

Consolidation of the plant-science workers under Galloway's influence proved to be an excellent idea. P. H. Dorsett was his intimate personal friend and played an important part in the spectacularly successful tests of fungicides on nursery stocks and grapevines. He also did extremely valuable work as an agricultural explorer in China, where he made the first successful large-scale importation of a number of soybean varieties. He was a true trailbreaker in the field of plant exploration.

Frederick V. Coville, who had been chief of the Division of Botany, came into the new bureau to continue his botanical investigations. His classic earlier work has been somewhat overshadowed by the remarkable things he accomplished later in breeding and improving the blueberry. Mark Carleton, who had but recently completed his spectacular introduction of durum wheats from Russia, headed work on cereal investigations and diseases.

O. F. Cook handled the tropical agricultural studies, but was to find his greatest field of accomplishment in creating new cotton varieties and developing improvements in the handling and growing of this crop. Walter T. Swingle went on to make the domestic culture of Smyrna figs possible by introducing the fig insect required for pollination, a piece of work widely reported in newspapers and magazines.

Swingle, also well known for his work in the breeding and taxonomy of citrus, brought the Garden of Allah to America by making possible the introduction and establishment of date-growing here on a commercial scale. This was the first planned introduction of a plant. Growers were told in advance when the date palm would be introduced and just what regions offered the best prospects for its profitable culture. They were even told which varieties would probably succeed best.

Carl S. Scofield pointed the way to successful dry-land (irrigation) agriculture in the West. Thomas H. Kearney went on to make possible a successful Egyptian (long-staple) cotton culture here. There were many workers in this remarkable galaxy. Some of the others who should be named are: L. C. Corbett, David Griffiths, Elmer D. Merrill, Carleton Ball, Rodney H. True, William A. Orton, Cornelius F. Shear, A. J. Pieters, L. F. Dewey, Charles J. Brand, Jared A. Smith, William A. Taylor, E. V. Wilcox, Ernest A. Bessey, Edgar Brown, V. K. Chesnut, and A. S. Hitchcock, whose *Grasses of the United States* is a book of fundamental scientific importance and lasting value.

Henry E. Van Deman, the Department's first pomologist, was so expert in budding trees at ten years of age that he produced better stock than his father was buying in commercial nurseries. The Civil War interrupted both his education and his fruit work, but afterward he moved to Kansas and returned to the latter so successfully that, in 1878, he became the first professor of horticulture at Kansas Agricultural College.

Then he left this position to return to his farm for life, or so he thought. However, he was mistaken. He was drafted in 1885 to form the Department's Division of Pomology. He was interested in all phases of horticulture and was a pioneer in advocating the introduction of plants from abroad. Finally, he believed no piece of research to be complete until the facts had been stated in such a way that others could use them.

In this belief he was quite in line with William Saunders and others. In 1869 Commissioner Capron brought to Saunders a letter from a missionary named Schneider at Bahia, Brazil, telling about a fine seedless orange which grew there. Saunders at once wrote for the plants, but when they came they were dry, worthless sticks. Saunders now suggested that the missionary hire someone to bud a few of the trees, then ship them billed to the Department.

In the course of time twelve budded navel-orange trees arrived. Buds from the Brazilian oranges were inserted on some orange trees then growing in a greenhouse which formerly stood on the north lawn of the present Administration Building's west wing. In 1873, two of the resulting plants found their way to the yard of the Tibbets home in Riverside, California. When they bore excellent seedless fruit, they attracted wide attention.

Soon propagating material was in great demand. The navel-orange industry, now a billion-dollar affair, thus rapidly got underway. The state of California has obtained far more value from it than from its famous gold mines. Perhaps because the California growers could not pronounce "Bahia," they began to call the orange Riverside Navel. When its culture spread to other sections, it was renamed the Washington Navel orange, possibly because it advertised Riverside too much.

One of the original trees died in 1921, but the other, or a shoot from it, bore four boxes of fruit annually as recently as 1940. It was then surrounded by a picket fence and duly identified by a plate. Incidentally, some linguists say that the word "citrus" itself resulted from a mistake on the part of an ancient Greek botanist who, 2,500 years ago, mistook an orange tree for a cedar and called the fruit "cedar apples." If so, misnaming oranges is no new game.

Considerably later than this introduction, plant exploration was placed upon a firmer foundation in the Department. This will be considered subsequently. In the meanwhile we should look into three extraordinary basic discoveries in the field of plant pathology, made late in the nineteenth and around the beginning of the twentieth centuries, when fundamental research was instituted by the above-mentioned Department scientists.

This brings us first to T. J. Burrill, a remarkable man born in Massachusetts in 1839, who was moved to Illinois as a child. Burrill attended a log schoolhouse, then graduated from the state normal school and became superintendent of schools in Urbana. He early gravitated towards botany mixed with entomology, and soon became assistant professor of natural history at the University of Illinois. For a half-century thereafter he was the moving spirit of the Illinois Horticultural Society and of the university's agricultural school, of which he later became vice president, then president.

Burrill was also president of the American Society of Bacteriology and the first modern microscopist. In 1877 he announced to the American Association for the Advancement of Science his discovery that fire blight of pears, then sweeping the Midwest, was caused by a bacterium. This view met skepticism in the United States and scorn in Europe. Burrill confirmed his finding and thus became a pioneer plant pathologist. He predicted that other plant diseases would be found to be caused bacterially, but did little to advance his view. That was left for Erwin F. Smith, though J. C.

Arthur of the New York (Geneva) Agricultural Experiment Station also held to Burrill's theory.

Although Thomas Taylor, the Department's microscopist, and others had done some investigation of plant diseases, dependable work of this sort was first inaugurated in Lamson-Scribner's time. Fundamental research, the value of which is still recognized, was conducted, as time and the increase of staff permitted, on the diseases of grapes and their control, on peach yellows and peach rosette, and on a rapidly increasing series of important diseases affecting other economic crop plants.

When B. T. Galloway assumed charge of this unit, it became almost at once the recognized center of phytopathological work in the Western World, and was probably surpassed nowhere. For some years particular emphasis was laid on life-history studies of pathogenes inclined to make economic trouble and on their control by spraying with fungicides. This line of work was by no means original with Galloway and his assistants, but they did advance it and bring it to general attention.

However, the work of Burrill and other American investigators who shared his views continued to be ignored and even ridiculed by outstanding German and British botanists. They took the purely a priori position that bacteria could not live and reproduce in plant tissue, hence certainly could not infect it with disease. It was the careful, detailed work of Erwin F. Smith which placed phytopathology on a firm basis.

Smith was a well-rounded man, an outstanding scientist, a father confessor to his men, a painter of considerable talent, a poet who wrote delicate and beautiful lines, a gentleman, and a scholar. I shall always remember him sitting in a cluttered basement room where he was as courteous to a brash young chemist as he could possibly have been to an eminent dignitary. He was to the bacteriology of plant diseases what Pasteur and Koch were to the early days of animal and human bacteriology.

Before 1901 Smith had founded phytopathology, or the science of plant pathology. He wrote its first textbook. Extremely versatile, his work ranged over a wide field, but his name is most closely associated with plant bacteriology. Typical of his thoroughness is the fact that he learned six foreign languages in order to read scientific papers in the original. His Bible was a Latin Vulgate, not an English translation.

Smith was born in New York but was educated at the University of Michigan. When he entered the Section of Mycology, Division of Botany, on September 20, 1886, he asked to be assigned the toughest problem it had. He was obliged—with peach yellows, then threatening to destroy the orchards. He gave relief by applying the technique of the cancer surgeon, cutting out the diseased parts of orchards, and the status of the problem remained the same thereafter until utterly new methods developed years later.

Here Smith foreshadowed his later work on the similarity between plant tumors and human cancer. For this he received a Certificate of Honor from the American Medical Association in 1913. Smith also did revolutionary work on the fusarium diseases of plants, on crown gall, and in 1920 he even forecast such things as penicillin. But most famous of all was his prolonged polemic with Alfred Fischer, outstanding German authority, on whether bacteria could cause plant disease.

This controversy began in 1893, and before the beginning of the new century Smith had gained complete acceptance for his point of view and had fully confirmed it in experimental work. Fischer took suicide as a way out. Smith thereafter continued his intensive studies of plant diseases for many years, his laboratory becoming a mecca for experts and students from all over the world. The crown-gall organism was discovered by C. O. Townsend and Nellie A. Brown, working under Smith's supervision.

Thus the occurrence of plant disease was removed from the sphere of mysteries usually attributed to Providence. For years farmers had regarded plant diseases as inevitable, and it was felt little could be done about them. Certainly the plant could not tell where it hurt or describe its internal symptoms. Even a veterinarian's life was hard enough; what a plant doctor could do nobody knew. Finally, the erratic behavior of these ailments, which often appeared suddenly and wiped out entire crops in large areas, brought growers to the Department of Agriculture for aid, and aid they received.

This brings us to Merton B. Waite, who joined the Department staff in 1888, retired in 1935 and lived in Washington, D. C., active in the Botanical Society and otherwise, until his death in early 1945. He was assigned the problem of pear blight, a disease which was devastating the pear orchards of the eastern states. Burrill, as we have seen, had proved that a bacterium caused this disease; Waite wondered how it spread so rapidly.

On the grounds of the Department of Agriculture in those days was a pear tree, which Waite began to watch as he came down to work. Sometimes he would find it in perfect shape one day yet entirely blighted the next, and he wondered about that. The honeybees liked the tree as a source of nectar and constantly visited its blossoms. Suddenly it occurred to Waite that these insects might innocently spread the contagion. He examined them, found the pear blight organism on their body parts, and reproduced the disease from these bacteria.

Thus Waite proved that insects could spread (act as vectors of) plant diseases, as outstanding a discovery in this field as was Theobald Smith's discovery in the Bureau of Animal Industry that they could also spread animal diseases—about which we shall talk later. This should not be taken to indicate that honeybees regularly go around spreading plant diseases. This useful and beneficial insect rarely does such a thing, but it can, and it happened to be the honeybee that was performing when Waite worked on pear blight.

J. G. Leach's *Insect Transmission of Plant Diseases* indicates that this was the first proof of the dissemination by insects of any disease affecting plants, animals, or men. Waite next devised and put into practice a method to control pear blight which is still used extensively, especially in the Pacific states. He also devised a method of diagnosis so rapid as to enable one to identify doubtful fresh material in twenty-four hours. The casual agent is named *Erwinia amylovora*, the first word commemorating Smith.

Incidentally David Fairchild tells of a Maryland Eastern Shore physician who had a fine pear orchard but doubted Waite's finding and dared him to come over and blight his trees. Waite took the dare and the orchard soon merited the doctor's utter chagrin. My mother remembered this incident, as the doctor was her father's family physician, as well as her own in childhood.

Waite was also the first to prove by experiment that many varieties of fruits (experts say clonal varieties of pomaceous fruits) require pollination by other varieties if they are to bear well. Hitherto varieties were planted separately and bore none too well. This finding was a great surprise to the horticultural world. It has had and is still having a profound effect on the interplanting of varieties to increase yields. We owe to it many more pears, apples, plums, cherries, and other fruits—grown both here and abroad— than we ever should have had otherwise.

Likewise, Waite was the first to show that the cedar is the alternate host of the rust fungus of apples. By patient and persistent effort he convinced the skeptical, hard-headed growers that the disease was only present when cedars were near, and the nearer and more abundant the cedars the more fungus spots on the apples. Thus the Virginia Cedar Law was enacted and has withstood many legal attacks by large landowners and others. Waite made many other useful investigations, but certainly those we have mentioned prove his worth to the American public.

Mention should be made at this point of the much later discovery by H. A. Allard that aphids were vectors of the mosaic virus affecting tobacco and other plants of economic value, and A. F. Woods first suggested that the tobacco virus (not then known as such of course) was nonliving material, perhaps a protein, a discovery later fully confirmed by others. In the category with Allard's finding was E. W. Brandes's work proving that *Aphis maydis* spreads sugar-cane mosaic. Both pieces of work, and many similar projects by Department employees, proved invaluable to growers.

We come now to a third remarkable discovery and a lantern-jawed New Englander named William Orton. He was a typical scientist in appearance and, though cursed with diabetes even before insulin became available, he let it interfere with his work as little as possible. Indeed, he made of it an opportunity for service, for Dr. Elliot P. Joslin tells how he cultivated in his own garden about one hundred different vegetables especially good for sufferers from this disease. Joslin says that his contributions to the understanding and treatment of diabetes compared favorably with his other scientific work.

When I knew Orton, he was in the terminal stages of the disease, which was complicated with heart involvement. He was physically weak, saw poorly through thick-rimmed glasses, and was almost totally deaf. Yet in the last months of his life he made a survey of Brazilian forests for the government of Brazil and, returning home, prepared so fine a document on the subject as to surprise those who thought only a specialist in this line could turn in such a performance. Soon afterward he died.

But we are concerned here with the events leading up to the publication of his classic bulletin on "Wilt Disease of Cotton and Its Control," *Bulletin No. 27* of the Division of Vegetable Physiology and Pathology. Orton was a very young man when he came to assist Erwin F. Smith. He had never seen a cotton plant in his life and when cotton wilt, then devastating the crop in many entire localities, was assigned him, he made a trip to the South to see what the plant looked like.

Orton almost immediately observed that for some reason certain plants did not contract wilt. Thus the great idea was born in his mind that it might be possible to breed from these resistant plants strains which would resist fungicidal or even bacterial plant diseases.

In his classic bulletin he showed that it was possible to select resistant plants from a population containing disease-resistant individuals and from them to breed strains resistant to cotton wilt. He turned to cowpeas and again developed wilt-resistant strains. Then he produced wilt-resistant watermelons by crossbreeding a palatable, edible melon with one not so palatable, which, however, was wilt resistant. In two years he had mapped out a solution, through selective breeding, to some of the most perplexing problems which faced Smith and which Smith had described in 1898 as the most threatening to crop plants.

The principles established by Smith, Waite, Orton, and their colleagues have had an inestimable but enormous monetary value. Scarcely a fruit, vegetable, or cereal crop exists today which has not suffered at some time from some serious ailment which threatened its annihilation. The breeding of plants resistant to bacterial, fungus, and virus diseases has saved many of these crops, the development of fungicides also doing its part—and Galloway and Waite had a hand in that.

Today fruits, vegetables, and cereals are bred not only for resistance to diseases but for resistance to drought, better tolerance for cold, improved palatability, enhanced processing quality, and increased food value. Department Bankhead-Jones laboratories are now working on the breeding of vegetables particularly adapted to growing conditions in the South, as well as on breeding for increased vitamin content, a quality that has been found to be genetically heritable. The same methods are applied to the improvement of pasture grasses.

More and more the agricultural scientist regards the fruit, grass, cereal, or vegetable as a mere complex of varied qualities and characters. He learns how to sort these out and he unearths the rules which govern their transmission. Thereafter he can tailor the desired qualities together to produce almost exactly what is wanted for a specific purpose. It is astonishing to think that this work all stems back to Orton's first look at a cotton field affected by wilt.

Work of this kind must be continuous because new plant diseases and new races or strains of bacteria, fungi, and viruses— with new insects to convey them—occur constantly. Plant resistance also appears to break down from time to time, probably because of mutations in the micro-organisms or viruses attacking it. The Department scientific work just outlined ranks with other basic scientific discoveries which established fundamental principles that, in turn, work successfully in a multitude of specific situations, only a few of which we can examine.

The toll levied by plant diseases on important crops averages from 5 to 17 per cent of their total value. This in part should be added to, but in part overlaps, the tax levied by insects. In an address delivered in December, 1936, G. H. Coons of the Bureau of Plant Industry tried to approximate the annual value to farmers of disease-resistant varieties of only the following: corn, wheat, oats, barley, flaxseed, beans, sugar cane, sugar beets, asparagus, cabbage, cantaloupes, celery, sweet corn, lettuce, peas, spinach, and tomatoes.

Coons arrived at the carefully calculated figure of sixty-five to seventy million dollars a year. This figure represents the value of disease-resistant varieties to farmers, as compared with the money these farmers would have obtained for their crops had they grown nonresistant varieties. This annual addition to farm wealth and human food and fiber production, in large part stemming from research by federal and state agricultural scientists, is seldom considered by the average layman sitting down to eat a meal in a city restaurant.

But it is right there, possibly in the sugar bowl. In 1926 sugarcane mosaic, a virus disease discovered in 1919, cut our total domestic cane-sugar production to one-fifth of normal. Thousands of acres of cane went unharvested because of this disease and its attendant root rots. Cane mills were virtually bankrupt, and the industry faced certain extinction. About the same time another virus disease, curly top, was causing failure of the sugar-beet crop in irrigated districts west of the Rockies. Uncle Sam was expected to do something about this.

Uncle Sam did. He found sugar-beet growing had been abandoned in many areas. Factories had been torn down and moved, only to fail again at new locations. Permanent shutdown of the western beet-sugar industry impended, involving loss or idleness of fifty million dollars' worth of machinery and equipment. Uncle Sam conquered both the cane and the beet virus diseases through the persons of E. W. Brandes and Eubanks Carsner.

Brandes became a plant explorer for the nonce. He went to the Dutch East Indies to find improved breeding stock of sugar cane. The introduction and resettlement of these mosaic-tolerant cane varieties in the United States was the first step in restoration of the cane-sugar industry. They, and a succession of resistant varieties bred from them, turned the trick.

Thus the cane-sugar industry was saved in the decade following 1926. The new varieties did more than merely meet the threat of the disease. They gave impetus to new phases of cane culture and so raised the level of productivity in the cane lands of the South that they now yield more sugar per acre than ever before in their history.

Breeding research also saved the western beet-sugar industry. Selection of the few resistant strains and plants here and there in fields stricken with curly top furnished the foundation material from which Eubanks Carsner and his associates produced a series of even more and more resistant sugar beets. Farmers now use these varieties in preference to others, knowing that curly top can reduce the crop 10 to 20 per cent but cannot annihilate it.

Heavy loss is being saved the beet-sugar industry by reason of this work. Indeed, it is questionable whether the industry could have survived at all in many parts of the West without this service by Department scientists. However, since still other diseases attack both sugar cane and sugar beets, continuing research is necessary here as elsewhere. Dr. Brandes has estimated that improved plant materials supplied by his Division of Sugar Plant Investigations have alone conserved capital and augmented the national wealth in the sum of one billion dollars.

In addition, our dependence upon Europe for beet seed, which lasted more than a century, ended through the work of this division, plus the discovery of photoperiodism by other Department workers, to be discussed later. Investigations undertaken in cooperation with the New Mexico Agricultural Experiment Station, showed that beet seed could be produced in the United States by a method differing radically from the conventional European procedure, which was lavish in the use of hand labor.

By this methodological revolution sugar-beet seed is readily produced with brief occupancy of the land and effective use of machines. Our entire domestic requirement of eighteen million pounds or more of curly-top-resistant sugar-beet seed can now be produced here, hence we entered the war entirely independent of Europe in this important respect.

It would be tedious to review all the instances in which disease in crops has been prevented by breeding work based on the discoveries of Smith, Waite, and Orton. A few, however, must be mentioned, J. B. Norton's work on asparagus, for one. His work began in 1906 and resulted in strains that were highly resistant to asparagus rust; after 1919 they replaced practically all other varieties the country over. Norton was among the early investigators to approach disease resistance from the standpoint of genetics.

The breeding of wilt-resistant tomatoes by Fred J. Pritchard is another example. As a result of his work such varieties made up one-fourth of this crop by 1933. The annual return to growers on tomatoes alone, based on work in the Division of Fruit and Vegetable Crops and Diseases, is at least six times what is required to finance the Division's entire program of work for one year.

For years the corn-canning industry was confined to New

England and the Atlantic seaboard because of a destructive bacterial wilt known as Stewart's disease. But federal and state breeders produced Golden Cross Bantam, a hybrid sweet corn well adapted to conditions in the Corn Belt as well as along the Atlantic coast. It is far more productive under adverse conditions than other varieties and the canning industry took to it and profited.

It was the plant scientists who developed a double-shot lettuce, resistant to both mildew and blight. The lettuce industry would have been ruined without plant research. Just recently Dr. Ross C. Thompson developed a lettuce which withstands midsummer temperatures without "bolting" to seed too quickly. It took ten or twelve years of selection and breeding to develop this fine Slobolt variety for home gardens, but the job was done.

A few years ago, while a lively politician poured ridicule on the "long-haired" scientists of the Department of Agriculture for spending millions of dollars to develop one potato, the Katahdin (named after a mountain in Maine) was developed. It was highly productive and likewise resistant to mild mosaic. The scientist who had overall charge of the work was bald! But from Katahdin better strains of potatoes de luxe have been developed. The introduction to the trade of these potato strains alone has more than paid for all the potato investigations ever undertaken in the Department of Agriculture throughout its history.

The National Potato Breeding Program developed from this work. Disease-resistant strains then spread rapidly. Ten varieties distributed under the program constituted 28 per cent of the nation's certified potato seed in 1942. They largely accounted for the 13.4 bushel-per-acre increase in average yield in that year, as compared with the 1930–39 average. As for Katahdin, it has proved highly adaptable and is the outstanding late commercial variety. It is very popular in South America and has revolutionized potato culture in Australia.

Nor have sweet potatoes been overlooked. Not only is there the entomological project in the southern commercial sweet-potato-growing country which is steadily pushing the sweet-potato weevil back to the wild morning-glories as explained previously, but disease resistance has been bred into this morning-glory itself. Disease used to reduce this crop by over 60 per cent. Growers

Famous galaxy of plant scientists

Top row: Walter T. Swingle, Merton B. Waite, Mark A. Carleton, A. F. Woods
Bottom row: David Fairchild, P. H. Dorsett, B. T. Galloway, Erwin F. Smith

On the "golden jubilee" of his entrance into the Department, David Fairchild receives the Frank N. Meyer Medal from Secretary Henry A. Wallace

worked more and more to produce less and less and hoped meanwhile that the agricultural scientists would come to their aid. They did, and these heavy losses are now things of the past.

Then there was cabbage, which broke down with the yellows, a disease caused by a soil fungus which never seemed to die out, no matter how long the land lay fallow. The breeding of disease-resistant cabbage solved the problem and saved the industry. Returns to growers rose, while dozens of sauer kraut plants which were rotting away in disuse were again put to useful purposes. L. R. Jones of the University of Wisconsin initiated this project, which soon became a co-operative task with Department workers.

Conquest of celery mosaic reduced losses of Florida growers from 60 to a mere 6 per cent of their crop. The newer strawberry varieties produced by research are finer and stand shipping better than those that were grown before. This tale could go on for a long time; it seems never-ending.

Quite as remarkable work has been done on cereals. In 1935 an epidemic of stem rust did damage to the North Dakota wheat crop which ran into millions of dollars. Co-operative research by Department and Minnesota Agricultural Experiment Station workers resulted in the development of Thatcher wheat, resistant to most of the known rust strains and able so far to resist any that have been present in quantity.

It is impossible to plan a production program based upon disease-susceptible cereals. Rusts and smuts not only decrease yields but also lower the quality of the grain. Gains in quality of resistant varieties are often as important as increased production. A few years ago a large part of the wheat from considerable areas in the Northwest was smutty, dockage was heavy, and prices suffered accordingly. These losses were eliminated by research.

T. Ray Stanton of the Department of Agriculture has become a national specialist on oats. There is an outpost of federal workers at Ames, Iowa, co-operating with the state scientists in breeding oats resistant to crown and stem rusts and the various smuts affecting this grain. Their efforts have met with remarkable success. The planting of new strains which they have developed has already increased average oat yields in Iowa about 20 per cent.

The disease-resistant strains are spreading to other states. In

general, Iowa oat growers annually profit from $25,000,000 to $50,-
000,000 more by planting these strains. These figures are based on
controlled field tests in thirty counties. In Wisconsin growers
gained sufficient extra from these oats in a single year to finance
all that state's agricultural experiment work for the past twenty
years!

Until late years comparatively little attention was given to
diseases attacking grasses and legumes. But they have undoubtedly
long caused heavy losses by both reducing yields and lowering
the nutritive value of forage crops. For several years prior to 1925
farmers in some of the best alfalfa districts reported losses of stands
within two or three years, whereas the crop formerly survived a
decade or more. In 1925 bacterial wilt, produced by a hitherto unknown organism, was found responsible for these losses.

The disease rapidly spread east and west, destroying hundreds
of thousands of acres of this crop. By testing alfalfas from all parts
of the world, scientists found resistant varieties in Turkistan. Unfortunately these were susceptible to other ailments which afflict
alfalfa. But, through selection and hybridization, it proved possible to develop a strain resistant to bacterial wilt and quite satisfactory in other respects.

Likewise, the development of red-clover strains resistant to
anthracnose and of improved sweet-clover types constitutes an
important contribution. The introduction and extension of the
use of lespedeza is another big accomplishment of recent years,
for from the first experimental planting of this crop—a Korean
lespedeza—made in 1921, have sprung the thirty or more million
acres now grown.

Here we are really considering a plant introduction. That
makes relevant the work of O. F. Cook who, during a visit to
Guatemala, in 1902, discovered that the cotton grown there by
the Indians was not troubled by boll weevils. In 1904 he set out
to learn the cause of this immunity. It developed that an antlike
insect protected the cotton. Cook was instructed to bring home
colonies of this insect for use in Texas. This he did. Weevil-resistant
characters were also discovered in native cottons of Central America and southern Mexico. These cottons were introduced here.

Though cotton had been grown and observed for generations,

Cook was the first investigator to observe that the plant had branches of two kinds. Growth conditions surrounding the young plants determined the development of these branches. Cook saw that the branching habits could be controlled by suitable spacing of the plants in rows. He proved this in many experiments. Fruiting branches appeared earlier if the plants were left closer in the rows. That considerably shortened the fruiting season and tended to prevent damage by the weevil, who arrived later.

The old method of spacing produced big branches which bore bolls that ripened at different times over a long season. But Cook's conclusions about spacing to defeat the weevil were contrary to current opinion among growers, planters, and scientists as well. However, Cook's ideas slowly gained acceptance, and they formed the basis for a fundamental change in cotton growing throughout the world. They helped to make the crop profitable where the weevil had formerly destroyed it.

Cook and others who worked with cotton also insisted that variations in the cotton plant in the South, which were customarily attributed to a so-called "running out" of the seed stock, were principally due to the fact that seed of different varieties became mixed in gins and thereafter cross-pollinated in the field. He therefor began a campaign for one-variety cotton communities, and again had difficulty, but he was finally successful. The method assumed new significance when Acala cotton was introduced from southern Mexico, improved here, and became well adapted to the areas where it alone is produced. Pure-seed, one-variety cotton communities rapidly extended plantings of Acala and other varieties in California and elsewhere.

Rubber, coffee, cacao, and other tropical plants were studied during the exploration for new cotton types. The first detailed study of rubber culture in southern Mexico was made by Cook in 1902. In 1903 he published a bulletin on the culture of the Central American rubber tree. He aided in the discovery of new species of rubber trees. Later his experiments showed that rubber trees could be grown in Florida, south of Miami—even the Brazilian or Para rubber tree called "Hevea," which was cultivated in East Indies plantations.

Cook's work leads naturally to a discussion of Thomas H.

Kearney, another Department cotton wizard, who retired in 1944 after a service of almost half a century. He entered the Department as a botanist and became notable for his work on cotton, but flowering plants and ferns of Arizona and many other subjects came within the scope of his activities. Early in this century he also visited North Africa to study date culture and the production of olives without irrigation. Subsequently he worked largely on dry-land crops suitable for our Southwest. He built up invaluable information on the alkali tolerance of plants.

This marked the beginning of his interest in cotton. Between 1900 and 1913 he was responsible, with a few others, for the introduction of long-staple cotton into this country. Hitherto we had imported this Egyptian cotton. Such fabric as is made from this cotton came into heavy wartime demand for airplane manufacture, heavy-cord truck tires, barrage balloon cloth, machine-gun belts, parachute webbing, and other uses where high-tensile strength is essential.

All-told Kearney developed four famous cotton varieties, each one of which proved better than its predecessor. Kearney's researches formed the actual basis for the American-Egyptian cotton industry in this country, and in 1943 over 145,000 acres of this cotton were grown here. However, we are now well over into the field of plant introduction, the first activity in the field of agricultural science that was undertaken in this country.

Indeed in the early days of the United States, Benjamin Franklin, Thomas Jefferson, and others sent back here from Europe plants and seeds which they thought would be of value to American farmers. As we have seen, exploration to find disease-resistant plants, and their introduction into this country, has formed an integral part of research on crop diseases. We have had many plant explorers, but David Fairchild, author of *The World Was My Garden*, who was from 1908 until 1928 in charge of the Division of Plant Exploration and Introduction, possibly became best known to the public of them all.

Since 1898, when the Department began to list its introductions, more than 150,000 items have been recorded as introduced for trial. At the so-called Bamboo, or Barbour Lathrop Plant Introduction Garden, outside Savannah, there are many grasses,

shrubs, trees, nuts, fruits, and other plants under trial after introduction, in addition to well over a hundred varieties of bamboo.
There are also other plant introduction gardens; David Fairchild
maintains one of these as a Department collaborator, in and around
his home, the Kampong, at Coconut Grove, Florida.

To Fairchild have been attributed the introduction of crops
which profit American growers $100,000,000 every year. How-
ever, many others assisted in this work, among them N. E. Hansen,
Frank N. Meyer, Mark Carleton, Wilson Popenoe, P. H. Dorsett,
W. J. Morse, and Seaman A. Knapp. (The last was also founder
of the Department's Extension Service.) O. F. Cook and Thomas
Kearney should be added, as well as the present chief of the division,
B. Y. Morrison.

To such explorers we owe durum wheat, Japanese rice and
Sudan grass. We also owe to them a large acreage of Egyptian
feteria sorghum, another of Peruvian hairy alfalfa, and others of
numerous soybean varieties. They brought us sugar canes and
bamboos of many kinds, Chinese jujubes and persimmons, tung
trees, Chinese cabbage, Japanese flowering cherries, the dasheen,
the papaya, Sarawak beans, yam beans, Quetta nectarines, figs,
dates, mangoes, and alligator pears.

There might have been more and many of them would quickly
have been more popular, had we Americans not been so tradi-
tion-bound in food habits, a perversity which disgusted Fairchild.
But our Division of Plant Exploration and Introduction is famous
now from Capetown to London and from Java to Rio de Janeiro.
Fairchild himself encircled the globe again and again, usually financed by his millionaire friend, Barbour Lathrop, who also bought
the grounds for plant-introduction gardens like the one outside
Savannah which bears his name.

Hansen gathered many plants in Russia, Siberia, Turkestan,
Finland, the Caucasus, China, Japan, and Manchuria. He discovered the Hollander, Meyer, in a St. Louis Botanical Garden and
sent him to China, Mongolia, Turkestan, and Manchuria, where
he was insulted, assaulted, denied entrance, denied exit, arrested,
mobbed, attacked by footpads, deserted by guides—but he brought
home the plants. His greatest gift to us was the Mongolian elm.
He finally was drowned, appropriately enough in the Yangtze.

Mark Carleton and his hardy cereals from the Kirghiz steppes we shall mention later. Popenoe was past master of tropical fruit culture, was discovered when twenty years of age by Fairchild, and is now memorialized by the avocado on our tables. Walter Swingle ransacked the oases of Algeria and Tunisia, the stately groves of the land of the Pyramids, the ancient plantations of Bagdad, and even the Garden of Eden, to find dates that would grow in his native land.

Dorsett and Morse roamed Manchuria, infested though it was with robber bands and Japanese agents, to procure useful soybean varieties. Cook we have mentioned. Knapp gave our dying rice industry a transfusion, which brought it back to life, by introducing upland rice from Japan. In addition, ladino clover, timber bamboo, mangoes, crested wheat grass, Bahía grass, hardy plums, hardier apples and pears, special broomcorn millet, Cossack alfalfa, cold-resistant almonds, blight-resistant chestnuts and pears, puckerless persimmons, odorless cabbage, and hardy yellow roses at least deserve mention here, for we owe them also to the plant explorers.

Fairchild's successors, Knowles Ryerson and B. Y. Morrison, have built well on the foundations put down by Fairchild. Ryerson started out knowing what he wanted and going to the place where it was most likely to be found. This new technique brought results. Morrison, educated at the University of California and at Harvard, came to the Department in 1920. His world-wide travels gave him a splendid background. He has been directing the National Arboretum since 1937, making it one of the finest in the world. Since 1926 he has been editor of the *National Horticultural Magazine*, and he is also a popular lecturer and after-dinner speaker.

Despite these activities he manages to keep fairly well in the background. He says he is a mere front to the real men who work with him. But his pride is justified in the well-equipped plant-introduction gardens and greenhouses and the staff of highly qualified workers he has developed in this country.

The techniques of plant exploration in use today are quite different from those of Carleton's time, but Carleton's also worked. Mark Alfred Carleton came to the Department in 1894, after having been educated in Kansas. He left on his first trip as a plant explorer on July 4, 1898, spent most of his time in Russia, and returned six months later with large collections of durum wheats, bread wheats, oats, barley, emmer, rye, corn, millet, buckwheat, and peas. He was a man of erratic and tempestuous personality who easily made implacable enemies, some of whom tended to deny him credit for his actual accomplishments which, on the other hand, were much overrated by certain popular writers.

Durum wheat was not unknown here, having been introduced by Russian immigrants to the Dakotas and elsewhere as early as 1864. It originally failed to establish itself in the East, often being dropped there after a single, unfavorable year. Its kernels were hard and difficult to mill and people tried to use it for bread, whereas it was better adapted to macaroni. What Carleton did was to recognize and publicize these facts, study the Russian soils and climates where this wheat was grown, and find similar regions here to which it would be adaptable. He then sent seed to his co-operators, asking them to continue their trials over several years.

As a result the production of durum wheat grew from 60,000 bushels in 1901, to 7,000,000 bushels in 1903, and 50,000,000 in 1906. The years fully vindicated Carleton's assumption that durum wheat had a real place here in the New World. The durum crop now comprises about 6 per cent of our total wheat crop; because of its high gluten content it is especially useful in making macaroni and related products.

But Carleton was also a distinguished plant pathologist. He wrote comprehensively on cereal rusts prevalent in the United States, and was one of the first to make inoculations under careful control and to recognize that both the rusts and the cereals must be studied. Carleton had advanced ideas on the possibility of improving cereals by hybridization. His *Basis for the Improvement of American Wheats* pointed the way in 1900. In 1916 he published *The Small Grains*, a landmark in creating the science of agronomy, much used as a textbook, in which he brought together in orderly form the vast literature on crop improvement. Hansen, Swingle, and Scofield also participated with him in wheat explorations. Indeed, it was their reports after trips to Russia which first interested him in going there.

Carleton is therefore largely responsible for establishing a new industry in this country, based on a plant not hitherto grown here on an important scale. Swingle, who was associated with him on durum-wheat experiments, retired in 1941 after fifty years of service. Today millions of us enjoy the fruits of his research, which later dealt chiefly with making successful the domestic culture of date palms and Smyrna-type figs.

When he undertook his investigations, the latter had been introduced into California but would not bear. He went to Syria and Greece to study the fig's sex life in its native habitat. There he found that certain wasps were bred by the natives and used to pollinate the trees. They were the missing factor in the United States. Swingle sent back wild figs bearing the fig wasp from Syria in 1899. The wasps became established in California. They fed first on the male fig trees, then fertilized the blossoms of the females by crawling into them laden with pollen. Many scientists of the day viewed all these activities with amusement, but the idea worked. The large Smyrna-type fig industry in California and Arizona today proves that.

Swingle also produced the tangelo by crossing the tangerine and the grapefruit. He developed many new and useful varieties of citrus fruits. He and Kearney established the date industry here, whereas we had previously depended wholly upon imports. Kearney tells how, when they were searching for good varieties of dates in Africa, some of the best disappeared, the very trees being uprooted. It developed that the rulers of local districts demanded the very best fruit for their banquets, taking the entire crop of finer varieties from whatever groves they wished, and the owners of the groves had uprooted the trees bearing the finest fruit to prevent paying the undesirable levy!

Old Gulian P. Rixford, whose life began at seventy, joined the Department at that age in 1908 to take charge of certain of the work on Smyrna figs on the west coast. Actually neither a botanist nor horticulturist but a civil engineer graduated from McGill, Rixford became interested in fruits and vegetables while a waterfront newspaperman in San Francisco. He worked for the Department for twenty years, received the Meyer medal for distinguished service in the field of foreign-plant introduction soon after he was ninety-two, and was going strong towards the century mark when killed in a railroad accident about a year later.

Turning now to grasses, we find that C. V. Piper was instrumental in getting that excellent emergency hay and pasture plant, Sudan grass, introduced into this country about 1909. From an original eight-ounce packet of seed the use of the grass spread to practically every state. In 1941 we produced nearly 93,000,000 pounds of seed alone! Sudan grass fills in admirably practically everywhere during periods of drought injury or winter killing. Piper also made vigorous efforts around 1907 to obtain additional varieties of soybean for seed, from consuls, missionaries, seedsmen, government agencies, and foreign explorers. Since 1898 the Department has secured more than fifteen thousand introductions of soybeans from many far lands, giving us a wide selection of varieties for many uses.

William J. Morse, who came directly to the Department from Cornell after taking his degree in 1907, has for years been testing soybean varieties. He made extensive oriental trips to procure them. He is the outstanding American soybean authority of the day and deserves particular credit for bringing about the use of this bean as human food in this country, as well as for providing varieties needed industrially. Incidentally the soybean is the only bean practically without starch, welcome news to persons trying to reduce their weight.

At present more than 150 varieties of soybeans are handled by growers and seedsmen, nearly all of which resulted from introductions and selections by Department workers. Before the Department took up the matter, not more than eight varieties were available. These were grown only in limited areas. By contrast, the value of the crop was $300,000,000 in 1942, and it increased immensely under wartime urgency as a source of fats and oils.

The introduction of crested wheat grass, a long-lived, cold- and drought-resistant bunch grass native to the cold, dry regions of Russia and Siberia, occurred in 1898, and by 1920 it was being produced commercially in Montana, the state experiment station of which ably aided this project. The grass is a soil saver and a fine native-range immigrant, superior to grasses already growing thereon. It is invaluable to many northern-plains stockmen and restores otherwise unproductive range land besides.

Plant scientists have not neglected the storage and transportation of fruits and vegetables. The development of oiled wraps to control apple scald, work performed by Charles Brooks, J. S. Cooley, and D. F. Fisher, provides an inexpensive means of protecting apples in storage or transit.

The early history of the refrigeration of fruits and vegetables will be found outlined in an article by William A. Taylor, then an assistant pomologist but later chief of the Bureau of Plant Industry, in the Department of Agriculture *Yearbook* for 1900. The work of G. Harold Powell on the decay of oranges in transit, and Powell and S. F. Fulton's work on apples, pears, and peaches in cold storage was pioneering and outstanding. Their early publications formed the real foundation for a tremendous expansion of commercial cold storage and refrigeration in transit.

The railroads have continually looked to Department plant scientists for advice and for the testing of new developments in refrigerator-car equipment. The improvements made in such equipment are based largely upon the research of federal and state scientists. More recently the development of portable precooling facilities by the installation of fans in the cars has resulted in the main from the investigation of these scientists. The technique is now used in hundreds of thousands of cars of produce each season.

The modern refrigerator car is really a war baby of World War I. The United States standard refrigerator car was built to specifications drafted by a committee working under the auspices of the Railroad Administration. It was composed of engineers representing the Administration, refrigerator-car lines, railroads, and the Department of Agriculture. Full advantage was taken of the store of data accumulated in this important field by Department scientific work.

Just recently when Georgia growers of tomato plants found that their product became diseased in shipment north—and 6,000 carloads, 500,000 tomato plants to the car, are shipped each season—Department scientists in Orlando were hurry-called for aid. Despite the idea of the growers that cooling would fatally chill the tender young plants, the scientists quickly solved the problem by developing a method of moderately cooling the cars which got the plants to their destination safe and sound.

The Department has also made notable contributions in the

matter of treatments, particularly the borax wash, to prevent citrus decay. It has established maturity standards for harvesting both citrus and deciduous fruits. It has found how to remove spray residues from fruits effectively, how to use carbon dioxide to supplement refrigeration in transporting certain fruits, how sulfur dioxide should be used in transporting grapes, and the effect of various temperatures on the ripening of fruits; and it has undertaken helpful investigations on diseases causing heavy losses in post-harvest operations.

When tung trees began to be grown in this country, it was not long before those who grew them clamored for Department aid, which was given by both chemists and plant scientists. Going their own way, using commercial fertilizers, they were often killing their trees, while the young trees rarely grew as they should. Department scientists discovered the proper conditions for the trees, told the growers what trace minerals were needed in the soil, how much water, the proper type of cultivation, and then went on to develop a superior method of expressing the oil.

Thus a new industry is being founded which provides an oil we hitherto had to import to make waterproof varnishes and for other purposes. It has been nursed along every step of the way by the patient activities of the same type of Department scientists who generally solve the problems that threaten the destruction of so many agricultural industries. At times it is the purest kind of pure research which provides the aid too.

Between 1920 and 1925 W. W. Garner and H. A. Allard were working on what is known as "photoperiodism." They showed that plants respond to length of day, as it was already known they did to temperature and light intensity. After that fundamental discovery, which was embodied in a research paper published by the Department that probably has been quoted more than any other it ever issued, experiments were carried out to determine the nature of these responses.

It developed that the growth, flowering, and fruiting characteristics of many plants, including many of great agricultural importance, varied with the light period to which they were exposed while growing. That seemed an interesting botanical discovery of little practical significance, but many useful results grew out of it.

Thus, instead of having to run lengthy and expensive field experiments to determine what plants will grow best in a given locality, scientists now carry out inexpensive experiments in a greenhouse, making the length-of-day conditions correspond to those of the locality in question. If certain varieties of plants prove poorly adapted to the day length and other conditions under study, different varieties can usually be bred which will thrive in the locality.

Now, as a result of this basic discovery, we produce our own beet seed; we have found onions which will produce bulbs in short-day or in long-day regions as needed; and we have strawberries which will fruit abundantly in the long days of the North and others which fruit best in the shorter days of the South. Even florists now hasten or delay the flowering of plants as they wish by control of the greenhouse light period.

Then it was found that exposure to light near the middle of a dark period gave results similar to those from a full-exposure. Grafting a single leaf of an Agate soybean, which blooms under long-day conditions, to a Biloxi soybean, which requires a short day, enabled the latter to bloom under long-day conditions. Facts such as these open fascinating fields for future plant research. The discovery that trees could be sprayed with dilute hormone solutions to prevent premature fruit-drop, and that the growth of roots, stems, buds, and flowers could be accelerated or controlled by the use of growth-regulating substances or plant hormones, combined to provide new horizons for plant workers.

Hundreds of workers in many places are slowly piecing together the great mosaic of scientific knowledge. Insofar as what they do is done well, it proves of value later. DDT was originally made in the laboratory by an organic chemist, and penicillin was apprehended by a medical research worker, much before these two substances became widely publicized and of outstanding importance in World War II. Many years ago a Swiss botanist discovered quite by accident that minute quantities of copper would kill an alga known as green slime and frog spittle. Fifty years later Department of Agriculture scientists put this information to practical use, thus ending a disease of cress that was running water-cress growers out of business.

Thus the work continues constantly and endlessly. Workers in the realm of pure research are making findings and codifying information that will be of immense value years or even generations hence. Among these are many Department of Agriculture research workers in the fields of plant science. In conclusion, a few more important projects in this field, some of them quite recent, will be listed.

Carl S. Scofield, who retired early in 1945 after forty-five years of service, did much to turn our desert regions into gardens. Graduating from Minnesota University, he came to Washington to do this about 1900, though he was unaware of his mission at the time. Eventually he had field stations in operation on six reclamation projects—all in addition to his work on durum wheat, Egyptian cotton, and other problems. Improved dry-land-culture methods have also tremendously increased the acre-yield of wheat even in arid and semi-arid Kansas counties.

Allard, who worked on photoperiodism, did outstanding work also on tobacco mosaic. N. A. Cobb was world famous for his exact researches on nematodes. Cornelius L. Shear became notable for his work on the sac fungi, carried on for fifty years, but only as a side line and as time permitted, for Shear did much other work of great economic significance on the life history of fungi causing destructive diseases of grapes, cranberries, and other small fruits. Preventive and control methods were then developed.

The discovery that bean seed grown in the West is free from anthracnose has proved valuable to farmers of the East and South. In June, 1942, it was announced that the waxy sorghums might be utilized in part as a source for starch that would substitute admirably for imported root starches. The Chinese have grown these glutinous sorghums for centuries, and they were introduced here some while back, but it was Department scientists who, in 1921, observed a resemblance between the endosperm of waxy sorghum and the waxy corn introduced from the Orient some years earlier.

Thereafter the investigators tracked down all the important American commercial sorghum varieties with waxy seed. Some of them had been grown here for sirup, forage, or grain since 1854, but they now went under test by food manufacturers and makers of adhesives and other starch products. It was found that a starch can be made from them which compares favorably with tapioca and other root starches, and commercial processing is underway.

The method of producing hybrid corn was suggested by G. H. Shull in 1909. The combined efforts of many state, federal, and outside breeders, including Henry A. Wallace, were required to adapt this idea to the point where it increased our corn yields 20 per cent. The Department has worked on the problem since 1916. The first hybrid seed involving inbred lines were produced in Connecticut in 1921. In 1943 the gain in corn yield due to the use of hybrid lines was sufficient to make an extra fifty-four pounds of pork for every man, woman, and child in the country.

When World War II cut off our quinine supply, the Department's plant scientists co-operated with heroic Colonel Arthur F. Fischer in starting cinchona to grow over here. Colonel Fischer somehow managed to get out of the Philippines after the fall of Bataan with two million cinchona seeds. The seed ultimately reached the Department, were planted in sphagnum moss in greenhouses, and 90 per cent of them germinated. By the end of 1945 nearly a quarter of a million vigorous seedlings could be shipped to South and Central America for planting. In somewhat similar manner abaca (Manila hemp) was successfully introduced into the American tropics by H. T. Edwards, a Department scientist, giving us an urgently needed raw material during World War II.

The Department also provided authentic information on hydroponics, the tricky business of raising vegetables in water culture. They showed the armed forces how to grow fresh vegetables on volcanic islands such as Ascension, using this method, which requires special skill and training, though it is neither feasible nor practicable for home food production. At the same time the plant specialists provided commercial food dehydrators with information regarding the species of fruits and vegetables which were best adapted to this form of food processing, just as they had given other firms basic knowledge on fruits which made the most acceptable products in freezing.

Too little room remains to do this agency justice. However, mention at least and at last should be made of versatile 2, 4-D (2, 4-dichlorophenooxyacetic acid, if you must be formal about it) originally discovered to be a plant-growth–regulating substance

useful in preventing premature fruit drop. More recently it has
turned out to be capable of making weeds grow themselves to
death in agony, while leaving lawn grass relatively unmolested.
J. W. Mitchell and J. W. Brown of Plant Industry Station, Beltsville, Maryland, have worked out its mode of action; it utterly
depletes the weed's food reserve. The chemical also speeds the
ripening of bananas and prevents growth of certain bacteria. It
has a great future before it—as does the plant-science work of the
Department of Agriculture.

From the standpoint of home food production the victory gardens represented the most widespread practical application of plant
science in the history of the world. More than three million copies
of the *Victory Garden Bulletin* were distributed in one year, and
they were really used. With this notable mass practical application of their knowledge is concluded the discussion of research by
the Department's plant specialists.

CHAPTER 8

Man Can Help to Make a Tree

Y[OU PROBABLY TEND TO THINK], offhandedly, that a forest is a queer place to do research.[1] Does one take to the woods when one desires to undertake scientific investigation? Well, consider this.

Along with its other magnificent endowments, from movie stars to tropical fruit, California has some of the most inflammable forests in the United States. When fire once starts in these chaparral forests, it burns everything to the ground. No debris is left, and a tremendous erosion problem is created. The steep Southern California mountains are composed of very old granitic rock which readily breaks up into sand or gravel in lack of binding material. The force of erosion during rainstorms is terrific.

How could this be remedied? It was imperative to prevent great damage to agricultural lands below. Scientists long pondered how to put a quick cover over these burned-out forests, to protect the soil and prevent the cutting action of water at the surface. After testing more than one hundred plants and plant species, Forest Service workers found the answer—in a mustard plaster. Common black mustard qualified in every way.

The seeds were readily available commercially, in a country largely populated by hot-dog consumers; they were very light, running 275,000 to the pound; and 10,000 acres a week could be sown with them from airplanes. The seeds lacked wings, hence

---

[1] The basic material from which this chapter was written is a manuscript document on the research achievements of the Forest Service, prepared some years ago by the late Clark F. Hunn, long a scientific editor in this agency. Many changes were made; many sentences had to be shortened; much technical matter had to be simplified. Considerable biographical matter, the material on forest pathology, and many new items were added to bring the account up to date.

could not be blown long distances, they germinated quickly even on slightly moist ground, rapidly sent down roots and, when they grew leaves, these formed a rosette flat on the ground. Temperature and weather permitting, the plants were waist-high in a few weeks.

So they passed the mustard around. It has been used not only in California but in Idaho and in Montana. A program of quick mustard sowing will follow any fires which may ravage mountain slopes similar to those in California or even elsewhere where rapid cover is necessary. This gives a mere peek into the kind of research foresters carry on in the effort to help God make more trees and better soil. That is why we have a Forest Service, constantly to view with alarm lest we be caught with our natural resources down; that is also why we have a Soil Conservation Service, to be discussed later.

Public alarm over the rapid depletion of our timber resources brought the Forest Service into being. The seed from which it sprang was a paper delivered in Portland, Maine, in August, 1873, by Franklin B. Hough, of Lowville, New York. Hough, who was mentioned in an earlier chapter, had made and published many statistical and historical studies, and was familiar with the plants and agriculture of New York. His paper was entitled "The Duty of Governments in the Preservation of Forests."

Meanwhile Congress was memorialized and pressure was put upon state legislatures to take action on forest preservation. Under an act passed August 16, 1876, the Commissioner of Agriculture was directed to spend, from the fund appropriated for seed purchase and distribution, $2,000 as compensation for a man qualified to report comprehensively on forestry. Hough was that man. He was appointed to conduct forestry investigations in late August of the same year.

After extensive western travel Hough made his report, a document of 650 pages, dealing broadly with forestry matters here and in Europe. Congress received the report on December 13, 1877. Hough served the Department seven more years. In 1881 a Division of Forestry was established. Later Nathaniel Eggleston succeeded Hough, serving three years. The investigations of these men were comparatively rudimentary, but they aroused sentiment. In one instance they sent questionnaires to local army posts for information on forest conditions near by. Hough made three reports to Congress, all told, and Eggleston made one. Special agents were used to some extent to study forestry methods abroad and in the far West of this country.

The Division of Forestry attained permanent statutory rank in June, 1886. Three months earlier Bernhard E. Fernow had succeeded Eggleston, and he now became chief of the division. The young research organization sought to make special studies in forest description, botany, influences, and products, and also to look into tree planting and forest mensuration. This was an ambitious program, but Fernow was a rather remarkable individual.

Born in Prussia, he had been educated at Königsberg and the Münden Forest Academy. Thereafter he came to this country and established, in Brooklyn, an electrolytic works to salvage scrap tin. Next he became manager of Pennsylvania forest properties owned by certain mining interests and, in 1883, secretary of the American Forestry Association. He was the first professional forester in the federal service and headed the Division of Forestry until 1898, when he left to organize the state college of forestry at Cornell.

Thereafter Fernow became professor of forestry at Pennsylvania State College and later dean and organizer of the forestry faculty at Toronto. Fernow's *Economics of Forestry* was the first work of its kind in the English language. He remained at Toronto until his death.

He initiated important lines of forest investigation in the United States, promoting both federal and state legislation to prevent forest fires. Mainly through his efforts legislation was finally enacted which provided for the national forest system he proposed between 1891 and 1897, and it went into the custody of the Department of the Interior, which, however, constantly called upon the forest experts of the Department of Agriculture for scientific advice.

Fernow's successor was Gifford Pinchot, to whom the woods were a childhood passion. He graduated from Yale in 1889, took a European trip to learn all he could about forestry, and then, in 1891, began the first systematic forestry work in this country at George W. Vanderbilt's Biltmore, North Carolina, estate. So successful was he that he opened a New York office as a consulting forester soon afterward. He became a member of the National Forest Commission in 1896.

From 1898 Pinchot was head of the Division of Forestry, of the Bureau of Forestry formed in 1901, and of the Forest Service created in 1905, when the national forests were placed in the custody of the Department of Agriculture. President Taft dismissed Pinchot for insubordination as a result of the widely publicized controversy he carried on with Richard A. Ballinger, secretary of the interior. His later life is well known. He was one of the founders of the Yale School of Forestry.

Under Pinchot and his successor, Henry S. Graves, scientific and practical experimentation began which added to our fundamental knowledge of forest management and the utilization of forest products. Information had to be obtained about the best management practices for many different types of forests all over the country, as well as about structural characteristics of native trees and of foreign woods, for purposes of comparison.

All of the following came under investigation: Experimental reforestation; the best silvicultural systems and the degrees of cutting most likely to foster natural reproduction; the effect of forest cover on stream flow, excessive wind movement, and evaporation; the deterioration of fire-killed and fallen timber; the damage caused by fires of different intensities; and the growth, yield, utilization, and life histories of trees of many varieties.

Later still, studies of forest products, undertaken mainly at the extraordinarily fine Forest Products Laboratory, at Madison, Wisconsin, have dealt with preservative treatments of woods used for different purposes; finding new uses for wood or lumber that was previously neglected or wasted; increasing the yield and quality of crude turpentine; the manufacture of wood-distillation products; the kiln-drying of timber; the physical properties of woods with respect to their adaptability for different purposes; how to keep wood from swelling and shrinking; and how to fasten wood together and to make plastics and other products from it.

In 1907 the Forest Service and the Bureau of Plant Industry together undertook investigations on the wise and systematic use of the vast area of range forage within the national forests. The fundamental principles of range and livestock management were developed and applied. Marked improvement was made. The Bureau of Plant Industry has also for years carried on research in forest pathology which has flowered today in large-scale tests, ranging over several states, in which DDT is spread by airplane.

Herein we shall be concerned less with the overall conservation of forests and reforestation, which are well covered in books by others, than with the research achievements of Forest Service scientists. This is a field, however, in which the discoveries and activities of individuals assume less importance than do the long-time achievements of teams, even generations, of workers. Furthermore, while the monetary profit from this research is undoubtedly large—a single bulletin dealing with proper methods of kiln-drying a single much-used type of lumber may profit the industry ten million dollars a year—these can rarely be spelled out in dollars.

The major job of the Forest Service is to establish a national program which will assure abundant timber supplies without further destruction of our forest resources. This means nation-wide application of such rules for timber cutting as will stop further depletion and retain forest lands in reasonably productive condition. It means more co-operative aids for forest owners to encourage good forest practices among them. It means the extension of public forests, especially on lands so depleted or so low in productivity that there is little prospect of their private rehabilitation.

In the three decades prior to World War II, our total volume of standing saw timber was reduced almost 40 per cent. Current annual growth amounted to only about two-thirds of the current annual drain. We are still using up growing stock without making adequate provision for new growth, and this process was powerfully accelerated during the war. When the Department took over the forest preserves, after their almost complete lack of management by the General Land Office, Secretary Tama Jim Wilson said they should be administered for "the greatest good to the greatest number in the long run," and that has been basic policy of the Forest Service ever since.

The knowledge upon which wise forest management could alone be based can be developed only by research. It is with that aspect of the matter that we are here concerned. As early as 1890

Congress, evidently impressed by the wide activities of the Division of Forestry, asked it to investigate rain-making—not as a forest influence—but the production of rainfall by the use of explosives. No progress was or has been made on this project. However, George B. Sudworth, as division dendrologist, was preparing the first check list of the common and botanical names of our forest trees, and that was valuable.

Forest range research began in 1895 when the first appropriation was made by Congress for grass and forage-plant investigations. This work was undertaken the following year by the Division of Agrostology. Three years later the Department of the Interior found itself in difficulties in attempting to formulate grazing rules on the Cascade Range forest reserve and requested help from the Department of Agriculture. Dr. Frederick V. Coville of the Division of Botany, made the investigation required.

Investigation of forest products began under Dr. Fernow. They covered studies of timber physics and the properties and uses of wood, and included data on railroad ties, heavy structural timbers, wood pulp, charcoal, and naval stores. Some forty publications issued between 1886 and 1898 describe this work. Included also is Dr. Coville's report mentioned above.

The demands were diverse. They had to cover the railroads' use of forest products, designs for timber trestle bridges, osier culture, timber physics, the characteristics and properties of wood, forest mensuration, tree planting, foreign introductions, and forest conditions in the Rocky Mountains and in Wisconsin. There was plenty for the young organization to find out in those days, and it tried hard to do everything that was necessary.

Until the national forests came to Agriculture, however, a real laboratory for forest research was lacking. By the act of March 3, 1905, the Bureau of Forestry became, on July 1 following, the Forest Service, and the forest reserves, thereafter called "national forests," totaling sixty-three million acres were transferred to the Department of Agriculture, along with a personnel of some five hundred. President Theodore Roosevelt was an outspoken exponent of forest conservation and better forest management; and, by some, Gifford Pinchot was regarded as Teddy's "fair-haired boy."

Since notions about forestry which were prevalent in Europe and elsewhere could not be superimposed upon American forests, the organization of research became necessary. A forest experiment station was established on the Coconino Plateau in Arizona in 1908. Later similar stations were established in Colorado, Idaho, Washington, California, and Utah—one to each administrative forest district. This first station carried out recommendations dating back to meetings of the American Forest Congress in the eighties and later echoed by Gifford Pinchot, Raphael Zon, and others. Soon also the Forest Products Laboratory was established at Madison, Wisconsin.

Today the Forest Service has charge of 160 national forests, which contain more than 176,000,000 acres. It is organized in ten regions, has eleven forest and range experiment stations, a tropical forestry unit, a guayule emergency rubber project, and a Washington office with twenty-three divisions. Twelve regional forestry experiment stations are provided by law. These study forest management and production, forest products, forest economics, forest survey, forest taxation and insurance, forest influences, and range research—each for the region in which it is located.

Just as an example, the thoroughly urban headquarters of one of these region experiment stations is in Philadelphia. The region contains eleven states which cut two billion board feet of lumber annually. This experiment station has shown that changing the cutting cycle, from clear-cutting at fifty-five years to partial cutting at twenty or thirty, practically doubles pulpwood production. It has demonstrated that sending small trees to war wastes man hours of labor, space in trucks, and results in a low output of poor quality.

It has shown how to increase labor output by selective cutting so much that Pennsylvania woodsmen could have produced almost 40 per cent more timber for war use in 1942 than they actually did, had this method been universally adopted. Proper cutting of the tree into logs (bucking) has been shown to save 16 per cent of the logging time, while it adds additional dollars to the value of the lumber.

What the station described as a "prosaic experiment, intended to solve a rather dull and simple problem"—how to reforest abandoned farmland with hybrid poplar, resulted in findings that will be of aid in the entire field of reforestation and offer a new outlook for forest genetics. Turning the sod over and weeding the newly established hybrids worked wonders. Experiments with grass-resistant poplars also pointed the way to the finding of grass-resistant maples, ash, conifers and other species, which can be used effectively on abandoned fields and pastures. Research in the woods is thus both important and profitable.

Turning from what goes on today, we should note an earlier research undertaking made jointly by the Forest Service and the Weather Bureau, one of the first large-scale experiments carried out in the new forest laboratory. It was in the field of forest influences and was carried on for sixteen years. It was justified as much by what it taught experimenters regarding the requirements of such studies as by the conclusions drawn from it. Now a Forest Influence Division carries on in this field.

Until 1915 Forest Service research was partitioned among its divisions. In that year a Branch of Research was created. Today the Forest Research Divisions are: Division of Forest Management Research, Division of Range Research, Division of Forest Products, Division of Forest Economics, and Dendrology and Range Forage Investigations. The prime laboratory remains the national forests. The objective is often half a century in the future of the investigator, when his successors will ordinarily be carrying on.

Forest products research had been mainly centralized; blister-rust control has concerned only the white-pine region; naval stores investigations are concentrated in the southern states. But most of the other research spreads through every forest area in the nation. Growth and yield studies must be carried on for every type of timber. Seeding and planting experiments must be made for every different type of soil, topography, and climate, and for all tree varieties. Harvesting practices cannot be prescribed for forests in the East on a basis of what works in the West.

Forest research spans geography and chronology as no other research does. Its followers work constantly in co-operation with others, some of their own time and nation, some who live years after they have passed on or who work in far parts of the earth. In some fields of agricultural research the worker may himself review the development of racial characteristics throughout thirty or forty generations. But no seeding of spruce or fir yet planted by a Department forester has attained maturity; no one who could have planted such a tree is here today. Individual contributions, therefore, have been mere beginnings, adaptations, the perfection of better methods, or the fruition of work by those who have passed on the torch long since.

Of course the results of this research have made a tremendous monetary contribution, not only to the lumber industry, but to the timber and soil wealth of this nation. Much of the benefit has merely gone into improved plant capacity—i.e., the preservation and upbuilding of nigh irreplaceable natural resources. Much has the negative value of preventing us from having had to go without sufficient wood, water, grass, and good soil. Where actual values can be hazarded in dollars, the totals are huge.

One of the country's oldest industries, that of naval stores, was largely rescued from disaster by Department scientific workers, including those in forestry. This dates back to the days when the navy depended upon forests for tall pine masts and strong timbers. The industry began crudely by hacking into the lush southern forests of longleaf pine for turpentine. Only large-diameter trees were tapped. But at the turn of the century these were worked out. The prosperity built upon their exploitation appeared about to end.

How would that have affected you and me? The gum as it comes from the southern pine trees is called "oleoresin." The refined products are turpentine and rosin, and the uses of the former in paints and varnishes are well known. It is not so well known that a camphor substitute we had to have during the war to make smokeless powder, when camphor imports were shut off, is prepared from rosin. Rosin also makes wrapping paper and fiberboard boxes strong and water-resistant.

About half of yellow laundry soap is a rosin soap, and rosin also appears in many cheap toilet soaps. Manufacturers of varnishes and enamels require rosin in large quantities, combining it with linseed or with tung oil to make their finished products. Rosin also occurs in various chemical and pharmaceutical products, in linoleum, adhesives, plastics, foundry core oils, shoe polish, matches, insulating materials, and insecticides. Any failure in this industry

William A. Orton

Frederick Lamson-Scribner

Theobald Smith

Maurice C. Hall

would be disastrous, yet it was hard hit at the beginning of this century.

This was the first of three times that the industry faltered and appeared doomed. Viewed from a hindsight standpoint the remedy was childishly simple this time. In 1903 Charles H. Herty issued his bulletin on "A New Method of Turpentine Orcharding," the result of his investigations on the adaptation of European turpentining methods to American gum-producing species.

In 1905 Herty gave to the industry his "Practical Results of the Cup and Gutter System of Turpentining." By Herty's method the worker, instead of hacking a destructive "box" into a tree base, merely affixed a tin trough or gutter just below the face, and from this suspended a cup to catch the gum directed into it by the gutter. Immediately turpentiners lowered labor costs and procured more gum. Moreover, the old diameter limitation was removed from this forest crop forever, for a cup and gutter could be affixed to a six-inch sapling. Hence the Department presented to the turpentine industry millions of acres of new forests to replace their worked-out stands of old-growth slash and longleaf pine.

The industry was soon in trouble again! This time the workers slashed ever wider and wider streaks in small trees to make the gum run faster. In five or six years faces ran up to ten feet. The trees and the industry appeared to be facing disaster again, but Department scientists had been looking ahead. Senior microscopist Eloise Gerry had been studying the anatomy and physiology of gum production. Her bulletin on "Oleoresin Production" appeared in 1922.

In it she resolved many puzzles that had long baffled turpentine operators. She also showed how effectively the industry was killing itself by its current methods of operation. Her basic discovery was that the turpentine pine had a definite rhythm of response in its efforts to cover its wounds through gum flow—which is what happens when the tree is tapped. In their haste to get as much gum as possible in the shortest time, operatives ignored this rhythm. Thus they discouraged the tree from responding fully.

On the other hand, preparatory streaks made in advance of the regular season started the gum response and increased the first season's yield. Half-inch streaks produced as great a flow as wider ones, and these made the tree last twice as long. Rapid chipping with wide streaks carried the face up beyond the stimulated area, lost the rhythm, and invaded unproductive tissue. Dr. Gerry's conclusions proved themselves well when tried in practice.

Additional discoveries were made by V. L. Harper, Lenthall Wyman, James G. Osborne, T. A. Liefeld, and others. They found that back faces must be placed so as to leave a continuous three-inch strip separating them from front faces. Chipping must be lighter and must be restricted to trees nine inches in diameter, or larger, while backfacing must be limited to trees of fourteen inches or larger.

Defoliation by crown fires so retards the gum that two years should elapse between the fire and the next chipping. Ground fires and air temperatures influence gum flow. Chipping schedules must be adjusted to seasonal changes, but doing that brings larger yields for the same labor cost. Even the sharpness of the chipping tools materially influences the flow of gum, for trees are sensitive beings. Now, if the turpentine operators could be persuaded to accept these facts, the industry could be put on its feet once more.

Austin Cary became research salesman of the program. Understanding both the subject matter and the men in the woods, he preached the new doctrines indefatigably through the South. Because he was trusted, he was successful, and the industry averted disaster, at least until the manufacturer of substitutes for naval stores, with his cheaper big-production methods, threatened to drive woods producers out of business. Yet another time the research men had looked ahead and had seen the operator's seemingly insurmountable barrier, his cost of production.

The production of naval stores from pines requires human care and skill that mere mechanics cannot supply. The work of local stills is usually costly, because gum is wasted and generally unsatisfactory grades of rosin are produced. Only research could remedy this condition. The Bureau of Agricultural and Industrial Chemistry performed ably here by promoting the construction and operation of big, centralized steam-distillation plants which offered markets for small producers.

Meanwhile forest researchers advised chemical chipping, which, as perfected by Liefeld, consisted in using a one-half-inch or larger hack and then covering the resulting streak with acid. In effect this makes a deeper wound and produces a much greater flow of gum, while new streaks can be made less often than before.

At the same time other forest workers set out to breed pines of high gum yield. Under the leadership of Harold Mitchell the Southern Forest Experiment Station has progressed far along this line by rooting cuttings of mature slash pine—the first time this was ever done anywhere. As these improved trees grow rapidly to producing size, they will supply operatives with two or three (maybe more) times the present gum yields. This and chemical chipping should save them again.

Saving the naval stores industry is a project upon which the foresters co-operated with other Department agencies. Forest-fire control they have had much more to themselves. Research came tardily to the forest-fire fighter's aid, but it did come. Only about twenty-five years ago enlightened methods of fire prevention, detection, and suppression, came into use. They were based on research. The first efforts in this direction were made by E. A. Beals of the Weather Bureau in his early attempts to forecast fire-weather.

It was a natural step from the correlation of weather with incipient forest-fire danger to studying the influence of weather conditions on fires already underway. For instance, unmanageable fires in the great Douglas-fir forests of the Northwest often slowed down at dusk, made few gains if any during the night, then blazed furiously the next day. Why should a forest fire lack a night shift?

W. B. Osborne, Jr., soon found startling differences in humidity in those Douglas-fir forests at different hours of sunlight and dark. He next associated these changes with the behavior of fires already underway, as well as with the likelihood of new fires starting. Here, at least, the progress of most forest fires could be roughly charted by the variations in relative humidity. Thus a fire fighter could gauge the rate at which a fire would burn, or the spread of fires that might catch, merely by ascertaining the relative humidity, which is a simple process.

J. V. Hofmann worked with Osborne; and when their conclusions were published in 1923, they were eagerly accepted throughout the West. Here was a simple index of fire danger anyone could apply. Just as important was the fact that its development opened the way to further investigations into the influences of fire factors and the possibilities of further forecasting. Here Harry T. Gisborne of the Northern Rocky Mountain Forest and Range Experiment Station came forward.

As relative humidity was not so valuable an index in the inland region, Gisborne turned to the moisture content of forest fuels as an indicator. He first examined the "duff" on the forest floor and, with M. E. Dunlap, perfected an instrument that would quickly and easily measure its moisture content. From this the rate at which a fire would spread in this fuel could be predicted. But even this was an inadequate indicator. How about dangerous fuels like dried-out branches or fallen timbers on the forest floor? Soon a method was devised for estimating their moisture content also.

Ultimately Gisborne concluded that no one instrument reading would suffice as a basis for fire-control administration in any region at all. Moisture, wherever found, was not the sole determinant of fuel inflammability. The season, relative humidity, fuel-moisture content, and wind velocity must all be taken into account. Gradually a more complex "burning index" was worked out which had much greater usefulness than any of its predecessors. It has been widely applied throughout the country in the form of varied fire-danger meters utilized in many forest types and conditions.

Fuel-type maps and fire-sighting schedules can then be worked out from which the number of men to send to a fire, or to have on call, can be determined with a high degree of accuracy. Fire-research programs have been reoriented as a result and greatly improved fire-control management was evolved. Many losses have been prevented, many values preserved. Stimulus has been offered to further investigation. This research has contributed enormously to the saving of timber, other property, and human lives.

While this research was under way, S. Brevier Show and E. I. Kotok were engaged in a series of studies in California forests which have yielded results of equal importance to government and private owners there and elsewhere. The studies included an analysis of such fire records as were available for the 1911–20 decade, an investigation of the effect of weather conditions on fires, estimates of latent damage from apparently unimportant fires, and noteworthy trials of current detection and suppression methods.

Thus was worked out what is called "allowable burn." This is the area that can be burned each year without serious menace to a sustained timber yield. The effort to suppress fires could then be better controlled. Resulting improvements in fire-fighting methods undoubtedly resulted in the ultimate saving of millions of dollars' worth of property all over the land.

The value of promptness in detecting fires and in the start and arrival of fire crews, as well as the importance of establishing goals suitable to different timber types and danger spots—i.e., deciding that the allowable burn was inevitably greater in certain instances, were all proved important. The necessity of transportation planning, so that the arrival time of the fire fighters was no longer a matter of chance for a known fuel type or danger spot was also stressed.

Obviously it would be a fine thing to be able to detect forest fires quickly. The forestry scientists thought of that, too. Show, Kotok, and L. G. Hornby began investigating this field and, by 1937, had pretty well upset existing attractive theories upon which previous elaborate detection systems had been based. Formerly it had been the custom to build lookout towers on the highest peaks with the widest horizon in order to see the greatest number of fires most quickly. Now it was proved that this rule led to useless duplication, costly blind spots, and waste of protection effort. Distance seen is one thing; area seen is quite another.

California's entire detection system was reorganized on the new principles developed. Chance was eliminated, and a high degree of certainty took its place, in that every spot where fires might spread rapidly was in direct view of some fire watcher. Areas seen rather than mere distances now formed the basis of the protection system. Meanwhile, in the Northwest, other scientists were asking how far away a column of smoke could be seen under different atmospheric conditions. The Pacific Northwest Forest and Range Experiment Station sought the answer.

It seemed simple just to set a small fire and find out how well it could be observed from surrounding lookout points. The problem was therefore tackled hopefully in 1931—and is still being investigated! Progress is being made, of course, but atmospheric conditions are adverse during much of the fire-fighting season;

smoke and haze spoil the view. Fixed outlook stations must often be supplemented with temporary posts when visibility is poor during the height of the fire season. When the haze deepens, more of these emergency posts are manned; when it clears, fewer are needed.

In the meantime foresters needed to know how far a small column of smoke could be seen under different atmospheric conditions. The further the men can see, especially under bad atmospheric conditions, the less the cost of a detection organization. Richard E. McArdle undertook research in the Northwest, assisted by various other workers, notable among them George M. Byram and H. D. Bruce. He found that no one had ever made careful investigations of the visibility of small smoke columns at long distances outdoors.

As a result of Byram's investigations possibly no individual in the world knows more about the visibility of small objects than Byram and no agency than the Forest Service. Immediate problems to determine were: How good is the lookout's vision and how hazy is the atmosphere at a given time? There was then no answer to either of these simple questions, no known test, for instance, that could measure the "seeing" quality of a lookout man's eyes. Byram had to invent such a test. Then it became possible to select the eagle-eyed or hawk-eyed men for lookout jobs. The test spread from Forest Service to the armed forces, where it was found invaluable for selecting and training plane watchers and other persons for various lookout purposes.

Having selected the lookout man, how should he be equipped to use his vision best? How about inventing glass that would remove sun glare? Byram did this also. Next, could he teach the lookout man to see through haze? That sounds impossible, yet lookouts should have every possible assistance in seeing through obstructive hazes. All lookout men have dreamed for years of a magic device which would enable them to make out a distant smoke column while looking towards it through thick haze. McArdle and Byram set to make magic for the lookouts, the latter drawing on his comprehensive knowledge of optics.

The result was a haze-cutter based on the fact that the light reflected from many types of fire smoke is not polarized. A simple polarized filter permitted the lookout to see these types of smoke without seeing the haze. There are limitations to the value of the instrument, but it is a great aid to lookouts nonetheless, and its development indicates the wide scope of knowledge required by forestry experts. Another invention followed of a haze meter which enables the fire-control operative to measure visibility conditions with some degree of accuracy. This tells him when his secondary lookout stations should be manned and also how to place his various lookouts.

The armed services frequently work on problems similar to those involved in fire detection. They profited from these results and thus avoided expensive and time-consuming investigations of their own, just as they profited from Forest Service's methods of photographing large areas from airplanes, upon which it began research in 1926. Between 1926 and 1943 the Department of Agriculture thus gained complete aerial photographic coverage of two-thirds of the continental area of the United States at a cost of three dollars per square mile. The techniques developed proved of vital value to the armed services in World War II.

Byram's work had a similar unearned-increment value to the army and navy. He and McArdle instructed the armed forces in methods of detecting long-range targets. They helped develop markings for airplanes which were of high visibility at close range but invisible at long distances, and vice versa. They developed long-range targets that could be seen at twelve times the distance of short-range targets. They thus advanced the visibility research of the armed forces by several years, not only effecting a monetary saving but also enabling us better to meet the war emergency.

We turn now to range research. The prosperity of the western half of the United States is largely built upon "the miracle of green grass." Range forage builds cattle cheaply enough to make good meat available to more people than would otherwise have it. Normally meat eating goes much deeper into lower income-bracket classes here than among industrial workers abroad, and largely for this reason. But the range has to be managed, otherwise it can be ruined, and in the old free-as-air days of western-range utilization calamity was coming quickly.

Many supposed that since grass naturally covered so many million acres and reappeared every year, it would continue to do so, regardless of how much the sward was abused. Nevertheless, heavy grazing gradually killed out some valuable feed plants altogether. Although the range was free, unrestricted grazing could not be permitted. Secretary Hitchcock of the Department of the Interior found, however, that when he prohibited grazing on certain slopes which controlled watercourses upon which some people depended for irrigation, the livestock owners protested strongly.

Not knowing how to solve the problem, Hitchcock appealed to the Department of Agriculture, where Pinchot, Coville, and a representative of the range livestock men were sent out to make an inspection trip. The livestock man, Albert B. Potter, underwent complete conversion, became a staunch supporter of the Forest Service's range policies, then entered the service and was there employed for many years. Discovery that the western range actually was deteriorating was made by technical men. The job now was to convince livestock men that such deterioration really was taking place.

To do this, the Department must undertake range research which would develop practices that livestock men could follow with safety. In the end, methods were devised which would insure for the industry the maximum nutritious and palatable forage consonant with a sustained or increasing crop. By accepting these methods, the livestock growers preserved their industry, increased their revenue, and came upon the secret of perpetual operation.

Fundamental in this work was the discovery by Arthur W. Sampson, published in 1913, that when the same range area is even moderately grazed for successive years in the growing season, deterioration ensues. If forage value is to be maintained, the seed of all range plants must attain maturity every few years. To effect this, livestock must not be on the range at certain times. Plants so protected are not harmed by grazing after seed ripening; trampling by the livestock actually tends to plant the seed. But until then, no grazing.

Thus deferred or rotation grazing came into being, grazing being discontinued each year on successive fractions of the range until the seeds have matured. Thus the entire area is reseeded every four or five years and the more palatable grasses, those least likely to reach maturity under continuous grazing, are perpetuated. This

Breeding new tomatoes that will be resistant to defoliation diseases
at the regional vegetable-breeding laboratory, Charleston, S. C.

grazing principle has been widely adopted on national forest and other public ranges and also, through the Agricultural Adjustment Agency, on millions of acres of private range.

Because it is difficult for even technically trained men to recognize range depletion, much missionary work has to be done. A range may look quite good, even though its forage value has been halved. In order to know how to rehabilitate depleted range, some accurate measure of the degree and direction of plant succession became necessary as early as 1918. Arthur W. Sampson published the first thorough study of "Plant Succession in Relation to Range Management" in 1919. This work provided great stimulus to those who strove to save the already imperiled range resource for the livestock industry.

Each period of heavy range use, such as accompanies wars, makes demands for certainty about what is happening to the forage crop. James T. Jardine, later director of the Oregon Agricultural Experiment Station and chief of the Office of Experiment Stations, in 1907 began his eastern Oregon studies which led to the formulation of practical methods for making range surveys and management plans. Jardine was a pioneer here and his work was of great importance and significance.

The necessity was shown for an estimate, based on minute sample plots and gradually expanding to include the entire 175,-000,000 acres of western range so far surveyed, which would inform the people of the available forage area and the condition of its vegetal cover. These basic methods of Jardine's, later extended and refined by others, are today standard procedure on the national forests, as well as on other public and much private land.

Jardine's classic *Department Bulletin No. 490* (with Mark Anderson as collaborator) on "Range Management on the National Forests" was published in 1919. It is still the range manager's Bible. The methods thus established have proved fundamental to the work of the Agricultural Adjustment Agency, the Soil Conservation Service, the Farm Security Administration, and the Division of Grazing and the Bureau of Indian Affairs in the Department of the Interior.

Full utilization of the range forest every year cannot be regarded as conservative grazing. There must be recuperative periods, otherwise unforeseen demands will permanently deplete the range. There must be provision to withstand years of drought. Too much faith cannot be put in the "normal" year of range growth and use. Dr. Jardine and his successor in charge of range research, W. R. Chapline, called attention to these considerations.

Years of research finally demonstrated that reserves of untouched forage of desirable species must remain at the end of the grazing season if the range is to be properly maintained. Then seasonal inequalities have no effect on long-time grazing capacity. Even severe droughts can be weathered without range deterioration. Subsequent research by George W. Craddock and Clarence L. Forsling of the Intermountain Forest and Range Experiment Station in Utah showed that proper stocking must leave something like a quarter of the forage as drought insurance.

More, rather than less, livestock than before can be carried on properly utilized ranges, however. On them it has been amply shown that calf crops, the weight of calves per cow, wool production, and lamb crops all increase materially. The cost of supplemental feed per animal is less, when such feed is needed at all. Conservative grazing results in general benefit all around. One reason war meat demands were met for the armed forces was that these research results were being used practically. It is for this reason also that we are one of the greatest meat-eating nations during peace. When you draw your chair up to the table to devour your roast, remember this.

We turn now to something that conforms more nearly to the layman's idea of research—the investigations carried on by the Forest Products Laboratory at Madison, Wisconsin, since 1910, when it was founded. Here research into the physics, chemistry, and technology of wood began in this country.

This Laboratory has performed a notable service in awakening America to the necessity for thrift in the use of wood and in showing how that thrift can be put into practice. It carries forest conservation through from the millpond to industry. It develops new uses for wood, new products from wood, and even new substances with novel uses, made from wood yet scarcely recognizable as such. It contributes directly to your welfare and to mine, as does every scientific agency of the Department.

Credit for the establishment of this laboratory goes to Mc-Garvey Cline, its first director. It resulted from his original proposal to Gifford Pinchot and his indefatigable labors to put that proposal into practical effect. Until that time small laboratories had been set up to perform research at the site of the materials. Henceforth the materials were brought to a finely equipped central laboratory working in close co-operation with the University of Wisconsin. Broad vision at the university made this possible and determined the laboratory's location.

Harold S. Betts, who retired from Forest Service in the fall of 1944 after more than forty years of service, also comes to mind. He was the first man in the Department to undertake timber testing. As a young mechanical engineering graduate from Stevens Institute of Technology, he joined the old testing laboratory in the basement of the old Bureau of Chemistry, which has long since disappeared from the corner of Fourteenth Street and Independence Avenue, in Washington. That was in 1902.

Since there was no tank, Betts soaked his beams in Tidal Basin to test the effect of moisture on the strength of wood. He kept them submerged by weighting them down with stones and hunks of iron. The testers, attired in hip boots, fished the beams out after a soak of several months. Later a tank was set up under a shed close to the storage yard; that ended the hazards of Basin wading.

Betts had plenty of excitement during the early days, especially when he traveled to the West. He got tangled once in a wild melee with men on horseback chasing an escaped prisoner. On the same trip he discovered the body of an Indian in the baggage shed of a small-town railroad station. The fellow had been shot to pieces for killing a near-by rancher, and Betts came by accident on the badly damaged corpse, while hunting for his baggage.

Betts it was also who terminated speculation in Eucalyptus plantations when this afflicted the West. Large quantities of "securities" backed by Eucalyptus forests yet to come were being sold far and wide. Betts and Stowell Smith collected specimens of eucalypts growing in California, tested them, and published a bulletin which blew up this commercial bubble. Then Betts aided McGarvey Cline in propounding the idea of the Forest Products Laboratory.

Accustomed as these men were to hauling their heavy equipment around the country to test timber in various regions, they began to wonder whether it would not be better to have stationary equipment and haul the timbers to it. Since the University of Wisconsin offered the best inducements in the matter of establishing such a central laboratory, Betts and Cline went to Madison to choose a site. Betts later worked at the laboratory for some years, then returned to Washington.

The laboratory's broad field now includes timber physics, timber mechanics, the chemistry and microscopy of wood, wood pathology, the conditioning of wood for use, the preservation, gluing, painting, and finishing of wood, wood pulp and paper manufacture, and the making of specially impregnated woods of great density and of plastics from wood. Only a few of these lines of research can be mentioned here, and those too briefly.

Work on the conditioning of wood for use dates from the artificial drying of timbers in the eighth century B. C. But the theory of conditioning wood by application or control of humidity, temperature, and air circulation is a development of the past eighty years, and it remained little more than a theory until thirty years ago. Then studies began by Harry Donald Tiemann, just before the laboratory was established. Lumber production was at an all-time peak in this country when Tiemann's first patent was taken out on a kiln-drying process in 1909.

Practically all this output was being conditioned by the slow, age-hallowed but uncertain method of air drying. Even a decade after his work began, Tiemann realized that no one in the lumber industry had any real understanding of the principles underlying either air or kiln drying. Tradition and rule of thumb were followed on the principle that wet lumber dried in air just as a wet shirt dried on the clothesline. Tiemann kept insisting that the two processes differed, but few heeded.

He knew that the physical properties of wood had to be taken into account. He knew that these differed not only from species to species but from piece to piece, and often within the piece. Meanwhile, the efforts of the industry to kiln-dry lumber with inadequate equipment and imperfect understanding of the process were wasteful and near disastrous. Much of the product even twenty years ago was ruined utterly or else seriously degraded. But Tiemann kept on working, and he and Rolf Thelen took out more than twenty public patents on kiln-drying processes and improvements between 1910 and 1926.

Transition was extremely slow in the industry from traditional to scientific methods. Kiln operation lagged far behind the knowledge established by research. Slowly exact information was accumulated on the behavior of different kinds of wood under various kiln processes and about procedures for the control of humidity, heat, and air movement, so essential to successful kiln-drying. Nevertheless, many operators regarded all this as some new form of nefarious white-collar folly.

In the long run, however, phenomenal improvements in the product were demonstrated. It was shown that run after run of softwoods came out with negligible damage, and the industry began to accept the principles of scientific wood conditioning. Today elaborate schedules for dry-kiln operation are regarded as wholly indispensable. Savings are enormous. Whereas a quarter of the hardwood forest in the Mississippi Valley bottom lands could not be used profitably, it now came into use. Six-by-twelve-inch Douglas fir could be kiln-dried from a green condition to 16 per cent dryness in two months, in lieu of the former year or more of air drying.

All lumber and all timber must be dried from the outside in, of course, and it is all but impossible to retard the drying of the outer layers so that they will harmonize with the drying of the interior. Hence stresses are set up and the lumber checks. Sometimes this involves degrading and heavy loss. Various expensive and uncertain methods had been tried to solve this problem. Then, after three years of intensive work at the laboratory, W. Karl Loughborough evolved a new method of seasoning which really worked.

Loughborough observed that moisture in a piece of wood moves from conditions of higher to those of lower vapor pressure, the water in a sense running down the vapor-pressure hill. Hence, if the vapor pressure of the wood's outer layers could be lowered, all would be well. It was already known that any of several chemicals would lower the vapor pressure of water when dissolved in it.

Planks were therefore soaked in solutions of such chemicals long enough to penetrate the outer layers. When they were dry-kilned, the inner moisture made its way outward where it evaporated. Indeed, the interior started drying even in the chemical bath, so that the seven or eight days spent in soak represented no loss of time in the conditioning process.

The method also made possible reduction in the humidity used in the drying process and that cut the drying period in the kiln in half. The end result was always an increased drying rate and much less degrading. The lumber industry now discovered that drying losses were not acts of God and therefore inevitable in hardwoods and in large timbers of any wood. These losses had run into millions of dollars and billions of board feet. Putting an end to this waste constituted a fine achievement in the field of wood conservation.

Another fundamental problem in the utilization of wood and wood products was their tendency to swell and shrink rhythmically as they absorb and lose moisture. This perversity makes wood unsuitable for many uses, hence efforts to overcome it were in order. Early attempts were unsuccessful. It finally became evident that wood must be treated or combined with some other material to alter its structure and render it impervious to water.

Here the researches of Alfred J. Stamm into the physical and colloid chemistry of wood assumed importance. By ultramicroscopic investigation he discovered in what part of its structure the water-absorbing qualities of wood resided. He then concluded that attempts to change these characteristics by forcing water-resistant materials into the larger openings in the wood could get nowhere. Some substance must be found which would solidify within the microscopic structure. Exactly this result was achieved by the use of synthetic resins.

It was found that if wood were impregnated with a water-soluble mixture of resin-forming materials, so that these entered the cell-wall structure, the wood could then be heated to cure the resins so deposited. The cell-wall structure was then entirely filled and acquired high antimoisture and antishrinking properties. The treatment also improved markedly many of the mechanical properties of the wood, hardness in particular. The material so produced was named "Impreg."

Further development proceeded from there. It was next found that the presence of the resin in the wood made possible its compression under lower pressure than that required for untreated wood. It thus became possible to compress uncured resin-treated wood with heat in such a way that the resin became bonded with the wood. This produced a substance of greatly increased density, hardness, and resistance to moisture, shrinking, and swelling. Indeed, the properties of the original wood were so changed and improved that what was essentially a new substance resulted.

When this product is built up into thick sections of plywood, in which the hard self-glossed layers known as "Compreg" are added to uncompressed cores of Impreg, numerous possibilities of use can be met. The material can be applied for making ground-test and flight propellers, airplane landing-wheels, electrical-control housing for torpedo boats, special deck planking, airplane semi-structural skin-surface parts, and other airplane fittings, as well as a host of similar or somewhat related products useful in civilian life.

Paper plastics have also been developed here, which bear little or no resemblance to wood or to paper, but which are hard, moisture-resistant, difficult to scratch, and take a high polish.

Finally there is "Uralloy." This is the laboratory's name for a group of products made by treating wood with methylurea. This treatment makes the wood harder, stiffer, and more stable dimensionally. Three public-service patents were granted to cover the basic work on treatments and products.

The laboratory has also done valuable work on processes of fastening wood together. This began with container work, long before the war. After the war started, this project became exceedingly important; and the laboratory was able to show how wood could be used most economically and efficiently to replace metals in making containers of sufficient strength to serve the particular purpose for which they were designed. Circulars on factors affecting the strength and rigidity of wooden crates and on the principles of box and crate construction were invaluable during the war.

This laboratory told shippers, manufacturers, and railroads how crates should be fashioned to secure the necessary degree of durability with economical use of wood and other materials. It told them how to protect articles adequately from shock, sea air, heat, cold, and other factors, while making each crate or box weigh not an ounce more than necessary and designing it so that it would take up the least possible space. Every article supplied to the armed forces, from delicate instruments to mammoth tanks and guns and from powdered eggs to block-busters, made its separate demand.

These demands were supplied. The work actually added to our merchant marine fleet by reducing the bulk of required containers from 15 to 25 per cent, and sometimes more. Heavy tanks were lifting the flatcars upon which they moved right off the rails until the laboratory supplied an equally secure but less rigid method of holding them down. Years of research in box construction by J. A. Newlin, Thorwald A. Carlson, and C. A. Plaskett now came into its own. Many improvements were made in containers, which saved space, cost, and weight and helped them give greater service than those used hitherto.

Although we cannot go into great detail here, a minor instance is a bomb container that was redesigned, using cheaper aspen, which was less in demand, instead of white pine. The quantity of lumber used in making it and the space required by it were both reduced; there were corresponding weight reductions. Yet the resulting container had greater strength than the original.

Equally interesting and valuable work was done in testing and perfecting metal connectors for wood joints. Joints and fasteners are, of course, the weakest part of any timber structure. This weakness long precluded the substitution of wood for steel in construction work. Metal connectors and bolts are commonly used to increase joint efficiency and prevent sideslipping. Timber connectors were devised as substitutes which soon diverted half a million tons of steel into more direct war operations which only steel would serve.

The gluing of wood together dates back to the dawn of the cabinetmaker's art, and as early as 1500 B.C., the Egyptians had gluepots on fires and were doing veneering. Forest products research has developed and established many new gluing techniques. This came about as a result of seemingly endless experiments in which several types of glue and many combinations of these types were applied to all sorts of commercial wood species to test serviceability, durability, strength, water resistance, tendency to stain, the effect on tools, and so on. Finally a manual of gluing technique was evolved, *The Gluing of Wood*, by T. R. Truax, under whose direction these studies were long carried on.

Many changes in glue requirements have taken place. Aircraft manufacture set up wholly new demands. Animal glue is used in the manufacture of wooden propellers, partly because it does not· dull tools badly. Casein glues, mixed and applied cold, are used chiefly for assembly operations where heat cannot be employed. Blood-albumen glues, which must be applied with hot pressure to develop full strength and moisture resistance, are used in making aircraft flat plywood. The glue has to be tailored to the wood and to the job. Indeed, even paint has to be tailored to the wood, and that is quite a field of research in itself at the laboratory.

Laminated-wood construction represents one of the greatest recent advances in the fine art of sticking wood together. The glued laminated-wood arch is a monumental achievement in itself, giving great strength, though smaller inferior pieces of wood can be used, held together with casein glue. The resultant material is as durable as a solid beam and has the same structural possibilities. Its strength is considerably in excess of that of solid timbers of the same size.

T. R. C. Wilson was a leader in developing the arch to its present high degree of efficiency. It has excellent appearance and makes a remarkable substitute also for metal or full-timbered arches. Moreover, up to 60 per cent of low-grade woods can be used without impairment of its strength or durability. In part this work represents an adaptation of existing European techniques to our own woods and needs. The arches have been widely employed in building construction, are adapted to farm structures as well as to theaters, churches, and gymnasiums, and give complete satisfaction.

Great progress has also been made in developing new types of glues. The phenol-formaldehyde and the urea-formaldehyde types of synthetic-resin glues are notable among these. They render the joints of plywood layers practically impervious to moisture or heat. They have proved superior to other types of glues in many ways, though it is still true that just the right glue should always be selected for the particular job. Hence gluing research is a continuous effort to develop full acquaintance with the possibilities of each type of glue and then to use each through carefully tested and perfected techniques.

Many other lines of research are carried on at the Forest Products Laboratory, some of which we cannot even hastily mention. They include studies of the pulping possibilities of southern pines, carried on for many years under the direction of Henry E. Surface and his successors. The resulting craft and fiberboard processes were adopted by numerous new pulp mills in the South just in time to meet war demands for fiber containers. Today southern pines are the leading pulpwoods of the nation.

Wood plastics have also been developed from a discovery that a wood component, millions of tons of which were formerly disposed of by the pulp-making industry as waste, would yield a number of compounds new to the chemical world and with promising future possibilities. Then there was the patient and persistent work of John A. Newlin and his coworkers on the mechanics of wood. This involved thousands upon thousands of tests before the data could be assembled for guidance in a bulletin on "Strength and Related Properties of Woods Grown in the United States."

Most of us know too little to realize how much we have to learn. The strength and the specific gravity of wood from a single tree varies as you run up the trunk from the ground. The growth and strength properties of trees are also affected by droughts, floods, irrigation, the seasons, and so on. No piece of wood from any tree is the same throughout as any other piece. Certain principles rule, however, and by discovering and formulating these, the laboratory has made much progress.

Then there is the matter of breeding trees to serve specific purposes. Trees could almost certainly be bred which would grow faster, produce more durable wood or wood which was more outstanding in some useful property than that now available, or which could manufacture more naval stores than trees now available. Naturally such forest genetics is a long-time proposition. But the Forest Service is gradually learning how to grow dense or soft pine, or tougher woods on the order of hickory. Further valuable progress is bound to come on this sector.

In addition, the service has made nation-wide surveys of our entire forest resource. It has also inventoried not only remaining stands but the growing stock and the degree to which it is being reduced by our urgent demands upon it. Extremely valuable contributions to the general welfare have thus been made in the field of forest economics. As a result of these studies we know more about the economic rotation of forest stands, what size trees should be cut, and the way to harvest timber most economically.

There must also be accompanying research on the forest soil. Unwise utilization of timber harms the soil in ways that can be prevented. The research is not conspicuous, but it is fundamental and valuable. It is one of the many forms of scientific investigation in which a man certainly will not hit the headlines and can scarcely be expected to make a name for himself—the more credit to those patient, quiet men who follow this path.

Recently work has been done that may enable cows to eat at least part of the woodpile. It concerns the art of making high-grade yeast protein from wood sugar, a sort of magic by which the principle nutritive element of a steak can be prepared from sawdust, chips, and shavings. About 1,100 pounds of sugar can be derived from a ton of wood. Then, by adding 250 pounds of ammonium sulfate, or 100 pounds of urea and 50 of superphosphate, 500 pounds of yeast can be grown on the sugar, alcoholic fermentation being prevented. Yeast consists, to the extent of one-half, of high-quality, very palatable protein, rich in vitamins.

This protein can be prepared cheaply, without putting a plow to the ground or a bit of feed into an animal. Combined with cereal grains, it makes an excellent livestock feed, and its possibilities as human food are large. In addition to the above products, 500 to 600 pounds of lignin are made in this process, a clean, brown powder of much interest to chemists who see in it great potential worth. More immediate is the fact that waste wood offers an excellent source of industrial alcohol needed for the making of synthetic rubber and other vital products.

With the beginning of the war the Madison laboratory went all out for war projects, co-operating closely with the armed forces, giving educational classes also to army and navy personnel and manufacturers' representatives who were training for airplane inspectors as well as instructing manufacturers in the technique of container design. The Matériel Containers Division expanded in a large building of its own, quickly to devise and test containers of any kind that wartime urgency demanded. Again, however, much of this investigation will benefit us at peace; that it will save railroads a great deal of money in claims for damage to packages goes without saying.

The Emergency Rubber (Guayule) Project was another wartime baby for Forest Service. What it actually did was to take over a former commercial development for growing this plant, which had been far from successful, and, by introducing scientific management, greatly increase the production of guayule at a considerably decreased cost. The oil-spray method used to kill all weeds and leave the guayule plants unharmed was only one of the ingenious developments in the Salinas, California nurseries.

Typical of Forest Service's scientific personnel was Dr. Raphael Zon, who retired as director of its Lake States Forest and Range Experiment Station in 1944. Born in Russia in 1874, Zon studied at the Imperial University of Kazan, with Lenin as a fellow student. He then went on to the universities of London and of Brussels, and came to the United States in 1898, a penniless immigrant. But in 1901 he graduated from the Cornell School of Forestry and entered the Bureau of Forestry.

He was a pioneer forest-research worker in this country. When the first forest experiment station was established at Flagstaff, Arizona, Dr. Zon not only planned the work but helped to shingle the roof and make the road to the main highway. He made some of the earliest studies on the relationship between forest cover, stream flow, and flood control. He helped lay the foundation for much that has since been accomplished in erosion and flood-control work and in the planting of shelter belts.

Dr. Zon was the author of more than two hundred scientific publications, many of which were widely translated. He was founder and first managing editor of the *Journal of Forestry*. In 1940 he was named one of six hundred foreign-born citizens who have made the greatest contributions to American democracy during the past century.

Forest Service has come a long way since Gifford Pinchot settled down as chief of the Forestry Division on July 1, 1898, and a few days later was, much to his delight, given the title "forester" by Secretary Wilson. The division then had an appropriation of $28,500 a year; Forest Service now has one of about $60,000,000 annually. There were ten people in the division when Pinchot raised the population to eleven. The division roosted in two upper rooms of the Department's old Red Brick Building, which was torn down in 1930.

The service has plenty of work ahead, however. Total war makes huge drains on every natural resource. Today we are cutting and destroying twice as much timber as we grow each year. There is a limit to how long that can go on. We have ample acreage to grow a sustained yield of forest crops if we but put it to work on scientific principles. Indeed, we can, if we wish, increase growth rather than reduce consumption.

With good forest practices used throughout the nation, we should in time be able to grow 21.4 billion cubic feet of usable timber a year. Wartime consumption and losses ran only about 17 billion cubic feet, but growth lagged along at 11.3 billion. Even the nonmathematical can see what these figures mean. Forest Service scientists know what to do, if we just follow their advice.

Finally, work in the field of forest pathology, long carried on in the Bureau of Plant Industry and its administrative successors, should be considered. Before 1900 studies in this field were mainly made in Europe. They were observational and qualitative rather than experimental and quantitative.

Then, under the leadership of Herman van Schrenk, the Bureau of Plant Industry started further studies in its Mississippi Valley laboratory at St. Louis. The results were published in a general bulletin on the diseases of hardwoods, which immediately became a standard work. In 1907 this work was moved to Washington, a special forest-pathology division being established under Haven Metcalf.

Not only man but organisms destroy timber. The immediate projects attacked by this new division were chestnut blight and white-pine blister rust. It proved impossible to control the first, and the disease is now being circumvented by the introduction of blight-resistant stock and the breeding from it of chestnuts of the American habit of growth and lumber-producing quality.

Ordinary methods of plant-disease control are impracticable in the forest, but some good results can be obtained by special adaptations. Prompt demonstration that the two major diseases mentioned had been introduced here via nursery stock led to good results. It became apparent that similar introductions could not be sufficiently safeguarded by the current state inspection system, so, in 1912, the Federal Plant Quarantine Act was passed. This formed the basis for work by the Federal Horticultural Board, now carried on in the Bureau of Entomology and Plant Quarantine.

It was found that chestnut blight came here from Asia, but it became necessary to convince many of our university mycologists, who were sure that some native organisms produced the disease, of this fact. Next the rate of spread of the disease was forecast, and assistance could be rendered Forest Service and private landowners in utilizing their timber before blight ruined it.

Then resistant chestnut species were introduced from Asia and tested both in plantings and for hybridizing with susceptible American chestnuts. Trees with blight resistance, a good yield of nuts, and a high tannin content have been produced. Gradually, in the measured manner in which things go in the forest, they should largely replace the susceptible chestnuts we lost.

As for white-pine blister rust, a most devastating disease which threatened to wipe out an entire species, it had been determined that currants and gooseberries were intermediary hosts to the causal organism. If these bushes were eradicated, the organism died out. Thereupon a nation-wide control plan was undertaken, later with the assistance of "New Deal" agencies, which saved the eastern white pine and which is being carried on vigorously in the western white- and sugar-pine regions.

White pine is unique in wood quality. Its perpetuation is essential. The Forest Service has estimated the stumpage value of the three principal white-pine species at $300,000,000, so that one can easily see what is involved here. The trees are completely killed out in areas with prevalent alternate hosts, i.e., where the bushes have not been destroyed. The disease is especially destructive to young growth.

The Dutch elm disease reached this country in burl elm logs from Europe. It was distributed around ports of entry, along railroads, and through veneer factories using the logs. An extensive control plan is underway, but no remedy is known other than the destruction of affected trees. Their quick, complete eradication is imperative.

Other epidemic diseases have reached us which attack minor species like persimmon, mimosa, and Monterey cypress, as well as the major species, American elm. The development of resistant strains is being undertaken to combat these diseases. Work is also being done on a disease-resistant eastern white pine.

Quantitative study of the heart rot of standing timber began about 1910. Already a basis has been developed for timing logging operations to get the most timber from affected western virgin stands and eastern balsam fir. Methods have been perfected by which high-risk and low-risk trees can be identified so that the former can be used before they deteriorate too greatly. Selective logging, thinning, pruning, and other practices have also proved helpful.

Oak sprouts which originated high in the parent stump were found affected much more often than those which originated at the ground level. The latter were as nearly safe from decay as seedlings; hence the former were pruned and the latter left. This one finding was of enormous aid in handling the rapidly increasing second growth in eastern areas, so largely composed of sprouts. Thousands of trees have been dissected by tree surgeons and the information applied to the stand-improvement operations of the Civilian Conservation Corps. More work was done with less man power.

Heart rot caused losses of 25 per cent or more in the ponderosa pine of the Black Hills and the Southwest. Modified management, including both the selection of safe crop trees and pruning to keep them safe, were developed in co-operation with the Forest Service and put into use by the CCC. Investigation made the same proce-dure possible with Douglas fir and made practicable large-scale control of the very destructive leafless mistletoe of ponderosa pine —two species which comprise nearly half our entire saw timber.

External signs of hidden decay in Douglas fir and white oak have been identified by research; even liability to decay can be predicted. These findings, put into effect on national forest land in determining which trees can safely be left for a later cut have been extremely valuable. Modifications in the management of these species greatly decrease losses and uncertainties caused by heart rot and bark diseases, without necessity for special disease-control expenditures.

Foresters have been aided in fire control in three important regions by studies of the decay of logging slash. It has been found possible to decrease fire hazard in the slash by using cheap and easy methods of slash disposal to replace the expensive piling methods formerly considered necessary. Deterioration studies in areas where trees are killed by bark beetles, fire, and windthrow have supplied valuable information on the rate of deterioration. Salvage schedules can then be devised which avoid heavy losses.

Again we are considering public service which goes on continually and about which the average person normally knows little or nothing. The results are taken as a matter of course. But we should each become exercised over the matter if the pinch hit personally because investigations failed of their objectives.

Early large-scale introductions of tree diseases via imported nursery stock have been mentioned. This has led to investigation of the damping-off disease of pine seedlings, the most serious cause of uncertainties in the production of native nursery stock. Because of difficulties such as this, nurserymen were inclined to turn to importation.

By distinguishing losses caused by excessive heat from those actually caused by fungi, and by developing chemical soil treatments for use when the damping-off fungi were responsible, the production of seedlings was made both cheaper and more certain in this country. Need for extensive importations was markedly reduced, another way of circumventing loss from forest diseases.

As our nursery production expanded rapidly, through the work by Forest Service, Soil Conservation Service, and the Civilian Conservation Corps, it became possible to provide tree-growing agencies with advice and technical service through which initial heavy losses, both in seedbeds and in storage stock, or in stock in transit, could be controlled. The most common and most serious nursery diseases no longer endanger our large-scale planting programs.

The decay and discoloration of wood has also been studied.

U.S.D.A. photograph by Madeleine Osborne

New wheats in the experimental nursery at Fargo, N. D., are carefully harvested by hand

U.S.D.A. photograph by Hunton

Collecting pine gum at trees that have been tapped (right) and chipping new trees, Lulu, Fla.

Their causes and their effect on strength and toughness have been investigated, in close co-operation with the Forest Products Laboratory. Special attention was given species commonly used for aircraft wood, resulting in the use of much high-grade lumber that was formerly rejected because of suspected infection, particularly in the case of spruce and yellow poplar. It is estimated that findings on yellow poplar, made available to producers and inspectors of plywood, resulted in an increase of 20 per cent or more in airplane grades produced. That is just like adding that much to our timber stand for a specialized purpose.

Blue stains caused in the sapwood of pine, sweet gum, and other woods by fungi reduce large quantities of it to lower and unprofitable grades. Studies of these began in 1929 with the co-operation of lumbermen and chemical companies. Methods, cheap and easy to apply, were developed which effectively controlled these stains. They were rapidly adopted by the industry, billions of board feet of lumber being treated annually.

Finally, there must be studies of the decay of wood in buildings and the factors favorable thereto. Factors involved are proper drainage of sites, substructure ventilation, wall construction so that water which enters joints can evaporate, and care in placing no untreated wood in contact with the soil. Proper attention to these matters will prevent serious sporadic decay, the possibility of which often induces builders to adopt much more expensive means of prevention.

Generally improved building practices have followed the educational effort to disseminate this information. They have gone far to prevent much decay that would otherwise have taken place in buildings. Special study to aid defense and wartime housing agencies began before Pearl Harbor. Such agencies had the advice and technical assistance they required to build nonbasement homes without exposing the wood in them to rapid decay.

Studies of locust for fence posts were undertaken in co-operation with the Soil Conservation Service. They showed that some varieties are much more subject to decay than others and also that decay resistance differs considerably with the age and even the position of the tree. This work provides a sound basis for the selection of planting varieties, as well as for better utilization of timber, not only for fence posts but also for other purposes where decay resistance is required. The studies have been extended to oaks. The fundamental facts ascertained have facilitated the study of decay resistance in woods available for tropical construction, a field in which wise advice could be given during the war.

Mention was made earlier of the spreading of DDT and other insecticides around the woods by the use of airplanes. Undoubtedly methods will be devised to protect our forest crop from insects better than ever before, and without injury to helpful wild life.

CHAPTER 9

"A Very Grievous Murrain"

THE BUREAU OF ANIMAL INDUSTRY is a very important research institution which came into existence because a milkman inadvertantly introduced an extremely devastating cattle disease into this country. Furthermore, so much good came out of evil in this instance that we probably built the Panama Canal as quickly and as successfully as we did because this bureau came into existence. If this sounds fantastic, read on.

In 1842 Peter Dunn, a milkman located near South Ferry, New York, bought a ship's cow from the captain of an English ship named *Washington*. Unknown to Peter Dunn this cow had contagious pleuropneumonia, an insidious, destructive cattle disease prevalent in certain countries which had never been able to eradicate it. The cow carried the malady to Dunn's herd, whence it spread rapidly to other herds near by.

Long prevalent in other countries, this disease was known in the United States only by its dread reputation. Our cattle owners either failed to recognize the condition or else kept quiet about it. Soon it was raging throughout the states of New Jersey and New York. In 1859 it was introduced into Massachusetts by four infected cows from the Netherlands. The infection continued to spread, and by 1879 livestock growers were fully aroused to the danger.

On February 6 of that year the British Privy Council issued an order that all American cattle arriving at English ports should be slaughtered promptly on the docks. This act forced the price of American steers down ten dollars below that of comparable Canadian animals. This alone meant a loss of a million dollars annually to our cattle growers, over and above losses to cattle which remained in this country.

The disease conformed well to the descriptive words of the inspired writer in Exodus (9:3), for it was indeed "a very grievous murrain." Study of it began early, and some of the Patent Office reports contained discussions of it. At the direction of Congress J. J. Woodward of the army had investigated the disease. Meanwhile state regulation failed to stamp it out.

Some states were vigilant and co-operated loyally, but others were careless, and the negligence of one state could upset the entire contagious pleuropneumonia–eradication program. Some cattle owners remained secretive about the existence of this disease among their cattle and even sold cattle suffering from it. Consequently the cattle industry made loud and insistent demands upon Congress for action by the federal government.

In 1869 Congress had appropriated $15,000 for the investigation of animal diseases. A year earlier John Gamgee, of the Albert Veterinary College of London, investigated an outbreak of tick (Texas) fever of cattle in Illinois, for the Pork Packers Association of Chicago. The Department subsequently employed him to make similar investigations elsewhere, the expenses being paid from funds of the Statistical Division.

Work of this sort continued and, in reporting the results to Congress, the Commissioners of Agriculture began to suggest that a veterinary division be established in the Department. Finally Dr. Daniel Elmer Salmon became Department veterinarian. In 1881 the funds for the study of animal diseases were increased to $25,000, and in 1883 Commissioner Loring set up a Veterinary Division in the Department with Salmon at its head. Salmon had made distinguished studies of hog cholera, cattle-tick fever, and contagious pleuropneumonia.

Dr. Salmon graduated from Cornell in 1872 with a bachelor's degree in veterinary science. He settled in Newark to practice, taking his doctor's degree in 1876, also from Cornell. Failing health induced him to go to Ashville, North Carolina, and, while in the South, he began the study of swine diseases. Next he was called upon to help in the campaign for the eradication of contagious pleuropneumonia from New York state.

He came to the Department of Agriculture in 1879, in the main to study Texas or cattle-tick fever, contagious pleuropneumonia, and some other diseases of cattle and poultry. However, he drifted into administrative work, having a flair for it, and became chief of the Bureau of Animal Industry from its creation in 1884 until 1906, when he was called to Uruguay to organize the veterinary department of the University of Montevideo. Returning to the United States in 1913, he engaged in the manufacture of hog-cholera serum in Butte, Montana, until he died there of pneumonia.

After Salmon entered the Department, a farm near Washington, D. C., was purchased to be used as an experiment station in the study of contagious animal diseases. On March 3, 1873, a law regulating the transportation of animals was passed and, under the act of Congress of March 3, 1883, the Treasury Department began the administration of quarantine laws regulating the importation of animals under the direction of a cattle commission.

In 1884 Representative William H. Hatch of Missouri, long chairman of the House Agricultural Committee, introduced a bill to establish a Bureau of Animal Industry. This agency of the Department of Agriculture was intended to "prevent the exportation of diseased cattle, and to provide means for the suppression and extirpation of pleuropneumonia and other contagious diseases among domestic animals."

The legislation was bitterly opposed, in the main by believers in states' rights who thought it unconstitutional for the federal government to give special aid to the livestock industry. They called this the "horse doctor bill" and petitioned Congress not to saddle still more Washington bureaucrats on long-suffering taxpayers. They said that the disease was a myth anyway, and, besides, state regulation was adequate to control its spread.

But to the livestock men the disease was no myth. They knew that it could never be controlled at all if it once reached the herds on the unfenced western plains. A rising tide of public opinion favored the bill. Since 1842 Great Britain had suffered an annual loss of ten million dollars because of this one cattle disease. Had the disease spread in the United States for five more years it would have produced losses of over one billion dollars.

The Hatch Act was approved by the President on May 29, 1884. It required that the chief of the Bureau of Animal Industry be a competent veterinary surgeon. The bureau personnel was limited to twenty. It was to promulgate regulations, through the Commissioner of Agriculture, capable of suppressing contagious pleuropneumonia, and other contagious, infectious, and communicable diseases of animals. It was to co-operate with the Treasury on regulations governing the transportation and exportation of livestock.

Dr. Salmon, as chief of the bureau, displayed the same marked facility for selecting brilliant assistants as had Lamson-Scribner and B. T. Galloway in the plant work. Contagious pleuropneumonia was wiped out in this country within a few years at a cost of $1,509,100.

There has been no outbreak of this cattle disease in the United States since 1892, when Secretary Rusk proclaimed our country free from it. No large country but ours has ever extirpated the malady. However, we had created a research bureau destined to make a revolutionary discovery in the field of human and animal medicine, to perform much other investigation of great value, and to engage in lines of regulatory work which benefit us all, but to which little consideration can be given in this volume.

Soon after the Bureau of Animal Industry was created, a shy, diffident but handsome young graduate medical student from Harvard joined its staff. Whether he asked for one of the toughest problems it faced is not known, but he got it—cattle-tick fever, then miscalled Texas fever. It had become a curse to cattle raising in the South and, ever since the Civil War, southern cattle had left a trail of it behind them whenever they were driven north. This they did even when not sick themselves.

Cattle-tick fever was introduced into this country in Colonial times from the West Indies and from Mexico. It caused tremendous havoc during the nineteenth century. Northern cattle raisers finally demanded that the federal government take action to prevent the spread of the disease, since they regarded state regulation as wholly inadequate. In 1884 Dr. Theobald Smith, the handsome young medical student, took charge of animal-disease investigations in the Bureau of Animal Industry. Working with him were F. L. Kilborne and Cooper Curtice, both veterinarians.

While Smith was just a little disdainful of these "horse doctors," they had done valuable work on cattle-tick fever. Curtice had made so thorough a study of the tick that probably nobody on earth knew more about its biology than he. Kilborne, by associating with cattlemen and observing keenly, had reached the conclusion that the growers were right who said that the fever disappeared when the ticks disappeared. Smith, however, felt sure that the disease was transmitted bacterially, and he set himself to discover and indict the guilty micro-organism.

He early observed that the red blood corpuscles of animals attacked by the disease were destroyed. He next found in them a peculiar micro-organism, a protozoan—a single-celled, very simple animal, but not a bacterium. He did not know how the protozoan got there, but he was at first reluctant to accept the tick theory of its dissemination, already espoused by some cattlemen and by his colleagues.

About 1890, however, Smith decided to give this theory a try, and he formulated a set of crucial experiments which would either convict the tick or else find it innocent. For this he deserves full credit, as he was probably the only one of the three who could have mapped out the strategy of this scientific battle so logically and so well. As a result it was proved that the tick transmitted the protozoan in its bite and that the protozoan caused the fever in cattle.

This was an astounding discovery in the field of medicine. For the first time in history it was shown that an arthropod, an insect, could act as the intermediary host in the transmission of a protozoan disease. Tick eradication promptly got underway, after it was proved that tickless southern cattle could not transmit the infection. But the proposal to eradicate the myriads of cattle ticks from fifteen southern states was initially regarded as fantastic.

However, further research showed that certain dips and sprays, along with the vacating of pastures, would destroy the ticks without injury to the cattle. Systematic tick eradication began under authorization of Congress in 1906. The most progress was made by dipping ticky cattle in arsenical solutions. Today cattle-tick fever exists in only a small fraction of 1 per cent of the area formerly ravaged by it. A discovery that has been worth about $40,000,000 a year to the cattle industry cost only $65,000 to make originally.

But, in addition, the discovery that infective agents can use an intermediary host in attacking animals and men solved the problem of the transmission of fifty or more other diseases, such as malaria, African sleeping sickness, Rocky Mountain spotted fever, yellow fever, tularemia, nagana, and many more. This brings us again to the Panama Canal, which you perhaps thought had been forgotten.

The French failed to dig the canal not so much for lack of funds and energy, but because of the prevalence of yellow fever in the Canal Zone. Once the role of the mosquito in the transmission of yellow fever became clear—and this happened because others followed the trail blazed by Smith, Kilborne, and Curtice—the insects could be killed off and the danger to human life all but eliminated. No wonder Bureau of Animal Industry *Bulletin No. 1*, issued in 1893, on the "Nature, Causation, and Prevention of Texas Fever" remains an all-time medical classic.

It was also workers in the Bureau of Animal Industry who devised the satisfactory arsenical dip mentioned above. At first a homemade dip was advised. Later many commercial dips became available which needed only to be mixed with water in the dipping vat. Vast quantities of these dips have been used and a thriving industry owes its inception to the work of the Department's animal scientists. Tick eradication also produced expansion of the southern cattle industry, using vast quantities of fencing, cement, and other products. Altogether huge dividends flowed here from a very modest original investment in research.

In 1894 there entered the Bureau of Animal Industry a modest little man named Marion Dorset. A few years later he was publishing work of fundamental importance on hog cholera, which Dr. Salmon, after studying the disease himself, had attributed to a "micrococcus" in 1881. Dorset was a many-sided research investigator. He was a pioneer worker on the biochemistry of the tubercle bacillus and, in April, 1934, introduced the new tuberculin since used as a test agent in tuberculosis-eradication work among cattle. He devised the medium upon which the tuberculosis bacillus is grown almost everywhere for laboratory study.

Dorset also investigated the keeping quality of meats. He produced the effective, harmless fluid used in marking federally inspected meat. He organized the system of federal inspection in establishments licensed by the government to manufacture serums, viruses, toxins, and related veterinary biologicals. He formulated the laboratory procedures used in administering the Federal Meat Inspection Act.

He was active in the formation of the Federal Insecticide and Fungicide Board, and he developed and tested dips and disinfectants. Under his direction and with his suggestions his coworkers devised a rapid method of detecting pullorum disease in chickens, a boon to the poultry industry which will be discussed later. At present we are concerned only with his hog-cholera work.

At the time the Bureau of Animal Industry was founded at least twenty-five to thirty million dollars' worth of American hogs (sometimes as many as six million animals a year) died annually from cholera. The disease appeared among hogs during the Civil War. Some regarded it as of human origin. Farmers worked hard and spent cash to raise many hogs which never got to market. Could the disease be controlled? At the time Dorset began his work it was presumed to be caused by a germ.

But, in 1898, two German investigators, Loeffler and Frosch, reported an attempt to immunize cattle against dread foot-and-mouth disease, an ailment also to be considered later. They had filtered a quantity of virulent lymph obtained from infected animals through a filter that would hold back bacteria. Yet they found that this filtrate would still produce foot-and-mouth disease if injected into cattle.

That meant that there were virulent agents so small that they could go through the finest filters known. They could not be seen with the highest-power microscopes. Here was something basic. Soon it was shown that such an agent, called a filtrable virus, caused contagious pleuropneumonia. Dorset began to wonder whether a similar virus might possibly be the cause of hog cholera.

He found this hypothesis to be correct. This was the first time in medical history that an animal disease supposedly caused by a bacterium had been found attributable to a filtrable virus. The discovery was epoch-making. Following this discovery, other scientists found that yellow fever, smallpox, measles, and many other human and animal ills were virus-caused. Competent experts classified Dorset's work with that of Pasteur and Koch.

Dorset and his coworkers next perfected a protective serum which was highly effective when used as directed, and commercial production of the serum began around 1907. It confers a temporary immunity to hog cholera. The serum was prepared in more than fifty plants by 1942. Just before his death in service, on July 14, 1935, Dorset developed a crystal-violet vaccine for hog cholera, which under some conditions had distinct advantages over the serum treatment.

The use of these remedies saves American hog growers from ten to twenty-five million dollars each year, depending upon the price of hogs, the prevalence of cholera, and the extent to which the serum and vaccine are properly utilized. Around 1933 the work of Dorset's entire laboratory, performed on many subjects, cost taxpayers about $130,000 a year. The entire Bureau of Animal Industry cost about twelve million dollars a year, and the basic discoveries by Dorset and his colleagues cost about $50,000. Make your own comparisons. And we still had the Bureau of Animal Industry.

In the *Eighteenth Annual Report* of the bureau, issued in 1902, there was a summary of work by Charles Wardell Stiles on "The Significance of Recent American Cases of Hookworm Disease (Uncinariasis or Anchylostomiasis) in Man." Stiles was educated at Wesleyan in Connecticut, then took work at the College de France in Paris, in Berlin, and at Leipzig. He became a Bureau zoologist in 1890 and in 1891 took charge of its zoological laboratory. Trained as he was under outstanding parasitologists, he carried on a variety of investigations in his chosen field, finally becoming interested in the hookworm problem.

Stiles originally became familiar with hookworm disease in the Old World. Among the symptoms of infestation was a tendency to eat dirt which he also observed among certain classes of people in our South. Thereupon he kept telling the students to whom he lectured at medical school all his life to keep a lookout for hookworms. Many physicians, including the famous William Osler, scoffed at the idea. Finally one of Stiles' students, Bailey K. Ashford, found hookworm disease in Puerto Rico and, in 1901, returned to Washington with a large number of specimens.

Then eight cases were found among students at the University of Texas Medical School at Galveston, and Stiles identified the worms. Next he took a long trip through the South to study the prevalence of infestation. In 1902 he found significant differences between the Old World hookworm and worms taken from patients in this country. He reported his findings before the American Gastroenterologic Association at its fifth annual meeting in Washington on May 1, 1902.

Stiles also announced his findings to the American Sanitary Conference in Washington the following December 4. Since he attributed to the hookworm much of the so-called laziness and shiftlessness of southerners in the low-income classes, he came in for many satirical comments as the professor who claimed to have found the "lazy bug." His discovery was hooted and denounced; he was caricatured derisively. But after he made his survey of the South, Stiles got the attention of Henry Wallace (father of Henry C., grandfather of Henry A.), Walter Hines Page, and Theodore Roosevelt.

He showed these distinguished gentlemen actual cases of hookworm infestation on train platforms as they toured with him. Page obtained the financing of Rockefeller, who put up a million dollars to fight the hookworm. Ridicule ended abruptly. By 1927 more than seven million sufferers had been treated, and it had been shown that the disease caused by the parasite could be eradicated. One method of eradication was to give poor southerners shoes!

About 1902 Stiles was appointed professor of zoology for the United States Public Health Service. However, the Bureau of Animal Industry retained him as a consultant. He later collaborated with the staff of the Rockefeller Institute at the Hygienic Laboratory. The sanitary and other measures he suggested went far to raise the social and economic level of millions of people. He lived until January 24, 1941, and died, almost wholly forgotten for his spectacularly successful early work, at Johns Hopkins, in Baltimore.

In 1920, Maurice C. Hall, who had previously worked in the Bureau of Animal Industry, returned to it from war work. He was a tall, conspicuously attractive man with a wide mental range. His major virtue was not humility, but he had much of which to be justly proud. An ardent anti–antivivisectionist, he was never too busy in his life to confute the antivivisectionists, telling them with perfect truth the many successful methods he had worked out to free lower animals from parasites, which findings had subsequently helped human beings too.

Hall always answered his own phone and cried out "Yea!" and you knew it was he. He worked daily and Sunday, cursed with gastric ulcers for many years though he was. He would tell you immediately you met him that he was a radical, that he had wild, eccentric views, and that what he said would inevitably shock you. He had a violent temper, which cooled readily. He had many adoring friends and was proud of his enemies. Once he told me that he returned to the bureau and tried to decipher some scrawled notes he had made before he left. In the notebook he said that he found this legible entry: "Try organic compounds to eradicate hookworm." As he had tried chloroform and found it moderately effective, he now tried a related compound on dogs, carbon tetrachloride. The trial was extremely successful. He seemed to have something really good.

Then, thinking of those stricken southern sufferers who could not afford shoes, he began to wonder whether he could put the liquid in capsules so that human beings could take them unharmed. So, stomach ulcers and all, he decided to be guinea pig himself. He took some of the capsules and at least felt no worse than he did ordinarily. (The stomach ulcers got him eventually, only a short while after he left the Bureau of Animal Industry for the National Institute of Health.) He next tried the remedy on human sufferers from hookworm. Ultimately fifteen or twenty millions of these victims received the treatment.

Later a related and less toxic compound was used quite as effectually by Hall and his associates. Victims of hookworm are often totally incapacitated. Even if they can get around, their work capacity is reduced by one-third. The successful treatment of so many people, changing them from inadvertently shiftless and inefficient humans to self-supporting members of society was indeed an accomplishment.

This conservation of human resources on a grand scale was worth dollars and cents, in addition to a restoration of human and cultural values. At the very low figure of two or three dollars per person treated this meant $75,000,000 added to the national wealth by making more self-supporting citizens out of many who had to live on charity relief.

The basic papers announcing this research appeared in the *Journal of Agricultural Research*, a fortnightly scientific periodical published by the Department of Agriculture. The results which flowed from these papers alone amply paid for the publication of the *Journal* throughout its existence even up to this moment—many times over. Yet large monetary returns have flowed also from many other papers which have appeared therein.

We can give but passing mention to the enormous *Index-Catalogue of Medical and Veterinary Zoology*, a virtual rogues' gallery and doomsday book of dangerous parasites, which provides reliable information on any of approximately one hundred thousand known animal parasites in the world, and the latest methods for their control or eradication. In 1891, Albert Hassall, a young scientist of the Bureau of Animal Industry, was assigned by his chief, Wardell Stiles, to look up references to such parasites. The project grew into a catalog with over one million entries, a bulletin published so far in thirty-six parts (the first volume appeared December 26, 1901), and co-operative work with medical arms of the federal government. Its direct and indirect benefits to livestock, livestock growers, public health, and international good will are inestimable.

One of the earliest publications on trichinæ, by B. H. Ransom and Benjamin Schwartz, also appeared in the *Journal of Agricultural Research*. That was in 1919 and the work concerned all pork-eating human beings. When it began, there was no effective method of protecting the public from trichinosis derived from pork. No existing technique of inspection could be relied upon, the German microscopic system being best but tedious, expensive, and untrustworthy.

Laboratory methods of this sort could be used to eliminate heavily infested carcasses, but many lightly infested ones were overlooked, and a false sense of security arose about the condition of the meat. Ransom and his associates developed effective methods for the control of trichinæ during the processing of pork products usually consumed uncooked. These methods, involving cooking, refrigeration, and special curing, were generally adopted by the packers.

They are carried out effectively at all plants operating under the close scrutiny of the federal meat-inspection service. Over a billion pounds of products undergo inspection annually. The Ransom method is so effective a preventive, that the costly German microscopic technique of meat inspection does not have to be applied later.

Ransom emphasized swine-sanitation methods, too, which enabled farmers to produce as many marketable pigs from two sows as they formerly had from three sows annually, for many pigs die before reaching maturity if the Ransom swine-sanitation procedure is neglected. If it is utilized, the pigs not only survive better but grow faster and are ready to sell sooner.

Pig feeding also is important. About 6 per cent of hogs fed raw garbage harbor parasites, as compared with only 1 per cent of those fed principally on grain. As a whole these studies offered a practical solution to the trichinosis problem and not only saved vast sums annually on pork inspection but provided a further benefit in reducing human suffering and death from trichinosis, a result upon which it is difficult to place a monetary valuation.

Brucellosis is another animal ailment of very direct interest to human beings, and the bureau has performed research on it since 1900, when the malady was commonly known as "contagious abortion." Later it was called "infectious abortion," then "Bang's disease," and finally, out of deference to Sir David Bruce, who discovered the first species of the genus in which the causative organism is classified, "brucellosis." The agent which produces this disease is closely related to the one causing undulant fever in man.

The conquest of the malady in animals is being accomplished in the main by applying knowledge obtained through research. Unfortunately, the disease has a habit of entering a quiescent or dormant stage during which cattle owners think it has died out, or possibly been cured by some quack remedy; but the infective organism is still present, though its manifestations have subsided, and the disease can return with new fury.

In 1930 the bureau could announce a new vaccine, developed by J. M. Buck and W. E. Cotton, capable of preventing the disease.

Earlier than that bureau workers had devised methods of herd management which went far to curb brucellosis. Finally Strain 19 (a vaccine) was found to produce serviceable immunity without causing the disease. Favorable results were also obtained in field trials with young calves, which led to official adoption of calfhood vaccination in 1940, as an adjunct to the test-and-slaughter method of combating brucellosis.

Here a research discovery costing less than $85,000 saves calves worth about $2,000,000 a year. An interesting sidelight was the subsequent use of the vaccine prepared from the same strain of the organism by the British Ministry of Agriculture and Fisheries in combating brucellosis in England as an aid to the wartime milk-production program there.

Likewise reaching over into the field of human medicine is the problem of bovine tuberculosis. Tuberculin was discovered by Robert Koch in 1890, and three years later the Bureau of Animal Industry began to produce it. It has been doing that ever since. Tuberculin contains no tuberculosis germs, living or dead, and no substance that could be detrimental to a nontuberculous animal. It contains instead a small quantity of material derived from the growth of the germs.

But animals affected with tuberculosis show a specific sensitiveness to tuberculin when it is injected. They react to it in somewhat the manner that sufferers from hay fever react to certain pollens, though those pollens have no effect on persons who are not susceptible. Through research by Marion Dorset and his staff tuberculin is now produced on a synthetic medium which results in a more potent product than used to be grown on beef-broth medium.

Animals will often react positively to this tuberculin when their tubercular lesions are too small to be found microscopically at post mortem. The value of the test is so well established that the courts uphold decisions based upon it which result in the condemnation of animals. The results of the test also become apparent during federal meat inspection of slaughtered animals. That the test can screen out reactors for slaughter and thus reduce the extent of the disease is obvious.

Conquest of bovine tuberculosis in this country resulted from a combination of public sentiment, skilled research, and well-organized field activities planned by federal and state veterinary officials, and sometimes carried out under actual fire by owners who doubted the test. Actual tuberculin testing of cattle for detecting the disease began in Pennsylvania in 1892. In 1910 systematic testing of all cattle in the District of Columbia began.

Following a thorough study of the bovine tuberculosis sanitation by federal and state veterinary officials, the United States Livestock Sanitary Association in 1917 formulated a specific program of "Uniform Methods and Rules for Tuberculosis-Free Accredited Herds." It planned to give official recognition to herds tested and found free from tuberculosis. Provision was also made for the eradication of the disease from county-size areas.

By 1919 concerted efforts to test all animals within entire counties began. Then the objective became the testing of all herds in the country. By this means reactors have been reduced from as many as 30 per cent in some localities, to a small fraction of 1 per cent in all parts of the United States. Hence this insidious disease of high morbidity has essentially been eradicated from the nation by repeated tests and removal of reactors.

Direct benefits to cattle owners include increased values of breeding stock while indirect benefits include a broadening of outlets for livestock products, often to the extent of establishing new local industries—creameries, cheese factories, and so on. Finally, some bank officials claim that deposits have increased as much as 20 per cent in certain counties which have been freed from bovine tuberculosis.

It is quite apparent now that animals suffer from "many grievous murrains," but, as in the case of plants and trees, the doctor can destroy the patient to protect the well if he sees fit, a procedure considered a little drastic for human beings. Foot-and-mouth disease has been known for centuries to be one of the most contagious and devastating livestock maladies. We mentioned it when speaking of Dorset's work on hog cholera. It is caused by a filtrable virus so infective that it will produce the disease even when diluted a million to one.

Practically all cloven-footed animals, especially cattle, hogs, and sheep, are susceptible. In malignant form it will kill or render

U.S.D.A. photograph by Madeleine Osborne

Testing DDT to determine toxicity and duration of effectiveness
as a larvicide

U.S.D.A. photograph by Peter Killian

Seeking new chemicals that will make better bait to lure Japanese
beetles to traps

valueless half the animals in a herd. It permanently impairs the productivity of less severely affected animals. Man usually resists but sometimes acquires the infection; he can easily carry it on his clothing. Yet the United States has repelled eight invasions by this disease and, since 1929, has been wholly free from it. Why?

Because scientists in this bureau got busy on it. A rigid federal-state quarantine has long been kept on a national basis to exclude the disease. When outbreaks occur, a "blitz" procedure goes into effect at once. The ailing animals are slaughtered immediately, their owners being paid specified appraisal rates for them, and the bodies are buried in quick lime. Premises are cheaply disinfected with 1 or 2 per cent solutions of caustic soda.

In 1924 the Department proposed to Congress the appointment of a commission to study this disease in European countries where it is always present. Congress authorized the study by special act and the commission consisted of P. K. Oblitsky of the Rockefeller Institute for Medical Research, J. Traum of the University of California, and H. W. Schoening of the Bureau of Animal Industry.

The commission visited eleven European countries and, in addition, conducted experiments in France. The results of its work appear in a 172-page report which has since formed the background for keeping the disease at bay here. The slaughter method of eradication is advocated in the report for this country, a few animals being sacrificed to prevent the disease becoming firmly established here. Research on the disease has cost American taxpayers all of $85,000; if the scourge became established in this country, it would be an expensive luxury, levying a tax of $200,000,000 annually.

The sanitary regulations covering the importation of cattle apply also to fresh meat. This is known to be capable of carrying foot-and-mouth disease virus. Canned, cooked, or otherwise properly processed meat-food products are safe in this respect. Dependable means of diagnosis and eradication and the formulation of sanitary regulations to prevent spread of the disease we owe to the commission's report.

In June, 1943, there was announced by O. Wilford Olsen a workable plan for the control of cattle-liver flukes. In its adult stage the fluke is a flat, leaflike worm, pale brown in color, about an inch long and one-third to one-half as wide. Cattle become infested by wallowing in grass or water containing cysts which lodge in their digestive tracts and dissolve, liberating the happy young flukes, which bore through the intestinal wall and seek out the animal's liver where they become blood suckers and cause anemia.

The animals lose weight because of inability to digest their food properly, they give less milk, produce smaller calf crops, and finally have their fluky livers condemned by inspectors in packing plants, a last indignity which perhaps bothers them little. Olsen devised a way of preparing a drench, containing hexachlorethane, which drug was absorbed from the alimentary tract, thus reached the liver and eradicated the flukes. Commercial production and widespread use of the drug for the purpose have followed demonstration of its value.

We now consider two interesting pieces of research not concerned with a cattle disease. However, the health of the animals was impaired and calf crops were poor in the Gulf coast region and other parts of the South. W. H. Black's studies of the cattle industry in South Africa around 1931 provided a clue, for though the land there was deficient in phosphorus, feeding affected animals a supplement of bone meal increased their fertility, their flesh development, and the quality of their bones.

When he returned to this country, Black and his colleagues found that the addition of small quantities of phosphorus to the ration of similarly affected cows here ended their troubles. This could be accomplished by giving the animals bone meal, by dissolving disodium phosphate in their drinking water, or by fertilizing their pastures with a superphosphate mixture.

In 1942–43 the Agricultural Research Administration, co-operating with the American Meat Institute and the University of Chicago, quickly worked out a practicable method for dehydrating meat for war use. This offers another example of research performed capably under the whip of urgent necessity. The immediate objective was to develop methods that would enable the meat industry to process meat under wartime conditions, so as to save weight and bulk and get shipments to distant destinations without refrigeration. The whole process was successfully worked out, clear to methods of compressing the dehydrated meat to save shipping space and reduce the cost of containers. Compression also helped in retaining palatability.

This research was relatively costly—$160,000. Its proved monetary value so far is only $800,000, a small rate of return for investments in scientific investigation. But millions of pounds of dehydrated meat were produced, most of it pork, and sent to Russia under Lend-Lease. This added nutritive value in the food supplies of the Russian army was of the utmost value in bringing victory, for they used the product during the critical period when they held, then beat back, the armies of Germany.

We return to animal disease by way of the hog, whose cholera has already been discussed. J. E. Peterman and A. G. Beagle of the Bureau of Animal Industry not long since devised a chart which aids materially in the prompt diagnosis of swine diseases. Many swine ills have similar symptoms in early stages and are difficult to differentiate. But certain combinations of seemingly minor symptoms become very revealing when they occur together. The chart has already saved the life of many a hog which might otherwise have been a sacrifice to misdiagnosis.

At Ames, Iowa, the Regional Swine Breeding Laboratory, directed by W. A. Craft, has under investigation the possibility of speeding up hog genetics by eliminating faulty genes which cause defects. Thus it is possible to produce strains of swine with enhanced vigor, improved prolificacy, possibly more lean meat and better bacon quality, coat smoothness, economy in the use of feed for growth, freedom from excess fat, and other qualities swine growers like.

The laboratory is trying to do the same thing for swine that the hybrid corn breeders have done for corn. Important information has already been uncovered on more effective methods of selection, and on breeding systems to fix desirable qualities. The speed of genetic improvement has been thrown into high gear and it operates sometimes as much as ten times as fast as prevailing systems of swine breeding for racial betterment among the hogs.

Two older pieces of bureau research should be mentioned before we depart from the hog pen. One concerns the sanitation system for the control of swine roundworms devised by the aforesaid B. H. Ransom and his associates. This system, now widely used in the United States, was based on Ransom's painstaking researches upon the life cycle of the roundworm or ascarid. Ransom found the worms often in young pigs that died unaccountably, after coughing and "thumping"—similar to hiccups in man.

He then found that the worms travel in the blood stream from the intestines to the lungs, visiting many vital organs socially along the way, and then returning to the intestine via the windpipe and esophagus. Damage to the lungs explained the coughing and thumping (hiccups) of the pigs. Ransom and his associates then evolved a complete system of sanitation that proved 98 per cent effective in protecting pigs against parasites and filth-borne diseases.

Finally we come to the soft-pork investigations. Southern hogs were eating something—mainly peanuts and soybeans—which produced soft pork, i.e., there was a lack of firmness to the fat so extreme as often to render the products shapeless. Investigation began in 1919. Lard from soft carcasses was then often fluid or semifluid at room temperature. The problem was solved by so regulating the feed intake as to permit consumption of some softening feeds along with other feeds which prevented the former from having too great an effect.

The age of the animal, length of the feeding period, the period of final fattening, and many other factors had to be taken into account. Formulas were devised in which peanut meal, soybean meal, or cottonseed meal could be fed, along with other feeds, in such a way as to produce normal, firm fat and normal-appearing meat products. The problem was thus written up as solved. Another call from farmers for help had been answered.

The automobile industry has accustomed us to new models. The Bureau of Animal Industry devises new sheep models.

It had long been believed that a wrinkled skin and an abundance of wool on the face and legs tended to make sheep have heavier and more valuable fleeces. This was proved fallacious. In fact, the sheep often got the wool in their eyes so badly that they could not see to feed themselves properly, became lost from the flock, and died from malnourishment. Wrinkled skins did not help a bit either; they just made the sheep harder to shear.

The upshot was the development of two new range breeds. They excel in the production of wool, lamb, and mutton. Their weight gain is rapid. Their wool does not get into their eyes, nor does it straggle down their legs to become soiled. The ewes wean more lambs than did those with hairy faces. So streamlined, tailor-made sheep came from the breeders.

The Columbia is one of these modern made-to-order sheep breeds, living proof that livestock can be designed and developed to meet social needs. It combines the most desirable characteristics of the Lincoln and Rambouillet breeds, and has been developed since 1912. It was designed for life on the western range, at a cost of something like $75,000. It should increase the net returns of owners at least $150,000 a year above what they garnered from stock formerly kept.

While they were about it, the Bureau scientists also devised an effective and economical dip that would rid sheep of ticks with a single application. The ticks so torment the sheep that they pull out and ruin their wool and produce less meat than normally. This dip, in which rotenone is the active ingredient, has already paid for itself, as the savings from its use in a single year would foot the entire bill for the research involved five times over.

Here phenothiazine should also be mentioned once more, as it is now the most widely used of all drugs for removing parasites from livestock. It has a wide range of effective action and is not so selective and discriminating about the internal parasites it will kill as are most other drugs. Smear 62, mentioned also in an earlier chapter, likewise curbs the spread of screwworms. In the Southwest screwworms account for 85 per cent of the usual annual loss of livestock, largely preventable through timely application of Smear 62. Losses within any areas where Smear 62 is widely used decrease sharply.

Horses share with men the unique but somewhat unenviable distinction of having venereal disease. That of horses is called "dourine." It is highly contagious, makes a mess of the animal, and usually results in its slaughter, again on the kill-the-patient principle which rules in the barnyard. But development of a quick test has made it possible for bureau scientists to test 2,500 horses a day. Control is based on this test, which has so far effected a saving of millions of dollars for horse breeders.

Investigations of equine encephalomyelitis produced evidence that a safe, efficient vaccine could be prepared. This formalized brain vaccine was introduced in 1934. It is made commercially and used widely. The improved chick-embryo vaccine was introduced in 1938. As a result of these studies, aided by the discovery and location of two types of virus, many horses are saved annually.

We turn now to an immigrant to this country who made good. In the early days it lived a life of lush lust and leisure in the jungles of New Guinea, Java, and Malaya. Explorers found it an interesting creature and brought specimens to various parts of Europe and Asia whence they came in time to the Western Hemisphere. I refer, of course, to chickens, which produce for us four times as much meat as sheep, and a third as much as our beef cattle, lay millions of eggs as a side line, and bring farmers an annual income of about two and two-thirds billion dollars.

Naturally scientists were dissatisfied with the chicken as it was originally, and as a result of their experimentation the average annual egg production of the hen rose from 83 to 113 during the past quarter of a century. Blood lines have now been developed which can produce 200 eggs per year, and Victory cockerels have been bred which can readily increase the average egg production of the flock. Bureau of Animal Industry scientists have done much to protect chickens from disease, discovering only recently that sulfaguanidine, one of the numerous sulfa drugs, prevents caecal coccidiosis, a deadly parasitic ailment.

Then there is that simple test for pullorum disease, developed by a group of workers in Marion Dorset's Biochemic Division. Announced in 1931, it is worth more than a million dollars annually to chicken growers, although the cost of the project was $36,000. This conservative estimate is based on the current volume of testing and the relative survival rates of chicks in tested and untested flocks. The test is rapid, simple, and reliable. Before development of the test permitted poultrymen to discover and exterminate chickens suffering from the disease, it ravaged their flocks. Diseases of this nature not only kill young chicks, but they reduce the hatchability of eggs, curtail egg production, and finally kill off the hens from generalized infection.

Gapeworms are a common poultry parasite which formerly caused extensive losses. Until January, 1939, there was no satisfactory treatment for removing them, though Mother used to thrust a feather moistened with turpentine or kerosene down the little sufferer's throat, and, if it survived, the bird might cough up some of the worms, which were thus induced to loosen their hold on the throat lining. The bureau workers found that when infested chicks breathed barium antimonyl tartrate, the worms became dislodged, because the chemical was 98 per cent effective in killing the pest.

As for the hen's eggs, they seemed hardly hatchable enough to suit the scientists. Therefore, three of them found that, before 1900, only three studies had ever been made on the best conditions for egg incubation. Meanwhile, though the use of incubators was rapidly increasing, an average of but 60 per cent of the eggs set actually hatched. Experiments were undertaken with apparatus for precision studies. The chicks in embryo were to get just exactly the temperature, humidity, oxygen, carbon dioxide, and so on that would most surely induce them to break their shells and live.

Between 1924 and 1928 more than four thousand eggs were incubated in forty-four tests. Any factor could be varied as required by the use of a respiration calorimeter. Finally incubators were designed to provide just the temperature, humidity, and combination of gases the eggs preferred in which to hatch. Hatches of 70 and 80 per cent thereafter became common among commercial growers.

More recently the bureau scientists have found out how to produce eggs of better keeping quality. They observed that the shells of eggs laid by some hens are naturally more porous than those of eggs laid by others. Eggs with porous shells lose weight in storage, but hens can be bred which will produce eggs that shrink in storage only half as much as is common. Therefore, through selection of breeding stock to get strains which lay eggs with the less porous shells, the scientists are able to produce better-keeping eggs genetically.

Finally the scientists thought with remorse of all the wet chicken feathers that go to waste when plucked at commercial poultry-processing plants. They could not bear that waste. The feathers were decomposing too rapidly to permit their collection and shipment to feather-processing plants. John I. Hardy and Harold W. Wolf found out how to preserve the feathers for future use by dousing them in an inexpensive mixture of water, common salt, and commercial concentrated hydrochloric acid.

At East Lansing, Michigan, the Regional Poultry Research Laboratory, under the direction of Berley Winton, is seeking to improve viability in poultry. Currently it works on lymphomatosis, so-called "fowl paralysis," which causes losses of about fifty million dollars a year to the industry. The disease entered here from Europe about 1917 and soon one-quarter of the chickens in New England were affected. Progress is slow in this investigation because the causative agent is unknown as is the method of infection.

In fact one man who works in the laboratory chicken pens actually changes his clothes sixty-four times a day, because he has a special suit to wear when he enters each of the sixty-four control pens. However, highly susceptible lines of chickens can be bred which are free from the disease, and it is also possible to breed both resistant and susceptible lines which remain true to type. There are indications also that the infection can be carried in the egg, and that is important. This combined scientific attack—pathological, cytological, genetic, and nutritional—is bound to win in the end.

We turn now from poultry to Abraham Lincoln's mother, without going outside the scope of the Bureau of Animal Industry. In Colonial days there was a disease of animals and of human beings, accompanied by trembling, and called "milk sickness" or "trembles." It was very prevalent in rural areas. The milk of cows was suspected of poisoning persons who drank it, causing the disease, hence its name.

Early writers report that whole villages were at one time depopulated by the disease and settlers were terrified by the frightful pestilence. It is reliably reported that the deaths of Lincoln's mother and of two of her relatives were caused by milk sickness. Nor did the cows fare well either. Suckling calves also often sickened suddenly and died of the trembles.

Various plants—poison ivy, water hemlock, Virginia creeper, marsh marigold, and mushrooms were imagined to poison the milk of cows which ate them. Some persons claimed that the disease was caused by molds and fungi which grew on plants. Then, in 1923, C. D. Marsh, J. F. Couch (now the "rutin" man at Northern Regional Research Laboratory), and A. B. Clawson cleared up the mystery. They demonstrated that milk sickness was caused principally by two plants which contain a chemical compound that was crystallized by them. They determined its structure and named it "tremetol."

One of these plants is white snakeroot, widely distributed in the eastern states and extending as far west as Minnesota, Oklahoma, Nebraska, and Texas. The other is jimmyweed or rayless goldenrod, which thrives from southern Colorado to western Texas, New Mexico, and Arizona, and extends on into Mexico. Further research disclosed that, though the cows secrete the poison in their milk, their meat does not contain enough tremetol to cause the sickness. Trembles can be entirely prevented by keeping livestock away from patches of the two plants.

Another plant, botanically related to the other two but so far lacking a common name, also contains the poison, but less commonly causes milk sickness. These findings sprang rather spontaneously from research on plants poisonous to livestock.

Useful information about human marriage as well as about breeding tender beefsteaks became known because Sewall Wright in 1922 published highly technical papers on such subjects as "Coefficients of Inbreeding and Relationships." Wright applied mathematics to animal breeding. Since inbreeding helps fix desired characteristics in animals, it is important to know the animal's degree of inbreeding. Closely related individuals are mated when animals are inbred, and certain animals thus appear several times as common ancestors in the pedigrees of their own progeny, their influence being increased by the number of times they appear. Wright worked out a formula to measure the degree of inbreeding. It can be applied to any animal of which the pedigree is known.

There is no way of setting a monetary value on a discovery of this kind. However, it is an important new tool at hand for workers in many different fields of scientific research. In that sense its value is beyond computation. Thus Wright put scientific principles to work in the field of inbreeding and crossbreeding, long lively topics of conversation and public discussion, often culminating in laws and customs relating to marriage. Primitive peoples had very definite views on the degree of inbreeding they regarded as socially and physically permissible, but the customs of different peoples varied all over the world. The opinions of livestock breeders varied quite as much in their own field.

Some held that inbreeding would produce progressive degeneration, evidenced by reduction in size, in constitutional vigor, and in fertility, and would lead ultimately to the appearance of monstrosities. Yet it was a matter of record that most of the modern, improved breeds of livestock originated from rather close inbreeding of selected stock. To provide some basis upon which to appraise these varying opinions, the bureau began its comprehensive study of inbreeding, using guinea pigs as "guinea pigs," as early as 1906.

The guinea pig, because cheap, docile, prolific, and easy to handle, often turns out to be the scientist's best laboratory biological reagent. Most of this experimental work was conducted by Sewall Wright, and, as early as 1917, he had one guinea-pig family which had attained its twenty-fifth generation of inbreeding. By 1924, more than 35,000 animals had been studied in connection with this inbreeding and crossbreeding work.

The results tended to show that inbred stock did suffer a genetic decline in vigor in all characteristics, as compared with the control stock. Each line of descent also tended to become fixed in outward appearance, as shown by color and pattern, while in some cases an entire family bred true to a given color and pattern. Relatively few monstrosities were produced by either the inbred families or the controls, two of the feeblest families producing few or no pronounced abnormalities. Ultimately both better matings and marriage and improved beefsteaks may result from the application of this knowledge to other fields.

Last of all we shall consider federal meat inspection, though this was carried on in the War Food Administration during its existence, then by the Livestock Branch of the Production and Marketing Administration, but was returned to the Bureau of Animal Industry in the fall of 1946. Here also it had its beginnings. Agitation and sentiment for the inspection of meat began as early as 1861. Meat was said to be unwholesome in many instances because it came from animals that were subjected to cruel treatment en route to market. Health officers also reported that diseased animals were often slaughtered and processed for food.

In 1870 Commissioner Capron, in urging the establishment of the Department's Veterinary Division, said: "The value of stock lost annually from disease is enormous and threatens not only to decimate the animals but to expose the human family to disease from the consumption of unwholesome meat." The pressure of public sentiment finally led to the first legislation in this field. This relatively feeble act was passed by Congress in August, 1890. It did not meet public needs, and the livestock and packing interests both appealed for a service that would inspect and certify to foreign governments the healthfulness of animals and the wholesomeness of meat from the United States.

A somewhat broader and more effective law was passed on March 3, 1891. However, this was designed in the main to provide inspection which would command the confidence of European purchasers of American products. The first inspection under that legislation took place in New York City on May 12, 1891, and was confined to dressed beef for export. About a month later inspection began in Chicago and later still at five other points.

It was about time that meat inspection was begun because foreign buyers of our livestock products had just about dropped us from their lists, so far as their beef and pork importations were concerned. It was mainly in order to regain their export outlets that the packers favored as rigid inspection as they did. As a result American meat again began to move into foreign markets, but conditions at home remained bad. Real reform did not come until the next century.

Then Upton Sinclair exposed such shocking details about the packing industry in his novel, *The Jungle*, that President Theodore Roosevelt was aroused, and Congress passed the Meat Inspection Act on June 30, 1906. It will be remembered that this was the date on which the first Food and Drugs Act was passed, indicating that interest in and agitation about the low quality of food was high. Congress yielded to aroused public opinion, as usual; and President Roosevelt's active interest had no little to do with passage of both laws.

The Meat Inspection Act empowered the Secretary of Agriculture to provide the inspection service and the Bureau of Animal Industry was designated to take on enlarged duties and responsibilities. Its meat inspectors assumed very considerable educational functions, also, and did their best to instruct the packers in rudimentary sanitary procedures.

It was a slow process, extending from questionable water supplies and many old wooden packing houses to modern establishments with excellent sanitary equipment, proper toilet facilities, laundries, and even landscaping, if you please. It was a hard road, but Dr. Edward C. Joss and other bureaucrats followed it painstakingly and in good humor, and meat-packing plants improved accordingly.

At the time this new law was passed, all officially inspected meats were marked by means of the Howard label, printed in a transferable ink on soluble gelatin. These labels were not wholly satisfactory, because they frequently failed to leave an imprint and, at times, could be removed and reapplied by anyone so inclined. Besides, they were quite expensive, costing the Department $158,000 the first year of meat inspection.

That very year, however, Dr. Dorset devised a marking fluid, both harmless and indelible, which could be applied to meats whether wet or dry, warm or cold, to produce a legible inspection mark. This fluid completely replaced the Howard label. The saving thus effected has now run into millions of dollars. Hence this chapter ends with another reference to one more small research contribution made by the little gray biochemist, Marion Dorset.

CHAPTER 10

Nation-wide Research Subsidy

D EMOCRACY HAS BEEN DEFINED as a form of government under which any organized group finally gets what it wants, if it just makes enough fuss and is persistent. Whether that is true or not, it does in part explain the passage of the Homestead Act and the act founding the Department of Agriculture in 1862, as well as the act passed in 1889 giving the Department head a seat in the Cabinet. It also explains the passage of Justin S. Morrill's Land-Grant College Act, the beginning of federal grants-in-aid.

This act endowed the states with public land which was to be sold and the proceeds used to finance colleges of agriculture and the mechanic arts. Finally, the statement made above would also explain the passage, in 1887, of the Hatch Act (the same Hatch who fathered the "horse doctor" bill founding the Bureau of Animal Industry), which provided what E. W. Allen once described as nation-wide subsidizing of research in agriculture by the federal government. This research is performed at the land-grant colleges.

The cause of states' rights thus came into its own. The state agricultural experiment stations so subsidized were the joint responsibility of the federal and the state governments, for the act authorized the establishment, under the direction of the land-grant colleges, of state experiment stations to conduct experiments relating to agricultural subjects. Under the act the states were to receive specified annual grants of federal funds to aid in the establishment and maintenance of such stations. A main difficulty in the Department's work had been lack of well-co-ordinated facilities to cope with the diverse topographical and climatic conditions in the various states. That lack was thus filled.

Among those who favored legislation in aid of state experiment stations was Norman J. Colman, who became commissioner of agriculture on April 3, 1885. He had established *Colman's Rural World* in 1865, and was prominent in farm and livestock organizations. As president of the Missouri State Board of Agriculture he had done much to foster the establishment of farmers' institutes. Both before and after he became commissioner of agriculture, he worked actively for passage of a law containing provisions similar to those embodied in the Hatch Act.

A number of states already had experiment stations. The first of these appeared in Connecticut, whose famous chemist, S. W. Johnson, began to agitate for the establishment of a station right after he returned from a convention of agricultural college people in Washington, in 1872. He was joined by Wilbur O. Atwater, later pioneer nutrition scientist of this country and some say of the world.

Atwater was born in New York and graduated from Wesleyan University in Middletown, Connecticut, in 1865, later taking his Ph.D. degree under Johnson at Yale in 1869. He next spent two years studying agricultural and physiological chemistry at the universities of Leipzig and Berlin, and in visiting agricultural institutions in several European countries. He was especially impressed with the excellent practical aid given to German farmers by small experiment stations which often had annual budgets of $10,000 or less. Later he began speaking and writing in favor of the establishment of such stations in this country.

On his return to the United States Atwater became professor of chemistry at the University of Tennessee, then taught chemistry at Maine State College until 1873, when he became professor of chemistry at his alma mater, Wesleyan. The proposals made by Johnson, Atwater, and others, followed by a series of farmers' meetings, resulted in a munificent grant of $700 a year for two years, made by the Connecticut legislature to finance experiment-station work at Middletown.

Meanwhile Orange Judd, who had personally donated a thousand dollars to the same worthy cause, had persuaded Wesleyan to offer free use of laboratory facilities, and Professor Atwater became director of this embryo experiment station on a part-time basis. It began to analyze fertilizers. In January, 1876, a meeting of fertilizer manufacturers and dealers and farmers resolved that it would be helpful if all fertilizers thereafter sold in Connecticut bore a guarantee of composition as determined by the station.

Since fertilizer frauds were rampant in those days, it was natural for state agencies to take such action. In 1887 the Connecticut legislature made the experiment station a permanent institution but removed it to New Haven, where it took up quarters in Sheffield Scientific School. These it quickly outgrew, land was acquired, and buildings were erected for it. A number of other states took early action along similar lines; Connecticut is mentioned only because it was the first.

From 1870 on there were continuous meetings and discussions in support of federal appropriations in aid of state experiment stations. These were attended by land-grant college staffs, members of farm organizations, and professional agriculturalists. Many individuals supported such action at every opportunity, the following among them: Norman J. Colman, S. W. Johnson, W. O. Atwater, J. Sterling Morton, Harvey W. Wiley, James Wilson, Seaman A. Knapp, George B. Loring, and Justin S. Morrill—not to mention a host of others.

The Commissioners of Agriculture also called repeated conferences and conventions in Washington which considered this matter. Largely through Commissioner Colman's personal interest a convention was held on July 8, 1885, and a second, composed of delegates from the states, was called for October 18, 1887, at which time a permanent organization named the Association of Agricultural Colleges and Experiment Stations was effected. Meanwhile William H. Hatch had embodied the ideas generally desired in a bill which began its way through a Congress constantly petitioned to pass it.

Hatch introduced the bill on January 7, 1886. Petitions favoring its passage came from thirty-four states—legislatures, state boards of agriculture, and the agricultural colleges doing much of the petitioning. After lengthy debate the bill was passed by both houses and was signed by President Cleveland on March 2, 1887. Beginning on July 18, 1888, Hatch funds were carried in Department appropriations, plus a fund to enable the Department to carry out the provisions of the act.

This resulted in the creation of the Office of Experiment Stations in 1888. After investigation had demonstrated some irregularities in the use of federal funds by the states, the office was given power regularly to investigate the use of such funds and also to appraise the research projects to be financed. Under this authority financial schedules are prepared and sent to the stations, which are each visited annually by representatives of the office.

At the time the act was passed, Alabama had two experiment stations, and California, Kentucky, Maine, New York, Tennessee, Vermont, and Wisconsin one each, all connected with land-grant colleges. Louisiana had two independent experiment stations, while Connecticut, Massachusetts, North Carolina, New Jersey, New York, and Ohio each had one. Some systematic agricultural experimentation was also being carried on in the following states: Colorado, Illinois, Indiana, Iowa, Kansas, Michigan, Minnesota, Mississippi, Missouri, Nebraska, New Hampshire, Pennsylvania, and South Carolina.

When the Office of Experiment Stations came into existence, W. O. Atwater became its director. Its immediate function was to act as a clearinghouse and to assume an advisory capacity. It also sought to indicate fruitful lines of inquiry, to furnish forms for the tabulation of research results, to co-ordinate the work and prevent duplication, and to render such advice and assistance as needed. At the end of 1888 there were forty-six stations in the United States, forty-three of which received Hatch funds.

Subsequent passage of the Adams, the Purnell, and the Bankhead-Jones acts granted further funds to the states for agricultural research. The Research and Marketing Act of 1946, authorizes yet additional grants. Examination and approval of research projects in advance of the expenditure of funds and the review of the work and examination of the expenditures at each station have been continuing responsibilities of the Office of Experiment Stations. Programs of research with proposed expenditures under federal funds are submitted by each station for review and approval at the beginning of each fiscal year.

Many of the stations feared that the Office of Experiment Stations might itself perform research overshadowing theirs, since it was close to Congress and could presumably get funds easily.

D. E. Salmon

Representative William H. Hatch

Marion Dorset

Charles Wardell Stiles

This fear was gradually dissipated. Finally the office did undertake research on human nutrition in 1894, on irrigation in 1898, and on drainage in 1902, without serious state opposition.

During the first six years, when the office had no regulatory functions, it collected and diffused information regarding agricultural experiment stations here and abroad. For this purpose it established the *Experiment Station Record* in 1889. The same year Secretary Rusk was persuaded by Dr. Atwater to begin issuing farmers' bulletins. A handbook of experiment station work appeared in 1893. Issuance of a card index of the publications of the stations began in 1891.

The state experiment stations operate as departments of their respective land-grant colleges. At one time it was common for the president of the college to be director of the experiment station, but enlarged functions of both have made it necessary to have different persons for these two jobs in most instances. College equipment and farmland are used in the experiments which are carried on by men who often have teaching jobs at the college as well; others devote all their time to research.

The line of experimentation followed extends over the field covered by the Department of Agriculture, but in a more local or specialized way. The projects usually concern single states or groups of states which co-operate on them, and also with the Department. Eight of the Bankhead-Jones laboratories also work in close co-operation with specified groups of states, while the ninth, the one at Cornell, is national in scope and co-operates with any experiment stations in the country as required.

Since the state experiment stations at Cornell and at Geneva, New York, were consolidated, the station at New Haven is unique in having no organic connection with a land-grant college. It has its own farm, grounds, buildings, and staff. W. O. Atwater's nutrition work has come down the years here from Middletown; in New Haven Osborne and Mendel long carried on their classic studies of the composition of vegetable proteins; and the latest in this noble line is Hubert B. Vickery, member of the National Academy of Science and New Haven's distinguished nutrition investigator of today.

It is an extraordinary experience to visit these state research institutions, finding each with its distinguished staff performing much work of great local importance and no little that is national in scope. Co-operation with other stations and with the bureaus and laboratories of the Department of Agriculture extends facilities, staffs, and scope of projects as required—nor is the work unprofitable even in a sordid monetary sense.

Director V. R. Gardner of the Michigan Agricultural Experiment Station announced recently that farm production of his state is valued at $500,000,000 a year, but only one-tenth of 1 per cent as much is spent on agricultural research there. Yet, of 230 research projects underway, a mere dozen, which have cost no more than $76,000 all told, have increased Michigan farm income by $16,370,-000, a return of 215 times the investment. This is not an unusual situation by any means. Practically any other state could give as good a monetary accounting of its research.

Returning to earlier days, we find that W. O. Atwater soon relinquished the directorship of the Office of Experiment Stations in order to engage in the nutrition researches which occupied the remainder of his life, and which will be recounted elsewhere. He was succeeded by A. W. Harris, Dr. A. C. True being his assistant as he had been Atwater's. About this time a compilation of the analyses of American feedstuffs was issued and also a bulletin on milk fermentation by H. W. Conn. Many other important and useful publications followed.

On July 1, 1897, funds were provided for a station in Alaska, a Hawaii station was authorized in 1901, the Federal Puerto Rico Station at Mayagüez in 1902, the Guam station in 1908, and that in the Virgin Islands in 1919. The latter two are no longer under Department jurisdiction, but Puerto Rico also has a territorial station at Rio Piedras.

On July 1, 1915, the States Relations Service was formed, with A. C. True, who had succeeded Harris as head of the Office of Experiment Stations, as its supervisor. This unit was dissolved on July 1, 1923, and the Office of Experiment Stations, Extension Service, and Bureau of Home Economics became independent agencies.

The Office of Experiment Stations now forms part of the Agricultural Research Administration. James T. Jardine assumed office in 1931, succeeding E. W. Allen, who had served from 1915 until his death on November 11, 1929. This is the same Jardine who did the outstanding range research as Pinchot's aid in forestry. He retired in the summer of 1946.

In its early days the office issued a number of important publications. One on the chemical composition of American food, first issued in 1896 and repeatedly revised and reissued, was a classic. It formed the groundwork for much later research. Famous also was the digest of metabolism experiments with men and animals in 1897, and the bulletin on cotton published a year earlier.

In its relations with the state stations the Office of Experiment Stations repeatedly touched lines of investigation not then carried on in the Department. Hence there was a growing tendency at first to place in the office special projects for which Congress provided funds. The first of these dealt with human nutrition. This work, which will be discussed more fully elsewhere, grew directly out of studies made at Wesleyan University, in conjunction with the Storrs (Connecticut) Experiment Station.

Results of these studies attracted the attention of the Honorable Edward Atkinson of Boston, who had compiled data on the subject from foreign sources. He had also been interested in the experimental and practical work of the New England Kitchen, conducted in Boston by Mrs. Ellen H. Richards, in collaboration with the Massachusetts Institute of Technology. Atkinson prepared a paper giving "Suggestions for the Establishment of Food Laboratories in Connection with Agricultural Experiment Stations."

This became a bulletin of the Office of Experiment Stations. It excited the interest of both Secretary Morton and President Cleveland. Congress was requested to appropriate money for investigations of this kind. It granted $10,000 for the fiscal year 1894. Dr. Atwater assumed supervision of the work, carrying it on at Middletown, using the facilities of the Storrs station and of Wesleyan University.

Information was collected regarding available foods and their uses. Dietary studies were made among both rural and urban people. Elaborate scientific experiments of a pioneering nature were carried on in connection with digestion and metabolism as well as on the nutritive value of various foods. The analyses of foods were compiled on a broad scale, and the results of experiments both in this country and abroad were published. Nutrition methods and apparatus were improved. Indeed, before he died on September 22, 1907, Dr. Atwater had founded the science of human nutrition. The work was brought to Washington subsequently.

To Dr. Atwater we also owe clarification of the objectives of the experiment-station system; his outline formulated in 1875–76 would serve quite well today. He made research the stations' primary function. He also planned and supervised nutrition investigations carried on in some twenty states. In the judgment of competent experts, the investigations carried on in this field under Atwater were more thorough in method, more extended in quantity and in scope, and more useful in practice than any other inquiry of the kind previously undertaken anywhere in the world.

We earlier mentioned two other lines of investigation carried on in this office. The spread of irrigation in the Western states during the latter half of the nineteenth century produced many problems concerned with available water supply, water rights, control of the appropriation and distribution of water, irrigation practice and methods, and the quantities of water required by different crops. In the mid-nineties the office was called upon to expand its work in this field.

Finally the appropriation act of the Department for the fiscal year beginning July 1, 1898, included an item of $10,000 for irrigation studies. The Department was also directed therein to collect from the agricultural colleges, experiment stations, and other sources, valuable information on the subject to be published in bulletins. Special agents were used for this work; Secretary Wilson assigned them to the Office of Experiment Stations which carried on these investigations until 1915, when they were transferred to the then Office of Public Roads.

Passage of the Reclamation Act in 1902 gave further impetus and importance to these studies. Largely through them improved legislation was enacted in the arid states and the general principle of determining water rights in accord with the actual, beneficial use of the water was firmly established. Later studies resulted in the far more economical use of limited irrigation water. Investigation of water loss in transit from stream to farmland led to improved conduits. Devices for measuring water were tested and new ones devised.

Much of this work was performed in co-operation with the states. Quite early also the office was led to attend the subject of drainage, without which irrigation agriculture becomes dangerous. In 1902 C. G. Elliott, an experienced drainage engineer, joined the irrigation staff. Under his leadership work relating to drainage was greatly expanded. His bulletin on farm drainage, published by the office in 1896, before he joined its staff, was a classic. In 1907 the drainage work was placed in a division separate from irrigation and so remained until it also went to the then Office of Public Roads in 1915.

Before that time great progress had been made towards a better understanding and solution of drainage problems on irrigated lands that had been injured by seepage and alkali. Much wider use of tile drainage had been promoted, especially in the Southern states. Drainage systems were first surveyed and planned on a large scale, involving community effort and the formation of drainage districts. In at least eight states laws for the establishment and financing of drainage districts were enacted. Under these laws hundreds of drainage districts were formed, and hundreds of thousands of acres of swamp and overflowed lands were reclaimed.

In the short space available a few of the interesting and important research accomplishments of the agricultural experiment stations will be surveyed. It would take a complete book to do justice to these extraordinary state institutions, which at last resolved the doctrine of states' rights in the very best possible way.[1]

The name of Stephen M. Babcock must be mentioned because he put the milk industry on the map at a single stroke. Graduating from Tufts in 1866, he pursued further studies at Rensselaer Polytechnic Institute, Cornell, and Göttingen. He then became instructor in chemistry at Cornell, leaving to work at the New York (Geneva) Agricultural Experiment Station, where he developed

[1] In this connection consult A. C. True's monograph on agricultural education in the United States, U. S. D. A. *Miscellaneous Publication No. 36, 1929,* and his *History of Agricultural Extension Work, Miscellaneous Publication No. 15,* 1928, as well as *Miscellaneous Publication No. 215,* to which reference was made in the foreword.

a simple method for analyzing milk. In 1887 he went to the University of Wisconsin as professor of agricultural chemistry and chemist at the experiment station. He retired in 1913.

Babcock's most notable achievement was the development of the "Babcock test," a simple method devised in 1890 for estimating the butterfat content of milk. Though Babcock developed many new methods for analyzing milk and curing cheese and paved the way for the discovery of vitamins, he is best known as the man who invented that test. During his later work Babcock came upon "hidden hunger" in animals fed complete synthetic diets upon which they appeared to starve on plenty. Dr. E. V. McCollum took Babcock's results as a point of departure and went on to the discovery of vitamin A.

The cream separator had been introduced in 1885. This stimulated the development of co-operative creameries, but the milk was still pooled and purchased merely by volume or weight, regardless of its butterfat content, and that constituted a serious handicap. Dairymen who produced high-standard milk bitterly resented its mixture with low-fat milk produced by others. They believed that creamery patrons should be paid for their milk and cream on a basis of its true value, but no ready method of estimating the fat content existed.

Babcock's simple method was especially adapted for use in creameries and cheese plants. It replaced the existing inefficient, time-consuming tests with one that was accurate and could be carried out in five minutes. No change has been made in its essential features to this day; its influence is tremendous. You can see Babcock test bottles in every dairy laboratory. The test, coupled with the separator, tended to determine the course of the dairy industry and to foster the development of co-operative dairy manufacture.

Incentive was given for the production of high-fat milk. Milk production was increased, because the test facilitated study of individual cow performance. Dairy breeds were improved for milk production, the unseparated cream in skim milk was reduced by half, and soil fertility was conserved by the expansion of dairying. The economic return from this test was huge, though it cannot be expressed with exactness in dollars and cents.

In *Science* for June 23, 1944, Dr. H. K. Wilson of the Minnesota Agricultural Experiment Station, gave an excellent account of how research in agronomy, carried on jointly by the Department and the experiment stations, had helped the corn belt and the Great Plains regions. Co-operative wheat research began with Minnesota in 1907. Black-stem rust then threatened the extinction of wheat growing in many areas producing hard red spring wheat. Co-operative development of Thatcher wheat saved the day.

In 1941 over eighteen million acres of Thatcher were grown. The president of the National Millers Association called Thatcher a "Godsend to the Northwest." Similar statements could be made about co-operative research on corn, which has helped spread hybrid-corn growing over many states. As a result of co-ordinated co-operative research, which facilitated trials in many states, hybrid corn increased the yield 650,000,000 bushels by 1943, over what it had been before such corn was widely planted.

Somewhat related is co-operative work with the Iowa station on waxy corn, a few years ago a genetic curiosity. Starch from Waxy Iowa Hybrid 939 appears to be a wholly satisfactory substitute for tapioca starch. Since we had been importing 350,000,000 pounds of tapioca a year from the Dutch East Indies, it is easy to see what it meant when, in 1945, we supplied all our own food and adhesive needs of this kind.

Crossing Victoria with Richland resulted in high-yielding, strong-strawed varieties of oats, resistant to black stem, crown rust, and both smuts that make life unhappy for this plant. Varieties from this cross, developed in co-operation with the Iowa, Wisconsin, South Dakota, and Nebraska stations are now growing on most of the oat acreage in these states. The development of productive smooth-awn barley varieties has meanwhile given impetus to barley production.

Crystal and Koto flaxes, developed by the Department in co-operation with the Minnesota and North Dakota stations, have better disease resistance, give better yields, and produce a higher percentage of oil of superior drying quality than older varieties. Sorghum varieties containing waxy starch also offer great possibilities in the matter of providing the food industry with a substitute for cassava starch.

The states have co-operated loyally in soybean researches which have had much to do with increasing our soybean production 1,400 per cent in the decade which ended in 1942. The movement of alfalfa into the North Central states has been accelerated. Ladak, a winter-hardy alfalfa brought by Department workers from India, is fairly resistant to wilt, and has proved more persistent than Grimm in Minnesota.

The Department has worked with several stations in improving red clover and in introducing and distributing crested wheat grass. It has aided in the development of smooth brome and reed canary grasses. It has developed a co-operative attack on bindweed and other noxious weeds.

The existence of these state stations permits widespread, rapid trial of methods and varieties under greatly differing climatic and soil conditions. That is exactly why hybrid corn spread so quickly throughout all regions where corn is grown. It yields better than open-pollinated corn, and is characterized by earliness, greater production of sound grain, improved resistance to lodging, plant disease, and insects, as well as to cropping hazards such as drought and heat. It readily adapts itself to various altitudes, climates, and degrees of soil fertility.

Each station working on this or any other project has promising combinations of growing conditions under test continuously. The results of performance tests under widely varying conditions can be quickly released to growers. Other lines of corn research are carried on simultaneously, as, for instance, at the Iowa Corn Research Institute, where Department and station workers co-operate. These projects concern everything that affects corn growth and production.

Some are concerned with soil types, fertilizers, crop rotations, and soil amendments; others with methods and equipment for seed-bed preparation, planting, cultivating, harvesting, curing, and storing corn. Others still relate to weed eradication, production as related to seed, time of planting, and adaptation. Then corn breeding has to be studied and new hybrids developed all the time. This leads to investigation of the physiology and development of the corn plant and its inner genetics.

Research must also be performed on diseases which attack corn and methods of combating them, as well as on corn-devouring insects, their life history, physiology, and control. The chemistry and qualities of corn as a raw product engage the attention of many workers, involving mechanical analysis and separation of corn constituents, and the industrial use of corn and its by-products. Finally, there are scientists who look into the economic phases of corn utilization and production and the sociology of corn growers.

The work on disease-resistant varieties of plants is, as we have seen, usually carried on by federal-state co-operation. The stations have constantly to meet local needs and conditions by carrying on long jobs of breeding and selection for resistance. The co-operation of the New Mexico station was invaluable in the development of curly top–resistant beet varieties and of the highly successful domestic sugar beet–seed program.

When some years ago domestic cotton manufacturers and foreign markets both complained of deterioration in American cotton, funds under the Purnell Act were made available for study of this problem in several cotton-growing states. In 1928 these states co-operated with the Department in securing adequate samples of the cotton crop for study. Thus was prepared the first authentic record of the quality of cotton produced in any country.

As a result of records then made, areas which produced good and poor cotton were plotted. Efforts at improvement were centered on the right localities. A program was then developed which enabled the Southeastern states materially to increase the production of high-quality cotton required by their local mills. Research undertaken to associate the properties of cotton fiber with superior spinning quality resulted in methods of correlating cotton quality with strength of fiber, of improving spinning economy and reducing waste. This information has been widely applied by cotton-breeding specialists.

Turning now to meat, the discussion of breeding tender steaks will be remembered in connection with the work of Sewall Wright in the Bureau of Animal Industry. Work at the Department's Range and Livestock Experiment Station in Montana has shown that beef production can be increased by breeding procedures. The bureau has also followed up Wright's work to the extent of proving that the tenderness and quality of meat can be improved—whether in cattle, hogs, or sheep—not only by proper feeding but by identifying and using breeding animals whose progeny yield meat superior in the desired qualities.

Thus the goal in breeding becomes not so much a physical type which appeals to the eye as a type of animal that produces highly palatable and nutritious meat and a large proportion of superior cuts. The stations have worked together on research projects such as these, as many animals must participate in many experiments to get any worthwhile results. When the Purnell Act was passed, there was no scientific basis for current marketing customs, practices, and prejudices concerned with the purchase and use of meat animals.

Effort has been made to discover those factors in meat that are responsible for its quality and palatability, and then to find what practices would improve the factors. For instance, it was long held that grass-fed cattle produced dark meat. Studies at the Kansas and the Virginia stations proved this belief false, by showing that the color of the fat and lean meat was related to the degree of finish. Investigations at the Nebraska, Missouri, and Illinois stations revealed that discrimination by packers against heifer carcasses was justified only from the standpoint of more waste to the cuts of meat.

This finding resulted in very large returns to cattlemen who produced finished heifers. Improved methods of chilling, preparing, and preserving farm meats, an outgrowth of the study, have been calculated to add 15 per cent to the number of meals obtained from farm-slaughtered animals. Apply this percentage to hogs slaughtered for home consumption only, and you arrive at a figure of $3,500,000 annually. Results at the Indiana, Mississippi, and Tennessee stations showed that suckling lambs on good pasture grew as well and were as fat as similar lambs fed grain while at pasture, producing an annual saving of $1,125,000 in feed.

Before turning to recent activities of the stations in the states, we should glance hastily at some of the outstanding accomplishments of the insular and territorial stations. Some years ago the Hawaii station found that a disease which was doing great damage to pineapples was the result of excessive manganese in the soil. Scientists demonstrated that spraying the plants with iron sulfate solution corrected the trouble and thus made possible the replanting of ten thousand acres on which pineapple growing had been abandoned.

This station also showed the value of cover crops in the tropics. It likewise found the types of rotations which should be used for the island's most important crops, sugar cane and pineapples, and this finding was instrumental in widely extending them. The superiority of ammonium sulfate over nitrate of soda for fertilizing rice was another important result of this station's work.

Investigations of the Alaska station demonstrated that agriculture could well supplement other industries in the territory. Such industries could become established in Alaska if more of the food requirement were locally produced. This fact had been doubted by many when investigations started in 1898. Crops were selected and methods of growing them were developed for the Matanuska and Tanana valleys of southeastern Alaska and, to a limited extent, for Kodiak. Livestock have also been maintained for a sufficient period to prove that raising animals is profitable. Considerable aid has also been given the fur-farming industry of the territory.

In Puerto Rico dipping-tanks for cattle ticks developed the livestock industry, and dairying also became possible on the island. Then improved forage plants were introduced by the station, which likewise assisted materially in developing the island's citrus industry and in establishing vanilla-growing as a profitable undertaking. The station likewise introduced Uba sugar cane, which resists mosaic disease, and is widely planted.

The introduction of the giant toad (*Bufo marinus*) and its colonization in Puerto Rico is an accomplishment of the Mayagüez station. The toad notably reduces the numbers of major pests like white grubs, mole crickets, weevils, and cockroaches and has proved a predator of great value. The white grub has actually ceased to be an agricultural problem on the island because of this outstanding success in the biological control of an insect.

A sweet-corn variety adapted to tropical conditions, and known as USDA 34, has been developed at the station by selection. It is now grown extensively in both Old and New World tropics. It is the only strain giving satisfactory yields under tropical conditions, and thousands of pounds of seed were provided for our armed forces in the tropics to enable them to raise this fresh vegetable for themselves.

An interesting and important project of this station was the distribution of derris cuttings to Latin America. This was an indirect way of aiding American farmers to get rotenone without having to depend upon the Far East. The station has also done research on quinine-producing cinchona and has made extensive plantings of high-yielding material.

There has also been built up at the Puerto Rico station a remarkable tropical-plant introduction garden containing a collection of over seven thousand species. They include valuable collections both of cinchona varieties and of high-yielding strains of hevea rubber plants. The station undertook extensive work on bamboo introduction about 1935. It has now determined by selection and testing that several species are especially valuable for industrial purposes as well as resistant to the powder-post beetle, which attacks and destroys bamboo. As a result of this work a new bamboo-furniture industry sprang up in Puerto Rico.

When the war emergency occurred, the work of the state experiment stations turned almost instantly to the solution of wartime problems. Effective assistance was offered families, producing increased foods on the nation's millions of farms. By July, 1941, a fifth of the stations' research projects that had been active under federal funds the previous year had been closed out and replaced by work on new problems of immediate significance.

Prompt and effective aid given by the New Jersey station to that state's tomato growers enabled them greatly to increase production. The effective work of the Pennsylvania and other stations in replacing seed of various kinds that we formerly imported enabled us to grow many of these seed domestically. The Puerto Rico station undertook an emergency study of food-canning and food-processing industries on the island, and all its agricultural agencies were co-ordinated so as to relieve the food situation as much as possible. Stations in Hawaii, Colorado, Connecticut, Oklahoma, Florida, Nebraska, and Tennessee all jumped in to increase food production.

Both New York stations and the California station co-operated with the Department on food-dehydration projects. The Wisconsin station gave aid to increased cheese production required by the British. Vitamin research at the Maryland station helped us fill large British requirements for canned poultry meat and eggs by showing growers how to avoid serious losses traced to deficient vitamins A and E in poultry feeds. The Maryland station also formulated a low-cost ration for the near-by broiler industry, in which by-products of alcohol manufacture and soybean meal replaced milk products. Thus the growers saved $300,000,000 a year in feed costs.

The Mississippi station developed a sensitive test for bitterness in milk caused by the milk cow's consumption of bitterweed, a serious pasture pest. As a result much "bitter" milk could be used in manufacturing which would otherwise have been discarded. The Alabama station found that sun-drying retains most of the carotene in carrots, sweet potatoes, and greens, and that winter milk can be maintained at a high level of vitamin A content by feeding sweet potatoes to cows.

The stations sought new anthelmintics and drug plants; they promoted the more efficient use of nitrogen fertilizers. They discovered new methods of making alcohol from cull potatoes and improving the yield of alcohol from molasses. The Delaware station developed a new pectin which promised relief during the sugar shortages and helped meet an increasing wartime demand. The Wyoming station shifted some of its current research work in nutrition to speed up projects on sugar substitutes used in cooking.

Various stations undertook emergency work on insecticides and fungicides; others worked out formulas for substitute sprays used to control insect pests. The New Jersey station obtained from cultures of micro-organisms two substances highly destructive to disease-producing organisms and of value in the control of human diseases and war-wound treatment. This adventure in biotherapy by Selman A. Waksman and associates also showed that many molds other than *Penicillum notatum* can produce penicillin. Meanwhile C. S. Pederson of the Geneva (New York) station found that cabbage juice contains something that kills objectionable bacteria and that onion juice acts similarly. The National Research Council asked intensification of such research, and the New Jersey station began extensive isolations of soil and compost micro-organisms to test their action against disease-producing bacteria. This led to Waksman's development of the new wonder drug, streptomycin.

The programs of many stations on processed citrus-fruit products, essential oils, tung oil, spices, and vanilla assumed enhanced importance. Station directors and staff members undertook missions to Latin America, and a lively interchange of information took place among the agricultural research workers of the Western Hemisphere.

Anywhere the visitor goes—New York, Pennsylvania, Connecticut, Florida, Iowa, Nebraska or elsewhere—he meets station directors and investigators who are alive to the problems about them, and has recounted to him progress reports on research of the utmost interest and importance to considerable areas. Something new in cattle feeding, in making orchids germinate synthetically (vanilla is an orchid), in food preservation or food processing, in deficiency diseases caused by lack of trace elements, on teaching honeybees new tricks, about the turkey as a grazing animal, or about insecticides, breeding blight-resistant chestnuts, concentrating orange juice by freezing, or preserving fresh fruits and vegetables in pliofilm—always something fascinating, novel, and useful is brought to the visitor's attention.

The Georgia, Virginia, and North Carolina stations point the way to better peanut yields by the use of new fungicides. The Massachusetts station shows that one-quarter to one-third of the total sugar used in canned fruits, preserves, and jellies can be replaced with dextrose without change in color or texture. The New York (Cornell) station tells how to use man power so as to decrease the cost of milk production. The Missouri station demonstrates that losses of one-half in young pigs can often be avoided by providing them with fresh forage or pasture.

The Michigan station developed the Robust and later the Michelite bean, thus increasing 1941 bean production 30 per cent over 1940 and saving growers 236,000 acres of land, 5,192,000 man-hours of labor, and $5,664,000. The Connecticut (Storrs) station proved that in one instance daily travel of 18,000 miles could be reduced by more than half if certain milk routes were reorganized. The Vermont station showed that an estimated reduction of one-quarter in mileage traveled could be effected by reorganization within milk companies, while an additional reduction of one-quarter could be achieved by reorganization of routes among different milk companies.

Early work of the Department on cattle-tick fever was co-operative with the Texas, Missouri, Mississippi, Louisiana, and other stations. The co-operative hybrid-breeding programs for wheat and oats with the Wisconsin, Iowa and other stations has been mentioned. Grazing and pasture-management studies were made in co-operation with the Florida and Mississippi stations, while the Regional Pasture Laboratory on the campus of Pennsylvania State University co-operates with all twelve experiment stations in the Northeast.

The Department developed the Sequoia potato with aid from North Carolina and the Houma potato with aid from Louisiana. Bacterial wilt-resistant Golden Cross Bantam sweet corn was developed in co-operation with the Indiana station, and of high-vitamin, high-starch sweet potatoes with the Louisiana station. The use of maggots in preventing wound infections was developed with the Texas and other stations.

The fundamental nutrition and calorimetric studies at the Pennsylvania station stemmed directly from work by Dr. Atwater in the Office of Experiment Stations itself in early days. There still stands the cow-sized calorimeter built and used experimentally by Henry P. Armsby and by his successor, E. B. Forbes. The Germans intended to reproduce this piece of equipment before World War I, but before they completed their model, their government took all their copper away from them for war purposes, and the job was never finished!

Nor is the job of research itself ever finished. Conditions change, pests mutate, and new factors enter into the picture. There must always be investigation both to uncover fundamental principles which are applicable to a wide variety of problems and to solve immediate difficulties. The state experiment stations have their hands full, too, in helping both farmers and industrialists make local applications, adaptations, and adjustments. Nor are calls from industry infrequent. Many experiment stations have almost as many requests from industry as from farmers. This is especially true where they get over deeply into the industrial utilization of farm products and by-products, as many of them do.

In 1944 it took over four thousand published bulletins, circulars, reports, and scientific articles to explain what these fifty-three stations were doing the past year. The stations employed about 5,000 technical workers and were reporting on about 500 of their research findings. All told, 3,419 research projects were active under federal-grant funds and 5,000 were supported with state funds during the year that had just elapsed. The entire work cost about $25,000,000, of which less than $7,000,000 were in the form of federal grants. Some 1,200 formal memoranda of understanding covered co-operation between the stations and other agencies, and had been approved by the Office of Experiment Stations. This is research of mass magnitude.

What all this effort is worth in monetary terms is another question. About the only careful, conservative study ever made appeared in a *Survey of Land-Grant Colleges and Universities*, published by the Office of Education, Department of Labor, in 1930, as *Bulletin No. 9* (see Volume II, Part VIII, on "Research"). Herein it is stated that our gross income from farm products in 1927–28 was about twelve and one-quarter billion dollars a year.

The combined federal and state governments during this time were expending about $2.00 for research per each $1,000 of agriculture's gross income. This amounted to only 43.5 cents per each $1,000 of invested capital for agriculture as compared with $13.00 per $1,000 for industry. Meanwhile, in 1928, agricultural research made contributions of economic value to the agricultural industry amounting to $842,470,995. This meant that each dollar invested in agricultural research by the federal and state governments brought a return of $33.00, or more.

That is a very conservative estimate, but it is not a low return. The dividends naturally accrue to some more than to others; they are paid socially rather than individually and they do not necessarily always return directly to the taxpayer who puts up the funds for all research in the last analysis. But they are there to justify federal-state research. It is up to us to evolve a social and economic system which will distribute the dividends more equitably and spread more widely the benefits of scientific investigation.

CHAPTER II

"A Good Soil"

THE PROPHET EZEKIEL in one of his more lurid moments beheld a vision in which he saw an eagle with a vine in its talons. Ezekiel continued: "It was planted in a good soil by great waters, that it might bring forth branches and that it might bear fruit." This idea was altogether correct agriculturally. But how find "a good soil?" When that problem engaged Department chemists in early days, they began to analyze samples of soil.

But at that time all work on soils was influenced by Liebig's balance-sheet theory of plant nutrition. According to Liebig, the soil was a great storage bin of plant nutrients. Therefore, if one analyzed the soil and the plants that grow upon it, one could easily calculate the number of crops the soil would grow and the exact quantity of fertilizer required to replace soil nutrients lost to growing plants.

The balance-sheet theory was simple and logical. It was really so simple that it only approximated truth. What went on was very much more complex than that. Some nutrients were in the soil in forms which prevented growing plants from absorbing them. Some plants seemed to remove nutrients from the soil more efficiently than others. Soil amendments often failed to make plants thrive, sometimes doubtless because they did not contain trace elements we now know to be indispensable to plant growth.

Besides, the physical characteristics of soils had to be considered. Milton Whitney, working first at the Maryland Agricultural College and later in the Weather Bureau, realized the basic importance of soil physics and saw the necessity for studying soils in the field and expressing the results of these studies on maps which would give farmers reliable guidance. The work on soils became diverted from the chemists to a group of soil specialists.

Then came the question of soil erosion, and the great waters entered the picture. Unless the great waters were controlled, there was soon no topsoil at all and agriculture faced calamity. Thomas Jefferson and many early farmers had realized the dangers of this and had advocated stopping the gulleys, but soil erosion went on nonetheless. Yet, if the agricultural industry were to be based on a firm foundation, the soil must be prevented from blowing and sluicing away.

A long avenue of research has been traversed here, stretching from simple chemical analyses of soils to the anatomizing of mountains. About thirty-five miles east of downtown Los Angeles, at San Dimas, Department scientists have set up apparatus to find out what makes a mountain tick. Here at a "small" mountain laboratory of 17,000 acres Forest Service men are investigating the influences of vegetation on rainfall, the most crucial conservation problem in southern California.

Not only is Los Angeles hard put for waters great enough to serve its normal purposes, but it is frequently racked by severe floods which periodically take many lives and also erode the soil as they come rushing to the metropolitan area. The scientists want to find remedies for floods, irregular water supplies, depleted ground water, mud, debris flow, and erosion. The San Dimas forest is the world's foremost watershed laboratory.

Here scientists use all sorts of gadgets and equipment to study precipitation, runoff, muddy water, vegetation, soil, and the percolation of water. There are four complete climatic stations; there are 370 rain gauges, spaced one-half mile apart, more than in any similar area in the world. There are stream-gauging stations to measure the rate of stream flow and retaining basins to catch debris so that it can be examined.

There are twenty-six huge, soil-filled tanks which collect and measure rainfall runoff and seepage, requiring a 307-foot tunnel to house them. There is a vecto-pluviometer to measure both the amount and direction of rainfall. Numerous plots have been set aside on the mountain slopes for more intensive study, some kept in normal cover, some denuded, others burned periodically and then permitted to return to normal cover. At the base of each plot is a concrete trough to catch runoff by means of a clever tipping

bucket that empties every time it contains a tenth of a cubic foot
of water, a moving finger recording this action on a chart.

There are many other installations, instruments, and plots. The
data recorded, assembled, and processed tell how a mountain ticks.
Every factor influencing the water cycle is thus revealed. The
behavior of rainstorms, the healing over of fire-swept soil, and the
control of floods all come into the scope of the investigation. Here
Nature's most erratic behavior problems come under close observation. What a far cry from the simple chemists' laboratory in
which a few soil samples were analyzed when the Department
came into being!

Quite as elaborate as anything Forest Service does are the experimental stations of the Soil Conservation Service, but we must
leave today and return to beginnings, when Liebig's theories overshadowed the field of soil science. An immediate interest of Department chemists was the remedial measures required to combat
soil exhaustion.

In that connection I think of Daniel Lee, first agriculturalist
hired by the Patent Office, who insisted in and out of season that
farmers were sending the riches of their soil to the city in the crops
they sold. He wanted to remedy the situation by devising methods
of drying human excrement so that it could be bagged, returned
to the country, and put back on the land to restore the balance of
soil nutrients. He wrote exhaustively and often exhaustingly on
this theme.

The Division of Chemistry early undertook to investigate the
spread of plant diseases via the soil. These studies of soil bacteria
continued in the Bureau of Chemistry and later wound up in the
Bureau of Plant Industry, Soils, and Agricultural Engineering, its
present inflated bureaucratic name. In 1915 work on the identification of definite but complex organic substances in soils was placed
in the newly organized Division of Soil Fertility in what was then
the Bureau of Plant Industry.

In 1928 the Division of Soil Chemistry and Physics was formed
by a merger of two divisions which had previously been independent in the Bureau of Chemistry and Soils; and, in 1938, this work
also went to the Bureau of Plant Industry. There, in 1942, it was
merged with the Division of Soil Microbiology and Fertilizer Re-

search to become the Division of Soil and Fertilizer Investigation. That was when the bureau got its long name. This bureau, therefore, today does all the Department's pure research on soils, fertilizer, and irrigation, and also handles the important soil surveys.

Now we must retrace our steps to find Milton Whitney again, a person I will always remember as a dapper old gentleman, attired in a frock coat, getting out of his buckboard after he had been driven to work, and turning the reins over to the Negro driver. In 1886 he, much younger, was in charge of a thirty-five–acre experimental farm the Department had established near Raleigh, North Carolina, for work on cotton varieties, grasses, clovers, permanent meadows and pastures, and the "high manuring" of cotton and corn.

In 1891 there was issued from the Weather Bureau a *Bulletin No. 4* on the physical properties of soils and their relationship to moisture and crop production. It was based upon original work by Whitney, who was then at Maryland Agricultural College. Soon after, he began to work in the Weather Bureau on the relationship between climate and soils.

In 1894 Whitney became chief of a Division of Soils, which in 1901 became the Bureau of Soils. Whitney headed this bureau until his retirement, when A. G. McCall took over for less than a year, whereupon the work was merged with part of the work in the Bureau of Chemistry to form the Bureau of Chemistry and Soils. It was from this agency that research work on soils was transferred to the Bureau of Plant Industry in 1938, while its other work on soils went to Soil Conservation Service.

Washing and gulleying have been mentioned in reports by Department scientists for many years, but especially since the turn of the century. A report issued in 1907 declared that American rivers took a billion tons of soil sediment to the sea every year, and then very clearly presented the facts known about soil erosion. The bulletin stated that eroding soils could be salvaged by contour cultivation, proper drainage, strip-cropping, and the reforestation of land unfitted for agriculture. It advocated public education for collective action to arrest soil erosion.

The great educator in this field appeared soon enough in the person of Hugh H. Bennett, who entered the Bureau of Soils in 1903. Better than six feet tall and always flirting with the 200-pound mark on the scales, he became our greatest militant soil evangelist of all time. For years he crusaded up and down the nation and the world, preaching against erosion and advocating protective programs to conserve soil resources. He and his message traveled to Venezuela, the Union of South Africa, Mexico, Canada, and many other countries.

He is equally at home at a club-women's luncheon, a crossroads farmers' meeting, a convention of businessmen, or a scientific seminar. He pursues the same theme everywhere, with minor variations to suit the occasion. He incites all who listen to rediscover the land, to learn love for it, and to try to stay the erosive processes which have already ruined or damaged a third of our cropland.

Bennett was born on a North Carolina farm. In 1905 he carried out a survey of a badly eroded section of the Virginia Piedmont in Louisa County, and was deeply impressed. In 1909 he became inspector of soil surveys and also in that year served on a committee to study the agricultural possibilities of the Panama Canal Zone. In 1914 he headed an expedition to explore the agricultural regions of Alaska.

In 1919 Bennett was a member of the Guatamala-Honduras Boundary Commission and in 1925–26 was engaged in making a soil reconnaissance survey of Cuba. From 1909 until 1933 he and his associates made numerous references to the extent of serious erosion in their many reports on soil types. During the last decade of that period Bennett was undoubtedly the foremost advocate of a national program of soil conservation.

Largely as a result of this agitation the Buchanan Amendment to the Agricultural Appropriation Act for the fiscal year 1930 was adopted. It provided an appropriation of $160,000 for research on the cause and control of soil erosion. Ultimately ten experiment stations were established for investigation on lands typical of special erosion problems in various parts of the country.

Next a Soil Erosion Service was established in the Department of the Interior and Bennett headed it. That was in 1933, but, when the Soil Conservation Act became law on April 27, 1935, Bennett and his work came back to the Department of Agriculture, where he has since been chief of the Soil Conservation Service. The service formed part of the War Food Administration during its existence of two years or so.

Into this service were moved the above-mentioned soil-erosion experiment stations of the Bureau of Chemistry and Soils. There also went to it work on drainage investigations and experiments and demonstrations in connection with the construction and hydrologic phases of farm irrigation and land drainage. These had previously been in the Bureau of Agricultural Engineering, the Office of Public Roads, and the Office of Experiment Stations.

Milton Whitney began his soil investigations with an appropriation of two thousand dollars. His immediate objectives were to ascertain soil-moisture and soil-temperature conditions and to make soil analyses. As early as 1895 it was suggested that soils could be classified on a basis of their analyses. During this time the work was closely related to geology, though publications were issued on soil moisture, texture, and soluble-salt content.

The Division of Chemistry, meanwhile, was reporting on soil constituents—humus, nitrogen, potash, and phosphorus, and on the physical character, overall composition, and water-holding capacity of soils. By 1897 the Division of Soils had undertaken a notable investigation on tobacco soils. Soil survey began in earnest in 1899. Detailed studies were made and localities in Maryland and Louisiana were mapped. Alkali soils received much attention.

By 1900 the tobacco-soil investigations had progressed to the point where shade-grown Sumatra was widespread in Connecticut and it was estimated that the results of this research alone would save producers and consumers of tobacco $15,000,000 annually. A little later Oscar Lowe, who had been in charge of tobacco fermentation studies, left for the Tokyo Royal Agricultural College at four times the salary the Division of Soils could pay him. It was estimated that the results of his work alone had saved tobacco dealers in Pennsylvania a million dollars a year.

By 1903 Whitney had concluded that there was no apparent correlation between crop yields and the dissolved salts in soils, and that many soils which contained plant nutrients in abundance varied widely in agricultural value. Some of them indeed produced very poor crops. Whitney had discovered that, while all soils contained necessary plant nutrients, the fertility level of a soil could not be forecast by mere chemical analysis. This was a far cry from Liebig's balance-sheet theory. Whitney was laying the cornerstone for a new science of soils.

Mechanical conditions, moisture content, soil management, and climate all entered into the picture as he saw it. His work continued to demonstrate the complex character of soils and the many factors which determined their agricultural use. Whitney wrote: "The soil is not static, as was formerly supposed, but is dynamic, with many functions continually at work producing changes and always mutually affecting one another, and these changes can also be profoundly influenced by substances ordinarily used as soil amendments."

The Bureau of Soils worked out a scheme of classifying soils with reference to both their origin and their composition, which was used as the basis of soil surveys and was modified as the surveys and related studies progressed. The special adaptation of crops to these soil types was next investigated. It was found that crops differ in their effects on soils and thus influence succeeding crops, and it was seen that there should be general orders of crop rotations for the best results.

By 1905 maps were being prepared which graphically represented the classification, occurrence, and distribution of different soil types. Then the use of fertilizers by farmers came up for study, since it had been observed that many fertilizers were wasted by unintelligent application. By 1914 the role of fertilizers in mitigating the harmful effects of what were thought to be toxic soil compounds was being studied, and plant ash was being examined for the presence of rare elements. The work of Whitney and his bureau was important if for no other reason than that it demonstrated the complexity of the problem and proved that there could be a science of soils.

Milton Whitney and C. F. Marbut were long the two principal Department figures in the development of soil science. Marbut was appointed a co-operative agent in the Bureau of Soils in 1909, leaving the University of Missouri at Whitney's urging. He came in to direct the soil-survey work, and he made it one of the outstanding scientific enterprises of the nation, to say nothing of the impetus it gave to soil research in other countries.

The surveys became basic studies of the physical and chemical conditions of soils, the types of crops or trees that will best grow on them, the kind, quantity, and quality of fertilizing materials they require, along with informative large-scale color maps. The surveys also indicate the crop yields that may be obtained from each soil type under different management systems, and the long-time effect of these systems upon soil productivity. These surveys are absolutely fundamental to any rational program of land utilization.

Marbut early conceived of soil types as geographic entities which must be studied both individually and in relation to the landscape as a whole. He visualized the urgent necessity for exact knowledge about these soil entities. When he came to the Department, soil data were scattered and isolated.

The general soil classifications had been based upon the geology of the underlying rock formations, the method of formation, the topographic similarity, relief, drainage—though soil texture, soil structure, and soil organic-matter content were all considered. Marbut developed a system wherein scattered facts and data acquired meaning and significance.

Marbut's most important work was probably "The Soils of the United States," which formed the final section of the *Atlas of American Agriculture*. Naturally he published many other books and papers. Death overtook him on August 3, 1935, while he was in Harbin, Manchukuo, en route to China to examine certain Asian soils for the Chinese government.

The first actual report of a soil survey was in the initial volume of the *Field Operations of the Division of Soils, Report No. 64.* Whitney outlined his views in the introduction, which was followed by soil-survey reports for the Pecos Valley, New Mexico, Salt Lake Valley, Utah, the Connecticut Valley, and some reconnaissance surveys. As the field work continued, lack of correspondence was found between the geologic character of the underlying material and the soil characteristics related to agricultural production. Drainage and soil color were also recognized as important factors to be considered.

By 1924 Marbut had outlined modern soil science, although his formulations were built upon pioneer work carried on during the previous thirty years, which had mostly remained without synthesis or interpretation. By 1927 Marbut was the world's greatest single figure in the field of soil science, and Liebig's balance-sheet theory was about dead. By 1930 the principles of soil classification had been quite well worked out. It then became necessary to interpret these in quantitative terms as related to agriculture.

The soil surveys are still carried out at a cost of a few cents per acre and to put a valuation of a dollar an acre on them in practical use is again a gross underestimate. The armed forces attributed a value of $300,000 to a single survey because of the useful information it supplied for them in the construction of one air port. Charles E. Kellogg is now in charge of the soil survey work; his book, *The Soils That Support Us*, well merits study.

Around the beginning of this century F. K. Cameron assumed charge of the Laboratory of Soil Chemistry of the Bureau of Soils. Under his direction notable work was done on the soil solution, soil fertility, and the physical chemistry of soils. It was shown that the influence of water, atmosphere, minerals, and biological factors keep the soil solution in a condition of continuous change. This concept greatly affected later work.

Oswald Schreiner and Edmund C. Shorey were associated with Cameron. Shorey's *Farmers' Bulletin No. 921*, on the "Principle of Liming Soils," issued in 1918, was the first publication summarizing information on this important subject. It was used widely and proved extremely valuable. Cameron's book, *The Soil Solution*, was also broadly influential.

Schreiner and his associates introduced the "triangle" method of expressing the ratios of nitrogen, phosphorus, and potash in fertilizers, as well as the Schreiner colorimeter and other methods for determining the water-soluble plant-food constituents of soil. They likewise discovered basic relationships between the so-called rare elements and the health of plants, and placed the foundation for an understanding of how soil organic matter promoted or inhibited plant growth.

The results of work by Cameron and Schreiner convinced Whitney that the soil water or soil solution was the principal factor determining soil fertility. Whitney then began to maintain that one of the chief functions of fertilizers was to counteract certain toxic substances which these two workers had discovered in soils and which they incorrectly assumed to account for infertility. Their mistake was in believing that substances which were toxic in water cultures also poisoned soils.

It was under Cameron's supervision that Schreiner and Shorey began their identifications of definite complex organic compounds in soils. Later their investigations were re-examined in various parts of the world in the light of their possible relation to plant hormones.

About 1919 work on the soil colloids was actively undertaken, and during the following decade definite progress was made in working out methods of preparing soil colloids. Thereafter their properties and the quantities present in soils were ascertained, and the relationship between their chemical composition and their properties was worked out.

By 1928 emphasis had shifted to relationships between the chemical composition of soils and their colloidal fractions and soil classification. A dozen or more technical bulletins and as many long journal articles reported these studies. As a result, many recent chemical data from different parts of the world tell us much more about the character of the soils than we could find out previously.

About 1931 investigations began on the causes of a livestock ailment called "alkali disease" occurring in several western states. The chemical element selenium, transmitted from soils to edible plants, was shown to be the cause. These investigations, published in a long series of bulletins and articles, constitute one of the most carefully conducted pieces of Department research. They led to noteworthy improvement in grazing practices in extensive western areas. Horace G. Byers, who did much of the work on soil colloids, also pioneered here.

Meanwhile Carl F. Kellerman and his associates discovered and described the soil bacteria which decompose cellulose. This discovery was a definite forward step in our knowledge of the decomposition of agricultural plant residues. The discovery that these bacteria function in composts has greatly influenced the addition of fertilizers to increase the decomposition of cellulose therein. This has had considerable economic effect.

Felix Löhnis and Nathan R. Smith studied the life history of the soil bacteria and reported their findings. Their work stimulated much investigation on the variations bacteria undergo. Bacteria were found to have various growth phases and to differ in appearance and characteristics, from time to time, though within prescribed limits. This knowledge has benefited both agriculture and medical bacteriology.

Harry Mumfeld and Nathan R. Smith found that green plants decompose when plowed under and thus liberate plant food. The effect of this rapid decomposition affects neither the soil microorganisms nor the composition of the soil more than a quarter of an inch away from the decomposing material. Such localized action in part explains why decomposition and nitrification take place only in acid soil.

In studying the control of root-rot diseases, Francis B. Clark and his associates found that the fungus is killed out if the soil bacteria are stimulated to develop during the weakest period in its life. They also found that wheat plants resist "take-all disease" if properly nourished with nitrates and phosphates throughout their life span. Practical utilization of these discoveries has great worth. Charles Thom, long in charge of soil microbiological work, who wound up his career on penicillin in the Northern Regional Research Laboratory, is a notable scientist who should be mentioned in this connection.

Just before World War I research on fertilizer was intensified. Investigation of our national fertilizer resources was undertaken. The fixation of nitrogen began to be studied, and, in 1914, laboratory experiments began to be carried on in special apparatus for the Haber process installed at Arlington Farm, a Department experimental farm in near-by Virginia, which was relinquished during World War II, when all such work went to the Agricultural Research Center at Beltsville, Maryland.

Work on the subject was soon subsidized by the War Department and much extended to include study of the preparation and use of cyanamide and the fixation of nitrogen by means of the silent discharge. Furnace processes for volatilizing and collecting concentrated phosphoric acid were undertaken, and large-scale apparatus was installed at Arlington. Our entrance into World War I made all this work increasingly important. Germany was fixing nitrogen from the air; why couldn't we? The War Department supplied extra personnel both at Arlington and in the Bureau of Chemistry.

On March 29, 1919, the War Department itself established the Fixed Nitrogen Laboratory at American University in Washington, D. C. Its primary purpose was to utilize the Muscle Shoals fixed-nitrogen plants for agricultural purposes and the staff at Arlington was transferred to the new unit. On July 1, 1921, the War Department withdrew its support and the Fixed Nitrogen Laboratory became part of the Department of Agriculture. Here it assumed independent status until July 1, 1926, when it entered the Bureau of Soils.

It was then absorbed into the Division of Fixed Nitrogen and Fertilizer Investigations, which in 1927 went into the newly formed Bureau of Chemistry and Soils. On July 1, 1940, the division was transferred to the Bureau of Plant Industry, and in February, 1941, it was moved to the Agricultural Research Center, at Beltsville, after having been located at American University since its creation. The work continues in the Division of Soil and Fertilizer investigations, created July 1, 1942.

Research on fertilizer began in the Department some thirty years ago when such investigation was practically nonexistent in this country. Fertilizers were then largely made from low-grade waste materials. Nation-wide surveys for raw materials were first undertaken, followed by work on the utilization and perfection of methods for synthesizing new products. Rapid progress added to the list of products available for use in the fertilizer industry.

As a result the industry was re-established on a true chemical basis with an output of manufactured products having an annual retail value to the farmer of a quarter of a billion dollars. We were freed from foreign sources of many fertilizer materials, the costs of plant food were lowered, the quality of the final products was enhanced, and more efficient methods of utilization were developed. The development of suitable fertilizers and methods for their more effective use in producing food is of vital importance at peace or in war.

Fertilizer producers performed research of course, but each was inclined to follow pretty closely a limited line. Each tended to specialize in a few types of fertilizer produced from specific raw materials and overall research on fertilizers as a whole was neglected. That is why the Department came into the field.

Investigations on the production of nitrogenous fertilizer ingredients from atmospheric nitrogen began in 1915 when this process was as yet undeveloped in the United States. By 1925 this study was far enough along to permit the establishment of an American air-nitrogen industry based on the direct synthetic ammonia process. Department scientists had also developed an efficient, rugged catalyst for the synthesis of ammonia which was generally adopted commercially.

By then it was understood how to purify the gases used, and the chemical and physical behavior of gas mixtures was sufficiently clear. The apparatus necessary was designed and the technique perfected. The solubility of various gaseous constituents in liquid ammonia and in water, at various temperatures and pressures, had been measured. The American synthetic ammonia industry thereafter developed rapidly, using these findings and under the direction of workers drawn from the Department staff. Much cheaper nitrate nitrogen resulted.

Department phosphate investigations have been concerned with the conservation and the best utilization of the nation's phosphate resources, as well as with the development of methods for the manufacture of cheaper and more efficient phosphatic fertilizers. Special attention has been given to the utilization of phosphate ores that are too low in grade for, or are otherwise not adapted to, the manufacture of such fertilizers.

Concentrated phosphoric acid suitable for direct use in the manufacture of concentrated fertilizers was made for the first time by use of the electric furnace in processing both high-grade and low-grade phosphate ores. This work formed the basis for the commercial establishment of electric-furnace processing for phosphate rock, including that of the Tennessee Valley Authority plant at Muscle Shoals. The first of these plants went into operation in 1920, staffed by Department-trained personnel.

Later the application of fuel-fired furnaces was studied for the manufacture of concentrated phosporic acid. This investigation led to the erection of a large blast furnace which produced phosphate chemicals and triple superphosphate fertilizer for a decade.

Attention was given to the production of both phosphorus and potash by the simultaneous smelting of phosphate and potash rocks. A process was developed which offered promise of economic operation on a commercial scale.

A method was also devised for simultaneously removing the fluorine from phosphate rock and producing a phosphatic fertilizer by heating the rock at high temperatures in the presence of water vapor. The product contains about 30 per cent of the available phosphoric oxide and is an excellent source of phosphorus for promoting plant growth.

As this product contains little or no fluorine, it has the additional advantage of being a very satisfactory phosphatic material for use as a mineral supplement in livestock feeding. Detailed laboratory studies of the process and the product have been made in the Department, while the large-scale development of the process has been investigated by the Tennessee Valley Authority and by several commercial companies.

Before the organization of the German potash monopoly farmers in this country had been supplied with low-priced potash produced under highly competitive conditions. All that ended by royal decree which placed the world's known potash supply in the hands of one monopoly and by that same act placed farmers of the United States at the mercy of this trust. The monopoly was organized for purposes of exploitation; in case of war between Germany and a maritime nation all supplies of potash would terminate abruptly.

This situation was clearly understood before World War I, when the wholesale price of muriate of potash rapidly increased. Nation-wide surveys revealed resources of potash in both natural deposits and industrial wastes; technological research showed how these could be utilized. The kelp groves of the Pacific were surveyed from the Mexican border to Alaska. Experimental kelp-products plants were established on the West Coast. Processes for the production of iodine, potash, and decolorizing carbons were developed and demonstrated.

Surveys were also made of the salines and brines of the western desert regions. The commercial value of the brines of Searles Lake, California, was discovered, and a study was made of processes for the production of high-grade potash salts. Commercial developments in the use of these brines resulted in the establishment of a manufacturing plant of large capacity. The Department also developed improved processes for the recovery of potash from cement kilns, blast furnaces, Steffen's waste, and distillery waste, and sources of potash such as these assumed importance during World War I.

The farmer became chief beneficiary of the establishment of an American potash industry. Not only was he assured of an adequate future supply of potash, but, in 1942, he obtained potash at a saving of $10,000,000, as compared with 1910–14 prices. Farmers are also bound to benefit from further reductions in manufacturing and transportation costs.

Finally there is the matter of mixed fertilizers. About a quarter of a century ago the Department initiated work that is gradually bringing about the elimination of filler and the use of high-analysis fertilizer mixtures in many parts of this country. Double-strength mixtures were developed and put to agricultural use. They are similar in composition and physical properties to mixtures formerly used, but they contain a much greater percentage of plant food. Their effects on crops are similar to those of the best grades of former single-strength mixtures.

Farmers who use double-strength in lieu of single-strength mixtures make greater savings in their fertilizer bills than they would if the wholesale cost of all the plant food entering into the single-strength mixtures formerly used had been cut in half. Since this work was initiated in the Department a gradual increase of over 20 per cent has been made in the plant food content of American fertilizers. The resultant saving in freight, storage, handling, and bagging costs of fertilizers totals $15,000,000 or more annually and is growing steadily.

The adoption of high-analysis fertilizers has been contingent on investigations which resulted in improvement of their mechanical condition, reduction of their tendency to burn crops, and decrease in their acid-forming influence in the soil. At the same time practicable mixtures which contained an adequate proportion of all essential plant-food elements were prepared. A granulating treatment, whereby the fertilizer is changed into spherical particles of uniform shape and size, was found best to improve the mechanical condition of the mixtures.

The Department's fertilizer investigations as a whole have been largely responsible for a current annual reduction in farmers' fertilizer bills of from $45,000,000 to $50,000,000, as compared with 1910 prices. Hence this research has made available an abundant peacetime supply of fertilizer for growing crops at lower production costs and without impairing soil fertility. Indeed, the investigations have been an essential aid to soil conservation.

That brings us to the fact that a Division of Soil Utilization was created in the Bureau of Soils in 1901 and a Division of Soil Erosion in 1908. Thereafter more and more emphasis was placed upon the use of drainage, dams, and proper tillage methods as soil-conservation measures. This work may be regarded as the small beginnings of what is now the Soil Conservation Service, but many state workers also had a hand in giving this vast project its start.

Among the earliest scientific workers to report on soil erosion and soil conservation was E. W. Hilgard, state geologist and professor of geology in Mississippi, 1855–73. Hilgard observed and widely publicized erosion in his state, describing the complete destruction of certain fields left uncultivated since the Civil War. N. S. Shaler and W. J. McGee also pointed out the widespread occurrence of serious erosion in various parts of the country, in publications issued from the Geological Survey around 1890.

One of the earliest Department of Agriculture publications to deal with soil erosion was *Farmers' Bulletin No. 20*, issued in 1894, as a joint publication from the Divisions of Chemistry, Soils, Forestry, and Botany. This bulletin both discussed the effects of erosion and suggested control measures. The material was based on field observations by several individuals. The work was not followed up immediately. Meanwhile, the field studies of soil-survey workers of the Bureau of Soils began gradually to present observations on erosion.

These reports began with the work of Jay A. Bonsteel and associates around 1900. J. G. Mosier of the Illinois Agricultural Experiment Station emphasized the seriousness of the problem and the necessity for adoption of soil conservation measures in 1908. The well-known geologist, T. C. Chamberlin, in the same year

Sighting a forest fire by means of an Osborne Fire Finder, High Knob Tower, Ill.

A badly eroded farmyard about twenty miles west of the Guthrie (Okla.) Soil Conservation Camp

pointed out the necessity for erosion control before a conference of governors at the White House. W. J. McGee gave an exposition of the mechanism of the erosion process and possible control methods in Bureau of Soils *Bulletin No. 71*, issued in 1911.

H. H. Bennett's part in all this has been mentioned earlier. His Bureau of Soils *Bulletin No. 96* was devoted to the classification and detailed description of our soils. His book, *Soils and Agriculture of the Southern States* was a helpful influence. His primary interest was soil erosion from 1903 on.

In his report on Lauderdale County, Mississippi, issued in 1910, Bennett gave an extended discussion of soil erosion and distinguished the eroded areas on a map by cross-lining. This was one of the earliest attempts to map soil erosion. Bennett also made therein the fundamental distinction between woodlands, pasture land, and arable land, which is still the basis upon which the Soil Conservation Service classifies soils in its land use-capability categories.

In 1923, Duley and Miller of the Missouri Agricultural Experiment Station announced quantitative measurements of soil and water losses covering a six-year period under a variety of plant-cover types and three fallow conditions in central Missouri. As a result of their work they concluded that soil erosion was the most important cause of soil depletion under corn belt conditions.

The net result of all this preliminary investigation was to indicate that no large geological division of the country was entirely free from problems raised by loss of soil and water. At the same time further information about the causes of erosion on important soil types and the best methods of control was unavailable. However, the aforementioned Buchanan Amendment provided funds:

"To enable the Secretary of Agriculture to make investigations not otherwise provided for, of the causes of soil erosion and the possibility of increasing the absorption of rainfall in the soil of the United States, and to devise means to be employed in the preservation of soil, the prevention or control of destructive erosion and the conservation of rainfall by terracing or other means, independently or in cooperation with other branches of the Government, State agencies, counties, farm organizations, associations of business men, individuals."

Plans were then made to establish experimental work on lands typifying the large problem areas of eroding soil the country over. Ten erosion experiment stations were organized and their research programs got under way. They were designed to investigate the causes and rates of erosion, and to ascertain the most effective practical means of checking and controlling soil and water losses from agricultural lands.

This work included the keeping of meteorological records, experiments with various types of vegetative cover, soil treatments, and cultural and cropping systems to determine their comparative effectiveness in preventing erosion, studies of the performance of terraces and check dams of different designs in removing runoff without injury to soil or crops, and attempts to reclaim and revegetate eroded land. The investigations were carried out in co-operation with the state experiment stations.

The early work of these erosion stations showed that very large amounts of soil actually had been lost by previous practices of continuous single-crop agriculture. The value of rotations in reducing soil loss was demonstrated, as well as the excellent protective effect of vigorous grass cover, which was found to be as efficient in this respect as a good stand of forest trees. The effectiveness and limitations of many cultural and mechanical methods of erosion control, such as subsoiling, contour tillage, strip cropping, and terracing, were measured. A helpful fund of exact information was thus accumulated.

The application made of this information was unique. For that Bennett was largely responsible. The entire farm business of each co-operator in the program based thereupon became a demonstration project. This project was placed under an integrated farm plan which correlated the erosion-control problem for related groups of farmers on a watershed basis.

To meet the varied problems of soil and water conservation presented, first by the operations demonstration projects of the service, and later by the Soil Conservation Districts—which operate in the states as semiautonomous units of local government—the program of the original research stations had to be expanded. Several closely integrated research divisions were established in the service. The work of the ten original erosion stations was finally expanded into a Division of Conservation Experiment Stations.

There is also a Hydrologic Division in Soil Conservation Service which studies the influence of land use and different types of cover on runoff, erosion, and stream flow in typical watersheds. The Sedimentation Division has determined the effect of movements of erosion debris into reservoirs, stream channels, and valley fields. The mechanics of sedimentation movement, transportation, and disposition is studied by hydraulic laboratory research.

A Climatic and Physiographic Division has determined the relationship between soils and underlying land forms in the occurrence of large-scale gullying taking place in critical erosion regions. Large-scale climatic studies have shown the way in which storms build up and the types of storms which cause serious erosion. Out of this have grown new and extraordinary methods of long-time weather forecasting which had critical wartime value. Work in erosion history has shown the course of early attempts at erosion control and the reasons for success or failure.

A Conservation Economics Division determines the effects of soil conservation programs on farm income and farm living. A Farm Drainage Division ascertains the best depths and spacings of drainage tiles on a variety of soils and crops. It has developed new, improved types of drain tile for acid and alkaline soils. It has also investigated drainage-district organization and pointed out possibilities of improvement.

The Hillculture Division tries out new erosion-control plants such as shipmast locust. It discovers how they can best be used on eroded, hilly farmland to save soil and augment farm income simultaneously. The Farm Irrigation Division still makes notable contributions to greater water economy in the western states. In recent years it has developed an effective system of forecasting stream flow from mountain areas by making snow surveys.

H. H. Bennett and his associates have worked out methods for making large-scale maps which show the physical land conditions in each field and each part of a field on farms. They also show the soil type, percentage of slope, degree of erosion, and present use of the land. Then there is a series of bulletins reporting what are essentially land-use and use-capability studies which cover larger areas and show exactly how each kind of land therein should be used.

It is difficult to evaluate any isolated part of the soil-conservation research program because it all fits together as an integrated whole. As such it is a composite achievement. But it does provide a guide for greater crop diversification. It does mean monetary savings in seed, fertilizer, labor, power, and the actual prevention of soil erosion. It permits the greatest possible protection and improvement of the soil and water resources under pressure of intensified production. It offers farmers and ranchers sound methods to shift types and intensities of production to meet varying markets.

By studying the private life of a raindrop, scientists have developed unique rain machines which can be regulated to produce variations in rainfall from gentle drizzles to heavy downpours. These are used to test the effects of different kinds of vegetative cover as protection for various soil types. Tilting plots of earth can be sloped to any degree to help determine the soil-holding power of grasses and other close-growing plants on sloping fields.

Wind-tunnel studies contribute valuable information about wind erosion in dust storms. Fine-gauged laboratory instruments and ingenious weather-imitating devices of all sorts add bit by bit to the store of tested facts contributing to the development of new and improved soil-conservation practices and the refinement of methods already in use.

Farms are redesigned, just as factories are, as a result of the multitude of laboratory tests and plot studies made, and of carefully watched field trials. The research scientists of the service delve into the innermost secrets of soil, rain, wind, and growing crops, assisted by other federal and by many state workers. Scientific farm plans are evolved to put every acre to its best use in accord with its individual capabilities. The farmer's plant is actually redesigned for more efficient operation.

Using a miniature river and reservoir in glass, the service and the California Institute of Technology have found out how to shuttle a silt-laden stream through and out of a reservoir, by making enlightened use of the stream's own action. This is of the highest importance, because the annual cost of reservoir silting is over $50,000,000, and it is not worth a cent. It has been found that streams retain their identity after entering reservoirs and continue to flow in a layer through, under, or over the still water.

Hence a silt-laden current can slide under clear water in a reservoir as heavy cream poured into a cup of coffee slides under the clear brown liquid. These flows have been tapped in glass and their action recorded. Engineers will next use layered streams of water as accurately as accountants use the keys of the adding machine. Clean streams of snow water can then be channeled through a reservoir to the city mains, right while muddy streams are being passed through the same basin.

Water containing sediment can be led into sandy irrigation canals so that the silt will seal leaks in the sandy ditches, while salty water can be layered off for storage in a known stratum until time comes to drain it out. At Brighton Dam and Reservoir, near Washington, D. C., the principle of stratified flow is used by a system of outlets to carry off two to ten times as much sediment as would otherwise go over the spillway with the same volume of water.

Protecting the soil against wind and water erosion by using the straw as cover after harvest, instead of burning or plowing it under, is another project. Stubble mulching has proved a most effective conservation practice in the West. It reduces runoff and improves soil structure; it slows evaporation and reduces erosion. A wide variety of new-type equipment has been designed and put into use to cultivate crops without undue disturbance to this mulch. Many of these machines have gone into commercial production and are now in use on hundreds of thousands of acres.

The service has also developed a slide rule for measuring the quantities of soil moisture available seasonally at various locations, as compared with the quantities actually needed in the same areas for ideal crop conditions. To do this, it has been necessary to determine the rate of evapotranspiration, which means the rate of release of moisture to the air both by direct evaporation and through plant exhalations. Mere rainfall data are insufficient.

The rate at which water is lost differs in cold and hot climates, but the development of a dependable formula makes it possible to measure this rate quite accurately, using Weather Bureau records of temperature and rainfall as a basis. The formula that was developed is already in practical use on irrigated areas to compute the quantities of supplementary water that can be used efficiently, and the length of time they will be required. It is also possible by this means to forecast the probabilities of crop failure or success from crops not grown before and to find the best locations for various types of crops.

In view of all these factors it is not surprising that the soil-saving gospel spreads throughout the world from the United States. Dr. Walter C. Lowdermilk is a notable itinerant bureaucrat, who, like Bennett, has spread the message to foreign parts. He began stalking soil erosion thirty-odd years ago as a forest ranger in Arizona. There he was initially impressed with what overgrazing can do to ranges in the dry-land country. Later, with the engineers of the A.E.F. he roamed war-torn France and decided to devote his life to soil conservation.

China claimed him in the early years after World War I. For five years he chalked up thousands of miles in China's vast loessial regions as he worked on a famine-prevention project for the University of Nanking. He discovered and charted incredible erosion in the uplands feeding silt to the Yellow River. He followed the trail of the engineers of past centuries in their attempt to stem the tide of China's sorrow. Here Lowdermilk set up the first of a series of studies of accelerated erosion as it affects human communities of the present and as it has affected civilizations of the dim past.

In 1933 Lowdermilk was called to help launch the United States' national soil conservation program. He has since been a veritable ambassador of modern conservation farming in his own and many other countries. He traveled the rolling hills and roads of Old England, surprised French peasants in the act of rotating fish crops and grain crops, plowed through the sands of Egypt and Libya; backtracked to Syria, the Trans-Jordan, Palestine, and the Valleys of the Tigris and the Euphrates.

Searching always for water-saving practices and erosion-control methods that might be adapted here, Lowdermilk piled up volumes of valuable data for the Department, too. He continued his studies, begun in China, of the effects of different farming practices and traditional land-use policies on human advancement. The outbreak of World War II found him in Syria. He had just completed a survey of the erosion-devastated lands surrounding the "hundred dead cities," once a region of rich agricultural soils and extensive forests.

Since his reports on Syria and the dead cities no one disputes this itinerant soil conservationist's conviction that accelerated erosion, if long continued, rings the death knell of civilizations. In 1942–43 China borrowed Lowdermilk as adviser to the government in an energetic program to increase food production while conserving the soil. With a staff of eight Chinese specialists Lowdermilk covered nearly seven thousand miles in China's romantic northwest—out to the borderlands of Tibet and the Desert of Gobi.

This group surveyed the land, evaluated farm practices, and charted areas where land wastage was most serious and famine hazards were most pressing. They then set up simple demonstrations of conservation practices for Chinese farmers to see. Farmers came to look and then asked that their own farms be used for demonstration purposes as the practices increased yields. The first soil-conservation association in China was organized. Chinese farmers thus set to work co-operatively to solve their erosion problems.

Before Lowdermilk returned to the United States, in January, 1944, a national soil-conservation program for all the land of China had been formulated in detail and bore the approval stamp of Chungking. Thus when we come finally to evaluate soil-conservation research carried on by the Department we must not overlook what it has done for lands other than our own, and that is an important consideration if we are to have "One World" of mutual aid following World War II.

Our annual bill for soil erosion in this country is not less than four billion dollars. Of our original 462,000,000 acres of good farmland, 342,000,000 are already in cultivation, the remainder being mainly in grass and trees. But only 62,000,000 of these good acres are not subject to erosion. Another 70,000,000 acres could be protected from erosion by proper clearance, drainage, irrigation, and cultivation practices. Only then would the United States have an acre of cultivated nonerodible land per person.

Wind and water erosion and bad land practices have been ruining about one-half million acres a year, at least until soil conservation really got underway. A billion acres, half the nation's land area, needs some degree of protection. Moreover, the use of soil-building methods developed by research not only saves the soil, it also greatly increases crop yields and decreases the need for fertilizer. The loss of a single inch of topsoil represents a reduction in the nitrogen supply of at least 350 pounds per acre, as well as of some 175–200 pounds of phosphoric acid in the form of phosphorus pentoxide.

Little use was made of terrace-outlet channels to control incipient gullying from runoff water in the Southeast before the Soil Conservation Service was created. When the service began its operations demonstration projects, the best practice known was the use of an expensive system of check dams. In the fiscal year 1936 some two million linear feet of outlets were put in to protect 130,000 acres at a cost of $1,625,000, an expenditure of $12.50 per acre. These structures were expensive and subject to occasional failure.

Experimentation at the Spartanburg Hydrologic Laboratory developed a series of vegetatively stabilized outlets in which grasses and other plants were used. As a result of this research terrace outlets could be installed at a cost of only about $4.50 per acre. The large saving made on 950,000 acres protected in 1940 alone amounted to more than the cost of the entire research program carried on since 1935, when it began.

Studies of sand-dune and wind-erosion control carried out in the Dust Bowl resulted in information that was widely applied. The protection afforded agricultural land has been worth millions of dollars. It has notably reduced menaces to the health and comfort of farm families living in this region. Over all hang those great and intangible values that inhere in a way of life and a maturing civilization. Unless we retain the good soil and the great waters are conserved, the vine will not put forth branches nor yet will it bear fruit.

CHAPTER 12

Food and Raiment

W̶E COME NOW to work on nutrition, foods, household appliances, and textiles, not to mention the most efficient methods of doing housework.[1] We also meet Dr. Atwater again. In Europe, he not only became acquainted with agricultural experiment stations and decided we should have some of our own, but he also developed a lifetime interest in the composition and analysis of foods.

When he returned, that and the experiment stations, of which there were thirty on the continent of Europe by 1866, became his life passions. Between 1879 and 1883 he made a series of analyses of fish for the United States Fish Commission and of the flesh of animals for the Smithsonian Institution. He published dietary studies carried on for the Massachusetts Bureau of Statistics and Labor in 1896. We have already discussed to some extent the manner in which he combined experiment station and nutrition work at Middletown.

For generations it had been theoretically recognized that the primary purpose of agriculture and industry was to turn out goods the public would buy and use, and that an efficient national economy depends as much upon efficient consumption as upon efficient production and distribution. But the problem of the individual consumer was so complicated, and the ordinary home represented

[1] In preparing this chapter free use was made of a manuscript account of the research achievements of the Bureau of Human Nutrition and Home Economics, written for that bureau three or four years ago by Helen W. Atwater, daughter of W. O. Atwater. In some instances the language of the manuscript was pretty closely followed so as to keep the facts straight, but this chapter contains a great deal of material, some of it recent, that was not in Miss Atwater's account. Her manuscript is still on file in the bureau mentioned for any who wish to consult it.

so small a capital investment and had so little to do with monetary profit that research was inclined to pass it by.

It is true that some research which had distinct consumer benefit was undertaken by the Department chemists in early days. This led, as we have seen, to the passage of the meat inspection and food and drug acts. We shall have occasion later to examine some of this research in more detail, especially that concerned with foods, when we come to consider the activities of the Food and Drug Administration.

But the Department of Agriculture was the first great scientific institution in this or any other country to establish an Office and then a Bureau of Home Economics. This agency had the double function of conducting research into the principles behind the efficient utilization of agricultural products in the home and of disseminating reliable information on these subjects. This bureau stood first among government research agencies dealing primarily with problems confronting the ultimate consumer.

An outstanding neglect here was in the field of food and human nutrition. For a century or more citizens had recognized the connection between diet and national welfare. Witness an article on the "Proportions of Nutriment of the Means of Living," in the annual report of the Patent Office for 1847 and a report issued in 1852 by the Board of Immigration on the "Food and Diet Suitable for Almshouses, Prisons, and Hospitals." The former was a translation of a German discussion of the nutrient elements in legumes, eggs, milk, vegetables, fermented liquors, and such matters.

Papers like these would scarcely pass as scientifically valid today. Indeed, really valuable work could not be done until methods of food analysis and physiological chemistry were greatly improved. It was not until 1869 that W. O. Atwater made the first published proximate analysis of an American food material—corn or maize. Then, as the Office of Experiment Stations and the state experiment stations were established, opportunity appeared for more work on food.

Atwater, himself, in his first annual report as director of the Office of Experiment Stations, wrote: "It has been urged by not a few of the best thinkers and wisest agriculturists and economists that in studying the food of animals we have no right to neglect the food of man. The principles involved are essentially the same. The majority of our people and practically all wage-workers spend and must spend at least half the money they earn for food. . . . The need and the wisdom of such studies require no urging."

From 1894 until about 1914 Congress provided special funds for nutrition investigations in the Department of Agriculture. Almost inevitably other phases of home economics received attention as public interest developed. Home economic courses in schools and colleges multiplied rapidly; agricultural and home-economics extension work appeared together. In 1914 the nutrition investigations so long carried on were enlarged into an Office of Home Economics under the direction of C. F. Langworthy.

The States Relations Service was created the following year and into it went the extension work, the Office of Experiment Stations, and the Office of Home Economics, as well as the Office of Farm Management. The Office of Home Economics was directed to carry on studies of food and nutrition, household labor and equipment, textiles, and clothing. The importance of economic data gained recognition. A bureau, sometimes "kidded" later by a hostile press, which did not understand the importance of its work, and ironically called "Mother's Little Helper," was in the offing.

In 1922 Secretary Henry C. Wallace announced that the Office of Home Economics would soon become a bureau. The following year he invited a group of experts in the subject to come to Washington and advise concerning the organization of the bureau and the lines of work it should pursue. Among them was Dr. Louise Stanley, head of the Home Economics Department of the University of Missouri, the land-grant college of that state.

When the States Relations Service was dissolved in 1923 and the Bureau of Home Economics was created (the Extension Service and the Office of Experiment Stations becoming independent units at the same time), Dr. Stanley became its first chief. The step was taken as part of a general departmental reorganization, but also in response to considerable agitation by various women's organizations. The bureau's home-economics research originally included food and nutrition, textiles and clothing, household equipment, and the use of money and labor in the household.

On February 23, 1943, the Division of Protein and Nutrition Research was transferred from the Bureau of Agricultural Chemistry and Engineering to the Bureau of Home Economics, which then assumed the name Bureau of Human Nutrition and Home Economics. At that time the distinguished nutrition scientist, Dr. Henry C. Sherman of Columbia, became chief of the bureau. In June, 1944, he was succeeded by Hazel K. Stiebeling, herself an outstanding research worker in a pioneering field we shall consider later.

The value of research into home problems cannot be measured in the same way as research intended to increase production for sale or, indeed, many other types of investigation carried on by the Department. It is all but impossible to reduce to statistics the money savings which accrue to American families through the wiser selection, care, and use of food, clothing, and household equipment. That they are large and that they improve standards of home living go without saying.

Still less can we tell how great an effect the application of systematized knowledge about these subjects has on health and the intangible values of home life and on the making of strong, self-sufficient citizens. The only indication of its value that is readily available is the extent to which the information is used. When the research is translated into practical terms and issued in published form, the demand for these publications and the letters they bring in prove that both American consumers and commercial producers find the material valuable.

It was fortunate for Department work in home economics that the beginning was made in the field of nutrition investigation. This was one of the best-planned programs of scientific research ever carried out in any part of the world. It placed its director high in the list of distinguished Department scientists, and it was carried on after Dr. Atwater's death by other devoted workers.

After he finished the usual classical course at Wesleyan, young Atwater went to the Sheffield Scientific School at Yale to study agricultural chemistry. He soon realized that to be abreast of developments, he must go to Germany. So he studied for two years there and also learned of German experiment-station work at first hand. This we have discussed earlier.

However, Atwater's interest tended more and more to center around food and nutrition upon his return from Europe. He went back to study physiological chemistry in Münich and Heidelberg and to visit the leading laboratories. Returning once more to the United States, he began the first systematic studies ever made of American food and diet. This included the work on fish and animal foods mentioned earlier.

At that time many laymen, as well as many agricultural and social scientists, were beginning to sense the vital relationship between the nation's food and its economic and social progress. The federal government was being urged to do something to encourage research in human nutrition.

For instance, Edward Atkinson, socially minded industrialist, and inventor of a sort of closed cooker designed to aid women in preparing family meals while employed outside the home, openly advocated the establishment of food experiment stations. He prepared two papers which were issued in annual reports of the Office of Experiment Stations, and he was by no means a lone wolf. It was an increase in this sort of public pressure which induced Congress to make its first $10,000 appropriation for nutrition studies.

As we have seen earlier, Dr. Atwater was placed in charge of this work, which was to be done under the Secretary of Agriculture but in co-operation with the state experiment stations and the land-grant colleges. He maintained his headquarters at Middletown, where he could both direct the new work and continue his own investigations.

As he saw it, he was to find out what the body needs in its food, what nutrients different foods supply, how the body uses the various and varied nutrients, and what foods and methods of food preparation will furnish the most economical and healthful diet. The fundamental question was: How can national food production be made to yield the best returns in economic progress and social welfare? Research in human nutrition still follows the broad general patterns Atwater then outlined.

Such a wide range of subjects could be handled by Atwater only on a co-operative basis. A man of broad scientific knowledge and unflagging energy and enthusiasm was required as director.

During the eleven-year period Atwater was in charge, more than a score of experiment stations and other educational, scientific, and welfare agencies co-operated with him, each working on special problems of local interest or which it was particularly well equipped to study.

Central direction prevented duplication, helped to encourage work on neglected subjects, and upheld high standards of scientific accuracy and uniform reporting. Because the field was wholly novel, the first publication issued was a summary of methods and results of investigations on the chemistry and economy of food in all countries.

This was the first reliable compilation on this subject in any language. It gave great impetus to nutrition research both here and abroad. The literature of human food and nutrition was also regularly summarized in the *Experiment Station Record* to keep investigators up to date.

In 1894 Atwater's *Farmers' Bulletin* on "Foods: Nutritive Value and Cost" gave citizens of this country the first simple and easily available account of what science has to tell them about food and diet. It was followed by a long series on special food materials and their use in the home. These publications would hardly be classed as popular reading matter today, but they were a pioneer step towards our present methods of putting nutrition facts to practical use—at which the Bureau of Human Nutrition and Home Economics is now a past master.

All told these initial nutrition investigations had a value quite out of proportion to the $300,000 of federal money invested in them. What is it worth to found a science? Essentially that was the service Atwater performed. When his health broke in 1904, the United States was the recognized leader in the field of nutrition research. With his courageous persistence and his skillful and far-sighted leadership, this eminence was won quickly. American nutrition science has ever since had an enviable reputation for scientific accuracy. In this, too, it owes much to the high standards set by Atwater for nutrition investigations.

Basic to all nutrition study is the composition of food materials, and this Atwater did not neglect. Even before his nutrition investigations were organized, he had begun to compile the results of available American analyses, finding most of the data in the work of the Division and Bureau of Chemistry and in his own analyses.

In 1896 appeared the first edition of Office of Experiment Stations *Bulletin 28* on the "Chemical Composition of American Food Materials." It soon became the food student's bible, both here and abroad. In 1918 this publication was officially adopted by the Inter-allied Food Commission. Most of the food-composition figures in American books and articles on food and diet have been taken from this great source book. Countless institutions, physicians, dietitians, and students have used it to calculate the nutritive value of diets. The army and the navy have found it invaluable for the same purpose. Before 1940 more than one hundred thousand copies of it had been distributed.

The bureau has continued to assemble data on food composition. In 1940 its long-awaited revision of *Bulletin 28* appeared. After vitamins entered the picture, compilations of proximate analyses were complemented with other data on vitamin content.

Because the bureau had the largest available collection of basic data on food composition, the National Research Council later provided it with personnel to expedite the compilation of such data. This was especially needful in connection with new and less familiar foods required to feed the armed forces. It also became urgent when substitute foods were required by civilians at home and other foods for the relief of liberated peoples.

Of course one must establish some sort of a standard from which to judge the adequacy of a diet in nutritional terms. This standard should show the amounts of various nutrients the diet must provide. These are ordinarily based on the daily needs of a man at moderately active muscular work. So-called dietary ratios or factors are used to translate these into the requirements of other persons according to sex, age, and activity level.

The first such commonly adopted standards were drawn up by Voit, a German physiologist, who based his figures on the diets actually consumed by families of German workingmen. In adapting them to American use, Atwater raised them to conform to our more generous diets and to avoid the danger of underfeeding in institutions and low-income groups. The Atwater standards were generally accepted here. However, as increasing knowledge of nutritional needs became available, they were frequently revised or modified by Atwater and his successors.

So also were the dietary ratios set for calculating food requirements for different groups of adults and for children of different ages. When minerals and vitamins assumed importance in nutrition, standards for these were added to the original ones for protein, fats, carbohydrates, and energy. In 1941 the Nutrition Committee of the National Research Council announced its technical standards and its much-popularized "yardstick of good nutrition." These now form the accepted standards for the United States.

Pioneering work in rendering theoretical dietary standards widely useful in practice was done by Hazel K. Stiebeling. She translated theory into terms of actual food materials the average family could buy. Then it became possible to estimate the use of certain foods on a national basis. Thus nutritionally adequate meals for families at different income levels were brought nearer, for the calculations were so made that dietary adequacy could be achieved at several different levels of income.

In doing this, Dr. Stiebeling divided our common food materials into about a dozen groups according to special nutritive value. Then she calculated the quantities and proportions of each that would be required in diets at four cost levels: restricted diets for emergency use, adequate diets at minimum cost, adequate diets at moderate cost, and liberal diets. The cheapest diet, slightly below 1941 recommendations, was made up of quantities and proportions of foods from each group that would provide the necessary nutrients at least cost, while the more expensive diets included more of the foods which improve flavor and variety as well as nutritive value.

Next there were worked out the quantities of food from each group needed annually by adults and by children of different ages. Then came estimates of the approximate per capita quantities required per year to provide the population of the United States with each of the four diets. This was a very important piece of research because it enabled us for the first time to appraise what foods we needed and then to tailor agricultural production accordingly.

224

Potato seedlings which are expected to produce improved varieties
of potatoes

Columbia ram and ewes

The work assumed enhanced importance during the war because, when these estimates were correlated with other estimates by agricultural economists, showing which foods could be produced most cheaply in terms of labor, equipment, materials, and drain on land resources, it became possible to work out adequate diets composed mainly of foods that could be produced the most efficiently. Meanwhile Dr. Stiebeling's work had immediate application in feeding depression-hit families during the thirties. Her figures for national dietary requirements were constantly referred to in planning national and local food-production programs when goals were set up for farmers during the war.

In 1942 the material was translated into handy weekly market lists for practical homemakers. Each list was accompanied by simple directions and blanks for working out the quantities of various foods needed by a family made up of specific numbers of adults and children. Even the cheapest diets permitted a wide range of individual choices within each group of foods. In the first ten months after the lists were issued three hundred thousand copies were distributed, more than one-third of them by sale.

Dr. Stiebeling has been an influential official representative of the United States at many international meetings of nutrition experts. The tremendous food problems of the war brought out the value of her work. Through her investigations theory became practice in terms readily understood by the ordinary layman.

Early in the history of this work the Department carried on dietary studies. These were designed to find out what normal people actually eat, as influenced by regional food habits, racial traditions, income levels, and other factors, including prejudice, fallacy, and custom. Since the early investigations were carried on co-operatively with the states, considerable opportunity for this sort of study existed, and nearly five hundred studies were made between 1894 and 1906. From these it was possible to get a clear idea of the diversity of our dietary needs and customs, and thus it became possible to plan diets for special groups without upsetting food habits.

The work had value in dollars and cents, too. One large public institution in an Eastern state where such a study was carried on reported a per capita saving of nearly 14 per cent in the cost of food served, without sacrifice of nutritive value. The attractiveness of the food was actually improved. Dietary studies thereafter became a routine in many institutions. States began to employ nutritionists who showed how food costs could be decreased and diets improved simultaneously in establishments which feed people at public expense.

The most comprehensive picture of its food habits that any nation ever gained was drawn from the food data collected as part of our nation-wide consumer-purchases studies made between 1934 and 1937. The food figures as analyzed by the Bureau of Home Economics demonstrated that over one-third of American families regularly had poor diets, about one-fourth had good diets, and something less than one-half had only fair diets. Farm families generally ate better than others.

Although low incomes tend to cut food expenditures and to make diets inadequate, large expenditures for food do not automatically guarantee good diets. Many well-to-do families spend lavishly for food, yet are poorly fed in terms of essential nutrients. The quality of the diet depends very largely upon the wisdom with which food is selected, and good diets can follow many different patterns. Education of the public regarding sound dietary practice carried on by this bureau has been highly beneficial.

Then there is the question of the actual good our bodies derive from the food we consume. Department nutrition scientists have looked into this also. Digestion experiments were carried on to see how efficiently the body utilized various foods. The proportion of the nutrients digested from a given food or diet was ascertained by comparing the food intake and bodily excreta during the experimental period. The proportions were called the "coefficients of digestion" of the food. Before 1906 nearly seven hundred experiments of this kind had been carried on. In general, the nutrients and energy of animal foods showed higher coefficients of digestibility than vegetable foods.

The chemical changes which take place in the body, the building up and tearing down of tissues which goes on constantly, are spoken of as "metabolism." To understand what they are is an essential step towards establishing the basic principles of nutrition. It was in this field that Atwater and his assistants did notable work indeed. The metabolism of digestion could be unraveled only up to a certain point by running digestion experiments. Something more was needed.

Digestion experiments told nothing of the gaseous exchange through the breath, nor did they give any direct measurements of energy exchange. It was generally assumed that the law of the conservation of energy held true even within the living animal, but nobody had proved this. It was a mere assumption, not a matter of precise scientific demonstration.

To supply this proof, accurate measurements and analyses must be made of the air inhaled and exhaled, and the heat and moisture given off by the body must be determined. Physiological chemists in Germany had been experimenting with apparatus to accomplish this complicated task, but the first successful instrument for use with human subjects was devised at Middletown by Atwater and his associates.

It was known as the "Atwater-Rosa [later "Atwater-Rosa-Benedict"] respiration calorimeter." It was set up in the natural science building at Wesleyan University. To the ordinary visitor it was just a big, copper-lined wooden box. But between the inner and the outer walls were several others, separated by air spaces for better temperature control. The inner chamber was 7 x 6 x 4 feet in size, large enough to accommodate a folding bed, cot, table, and the apparatus a particular experiment might require.

There was an especially constructed window, big enough for a man to climb through, and a smaller aperture through which food and other articles could be passed in and out without loss of heat or air. Ventilation tubes took care of air intake and outgo. These were connected with measuring devices to show the temperature and water content of air entering and leaving the chamber. A system of aspirators permitted frequent sampling and analysis. Thermocouples were installed at frequent intervals in the walls of the calorimeter, and were connected with recording devices outside, so that temperature changes might be followed.

Probably the most amazing thing about the contraption was that it worked. Not only did subjects remain well and reasonably comfortable through their incarceration—commonly four or five days and nights, though some experiments were much longer—but the balance of matter and energy checked out perfectly to support the law of the conservation of energy. This was the first proof that physiology was amenable to a fundamental law of physics.

Because the construction of such an instrument called for work by a competent physicist, Atwater enlisted the assistance of his Wesleyan colleague, E. B. Rosa, later assistant director of the National Bureau of Standards, who developed many of the physical features that made the calorimeter successful. Later improvements became possible through funds from the Carnegie Institution of Washington and were under the immediate direction of F. G. Benedict, a physiological chemist on Atwater's staff. Benedict won an international reputation as director of the Carnegie Institution's Boston Nutrition Laboratory.

About five hundred experiments were carried on in the respiration calorimeter in Middletown. One series was planned to show the effects of different degrees of muscular work. For this a special stationary bicycle had to be developed, with an ergometer attached (an ergometer measures work done or energy expended). The subject then could pedal away and get nowhere at different rates of speed and for different periods of time.

The question also arose whether expenditure of mental energy in thinking or brain effort made any drain upon the body over and above that of necessary muscular activity. So college students took their examinations in the calorimeter and other subjects made abstruse mathematical calculations therein. The results were negative. Little light was thrown upon the problem of mental fatigue. Years later other work indicated that the food energy in a peanut would sustain a disproportionately large amount of brain work.

Then there were experiments to determine how high- and low-energy diets affected the metabolism of different subjects. A picturesque feature here was the use of a professional faster as one subject! Subjects of these experiments were sometimes given diets supplying different quantities of protein or fats from different food materials. Other experiments were concerned with the mineral constituents of foods.

Conspicuous among the experiments made in co-operation with outside agencies were those planned for and reported by the Committee of Fifty for the Investigation of the Liquor Problem. These were designed to show how alcohol was utilized by the body. As expected, the energy of alcohol was used as completely as that of other foods, but more quickly. This proved that alcohol was a food in the sense that it could provide bodily energy. However, newspaper and other notoriety attendant upon the experiment distressed Atwater, both as a scientist and as a sincere believer in temperance temperately promoted.

About two years after Atwater's retirement in 1904 the headquarters of the famous nutrition investigations were moved to Washington, D. C. It is of incidental interest that one of Atwater's aids on his calorimeter work was the same Henry C. Sherman who became Columbia University's outstanding nutrition investigator and also chief of the Bureau of Human Nutrition and Home Economics many years later. In Washington C. F. Langworthy took charge of the work.

The calorimeter was installed in the basement of a Department building. There it was used not only with human subjects but also, in co-operation with the Bureaus of Animal and of Plant Industry, to study changes in meat during storage, the incubation of eggs, and the ripening of various fruits. When the Bureau of Home Economics was organized, the calorimeter was turned over to the Bureau of Animal Industry.

An apparatus similar to Atwater's, but larger, was constructed at the Institute of Animal Nutrition, at Pennsylvania State College and Experiment Station. It was successfully used by Director Henry P. Armsby in studying problems of animal nutrition. This is the apparatus German scientists were about to copy when World War I took away all their copper. Several other installations were built at the Nutrition Laboratory of the Carnegie Institution, some for human and some for animal subjects.

Thus a whole new line of research grew out of Atwater's pioneering work. Basic study was made of such fundamental problems as metabolism in persons of different age, sex, and physical condition, in cold-blooded animals, and in connection with many and varied types of muscular activity. These calorimeters were expensive to build and operate. After aiding in the establishment of the underlying principles governing metabolism, they gradually gave way to less complicated methods of investigation.

Modern times bring modern problems. The vitamins had already been added to the list of essential nutrients when the Bureau of Home Economics was established. But there was a great dearth of information about their occurrence in different foods and the effect of cooking, freezing, processing, and storage upon their potency. Therefore the bureau set up a laboratory to investigate such questions, using the customary laboratory animals as subjects, rats and guinea pigs.

There vitamins tests were made with hundreds of foods, both in the fresh state and after treatment by commercial and household methods. A large proportion of these tests were carried out at the request of other government agencies or of industrial food concerns. Others still formed a natural part of the regular home-economics investigations into the effects of home methods of cooking, canning, drying, and food storage on the vitamin content of the foods concerned.

A basic study was also undertaken to determine the vitamin A requirements of normal human subjects. Their visual adaptation to changes from dark to light was used as a measure of the vitamin A sufficiency of the diet. A few experiments were also carried on with human subjects to determine their utilization of vitamin A from different food sources. The work with human subjects was discontinued during the war.

One complication in vitamin A determinations is the fact that the vitamin does not occur as such in plants. Many plants, however, contain the so-called precursors of vitamin A, mainly carotenes. From these the body manufactures the true vitamin A it needs. If it makes more than it requires at any time, this can be stored in the liver or in certain other organs, occasionally even in the fatty tissues.

Carotene also may be deposited in the body tissues. Little was known about the comparative values of carotene from different foods in relation to vitamin A formation. This subject assumed enhanced importance when our supplies of fish oils and other sources of vitamin A were reduced by war. Work on this problem began at once. It was found that the body needed from 30 to 60 per cent more carotene, as found in vegetable foods, than it did of vitamin A found in animal foods.

From all these data it became possible to estimate the daily minimum vitamin A requirements of average, normal adults. The findings became a basic part of the material used by the Committee on Food and Nutrition of the National Research Council in recommending daily allowances of vitamins and other nutrients for Americans.

Other experiments gave fairly definite facts about the body's vitamin A savings bank. It was found that moderate amounts of vitamin A regularly in meals were used more economically than occasional massive doses. Hence regularly eating the daily requirement of this vitamin to keep the body's bank account in order was stressed. Analyses of the vitamin A content of 128 common foods in both raw and cooked state were published to make the information of practical value. Dr. Lela Booher, Dr. Elsa Orent-Keiles, and Mrs. Elizabeth Callison led in this work.

Vitamins caught public interest from the start, and this bureau was most skillful in making accurate popular presentations of information on the subject, often using advertising techniques in its folders. One of these, a very simple folder, "Vitamins from Farm to You," issued in August, 1942, was immensely and deservedly popular. It is an excellent nontechnical presentation of this subject. Few better examples of translating technical matter into a form easily comprehended by laymen could be cited.

Naturally the bureau took a long look into the cook pot and observed what happens there. It found that early experiments designed to show the changes taking place in the nutritive value of food during cooking were poorly planned, but they did furnish a basis for later work on household and commercial methods of food preparation. For example, while H. S. Grindley and his associates at the University of Illinois were developing scientifically accurate measurements of the chemical changes produced in meat by cooking, Isabel Bevier and Elizabeth Sprague, of the same institution, were pioneering in laboratory studies of household methods.

During the food-conservation campaign of World War I the demand grew for practical, reliable information about cooking, drying, and storing food. An experimental kitchen was established, therefore, in the Office of Home Economics, with Minna C. Denton in charge. The plan was to combine methods of scientific measurement with ordinary household procedures, and to organize service testing in such a way that it would yield practical information. At the same time there would be accumulated a systematic body of knowledge about the effects of preparation, preservation, and storage on the nutritive value, healthfulness, palatability, and economy of food used in the home.

Despite wartime pressure for special services, Dr. Denton succeeded in carrying on regular work on subjects such as canning, bread making, jelly making, and the use of fats in cookery. She succeeded in maintaining high standards of scientific accuracy in all kitchen work. Many farmers' bulletins and popular articles told about this work. It established the Department's reputation as a source of information at once scientifically valid and practically useful to the homemaker.

Studies on home canning have been carried on continuously. In early days there was much discussion about the safety of different canning methods. The bureau's own work on the bacterial count, palatability, and appearance of foods put up by different methods and stored for different lengths of time under conditions like those of ordinary home storage, proved of great practical value. This, added to compilations and evaluations of work done elsewhere, facilitated the preparation of simple publications embodying practical directions based upon sound research.

The first farmers' bulletin issued on home canning was widely adopted as a standard. Over thirteen million copies of it have been distributed. Constant insistence by the bureau's experts on safe, thoroughly tested methods largely accounts for the current high standards of home canning in this country. During World War II this bureau also participated in the food-dehydration studies of the Agricultural Research Administration, studying the palatability and nutritive value of the rehydrated foods.

The study on meat cookery perhaps leads as an example of long-continued, carefully planned research. This investigation was carried on by the Department in co-operation with the experiment stations and the meat industry in order to discover how the table quality of meat is affected by the breed, age, and feed of animals. The work involved the examination of thousands of cuts of meat and nearly a thousand turkeys and chickens.

The methods used stemmed from those practiced in Illinois around the turn of the century. Grindley and his associates had measured the internal heat of the meats by means of specially constructed thermometers. Similar thermometers had been made for later work. The co-operative meat project adapted various other Illinois methods for determining changes.

Accurate records were kept of the cut, general character, weight of each piece, the temperature and length of cooking, and losses in weight. Palatability was tested by a carefully selected group of tasters, who judged and considered each cooked product for aroma, texture, flavor or fat, flavor of lean, tenderness, and quality and quantity of juice. This was really getting at the factors which make a roast of beef superior.

The results of this work not only improved the standards of the home cooking of meat but also had considerable industrial and commercial value. They showed, for instance, that holding the juices in the meat is a matter of temperature control, one of cooking at moderate heat, rather than searing from the outside as had long been supposed. Recipes in standard cookbooks, women's magazines, newspapers, and even in advertisements have been so changed since the results of this study were announced that one writer called it a "revolution in cookery."

The Department's home-economics staff is constantly called upon to study the possible home use of a great variety of new products, too. Study of the baking qualities of the soft-wheat flours which came to market from new wheat-growing areas after World War I is merely one example. Another is concerned with the use of soybeans as human food, for this protein- and fat-rich vegetable can be an important substitute for meat, eggs, and animal protein and fat generally.

Despite romantic notions about how much better cooking was in grandmother's time than now, you will find articles in early reports of the Department which attribute widespread indigestion to the fact that the women and girls of the mid-nineteenth century simply were not taught how to cook properly! Present standards of food preparation in the average American home, which owe much to advances in experimental cookery made by Department scientists, are much higher than they were a generation ago.

The Department of Agriculture owes much of its prestige in the field of interpreting scientific knowledge on foods and nutrition into terms of the ordinary daily diet to the distinguished and original work of Caroline L. Hunt. Unconventional, friendly, always on the search for new ideas, she was a striking and familiar figure around the Department from 1909 until her death in 1927.

While living at Hull House, Miss Hunt was asked to conduct dietary studies of low-income groups in that part of Chicago for the Department's nutrition investigations. In the course of this work she became so convinced of the social value of applying scientific knowledge to everyday life, that she threw herself wholeheartedly into the home-economics movement. Her unusual talent for clear, simple, accurate, and readable writing on science applied to home problems led to her employment in the Department.

She first popularized the idea of discussing the well-balanced diet in terms of five food groups. Her *Farmers' Bulletin*, "A Week's Food for an Average Family," issued in 1921, is typical. Therein she made many calculations of dietary values after long-continued testing, preparation, and planning of inexpensive, palatable meals which illustrated the principles she advocated. By her consultations with nutrition experts, extension workers, and homemakers in all parts of the country she tremendously aided the popularization of dietary facts.

Dr. D. Breese Jones and his associates have carried on protein research in the Department for more than thirty years. They have developed a reservoir of exact information about these complex organic chemical compounds which are so important and indispensable to us as food. These facts provide a means of evaluating the proteins in foods and feeds and, in many cases, the analyses have been supplemented by actual feeding experiments.

Among the hundred or more proteins isolated and studied in this work are those of peanuts, soybeans, corn, wheat, and ten or more varieties of beans. Dr. Jones isolated and determined the nutritive value of proteins of wheat bran for the first time. The first exact information on peanut proteins also came from his laboratory. In this connection it is of interest to note that two other Department scientists, Drs. J. Davidson and J. A. LeClerc, showed conclusively that the protein content of wheat could be increased as much as one-half by applying inorganic nitrogenous fertilizer at the heading stage of the growing wheat plants.

The proteins are made up of a group of simpler compounds called "amino acids." There are a score or more of these, which combine in various ways to form the multiplicity of proteins known. Our bodies can manufacture some of these amino acids; others, the dietary-essential amino acids, they cannot produce. Hence proteins which lack important essential amino acids are regarded as incomplete or deficient. Jones and his coworkers broke the proteins down into their constituent amino acids and then ascertained which are really complete.

They also showed that proteins from one source may supplement those from another so well that the resulting combination is better than either of the components. Thus, if soybean, peanut, or cottonseed flours are used in conjunction with wheat flour, the resulting bread is more nutritious than bread made from any of these materials used alone. Again, very little meat, milk, or egg protein will supplement deficient vegetable proteins and make a highly nutritious combination.

Thus, while the work of this protein laboratory sounds remotely theoretical, it actually has valuable results in practice. It aids us in making wise dietary substitutions, and it also points out for us the proteins that are nutritionally complete. The work is complex to the last degree and is another line of pure research which requires much time and much skill but does fructify in knowledge that has very definite practical use.

However, the bureau we are discussing does not devote itself entirely to studies in nutrition. Many years ago, even while it was an Office of Home Economics, tests were being made of household equipment of various types. Much later on, after the office became a bureau, work on textiles and clothing was undertaken. There was need for efficient utilization of cotton, wool, and other agricultural products for clothing and home furnishings.

Therefore, in 1924 Ruth O'Brien was appointed to organize the textile and clothing work and, at this writing, is still in charge. She has proved tremendously capable in a novel field of investigation and study. As she saw the work originally, it should cover the relative merits of different kinds and grades of fiber when made into fabrics; the effects of use and methods of care on fabric deterioration; the development of suitable designs for different garments and materials; and the systematic study of construction and repair.

Here again was a field wherein one might suppose commercial agencies had performed all the necessary research. Actually they had done nothing of the kind and so simple a matter—at least basic if not simple—as the sizing of women's and children's clothing was in complete chaos. It was therefore an ideal field for investigation financed by public funds, for the findings could be used to conserve materials and render valuable public service.

The textile work, which began in two small rooms of an office building, now occupies expansive and fully equipped quarters at the Beltsville Agricultural Research Center. Few large industrial organizations have better facilities than those at the center.

Cotton is our cheapest and most abundant fiber; consequently, some of the earliest research dealt with determining the characteristics of widely used cotton fabrics and the effects upon them of laundering and wear. For the first time varieties of cotton were followed through from the field where they grew to the wearing quality of the products into which they were woven.

The work on turkish toweling, sheeting, and cotton broadcloth ultimately led to specifications for their construction. These were drawn up by the bureau and were adopted by the American Society for Testing Materials and other recognized standardizing agencies. Similar work on blankets, corduroy, upholstering materials, and other fabrics soon began helping ordinary consumers to judge the quality of the goods they bought.

Reprocessed wool and rayon were combined with new wool in fabrics used for making suitings which also went under test. Studies of the construction used in ready-made garments became the basis for consumer-buying guides for boys' suits, women's coats, and women's dresses. Various government agencies began to use bureau findings in attempts to prevent the hidden degrading of goods during war.

One frequent cause of fabric deterioration is mildew; therefore, a new process was developed to render fabrics mildew-resistant. This was released under a public service patent granted to Helen

Robinson of the bureau staff. Another patent was granted three other workers for their method of sterilizing wool and other animal fibers without damaging them. Microbiologists of the Bureau of Plant Industry co-operated in this work.

When the nation found itself with a huge cotton surplus, Congress assigned the bureau the task of studying means to stimulate its use by glamorizing cotton hosiery for women. David H. Young, a well-known, widely experienced textile designer, was called in. A small experimental knitting mill was installed to help develop cotton stockings which might hope to compete with silk in style, sheerness, and other qualities women prefer.

By the time silk imports were cut off in late 1941 a hundred and fifty designs were ready for release to the trade. They are widely used by the industry. Experiments continue with chemical treatments and knitting designs that will still further improve the end product. The work on elasticity led to other promising experiments in the development of cotton fabrics as a substitute for yarns with rubber cores.

A striking project involved the use of anthropometry in determining the best means of providing reliable standards for sizes in women's and children's clothing. This is actually not half so bad as it sounds. The state of sizing in these branches of the clothing industry was chaotic. No one knew what "size 36" or "age 4" meant in terms of garments put out by different manufacturers, and what relation they might have to actual human forms was still more mysterious.

Consumers were bewildered, and retailers claimed that they lost $10,000,000 a year on the return of off-size children's clothing alone. So WPA help was enlisted in actually measuring 150,000 school children and 15,000 women the country over. Actual authentic data were secured on the human form divine as it occurs among the female of the species. All of the results were not highly complimentary, but they were very useful.

That is where the anthropometry came in, the science of measuring the human body. Experts in this science and representatives of the trade met in consultation on the measurements made. The data were analyzed by methods dear to every statistician's heart. Finally the combination of measurements that would prove most reliable in fixing sizes was revealed, and garments could be constructed to conform to each size as it existed in nature, not as it existed in the figments of some clothing maker's imagination.

It was found, for instance, that age was a poor guide for sizes in children's clothing, as anyone might have suspected who noted the difference between six-year-old Mary and six-year-old Ruth. The use of sizes based on a combination of height and hip measure was recommended. Leading manufacturers almost tumbled over one another to put these sizes and patterns into use. The bureau has had many a pat on the back from the best commercial sources for its work in this field.

The American Standards Association next established an American standard of body sizes for boys' garments, based on this study. Manufacturers of women's garments gave serious heed to the recommendation that they base their sizes on a combination of height and weight instead of on bust measure. Next the much more difficult problem of shoe sizes came up for study. The first step here was to devise a practicable instrument for three-dimensional measurements of the human foot. Obviously industry had left many primary points for investigation by government agencies.

Clarice L. Scott made a definite pioneer attempt to use function as a basis of design in women's clothes. Her idea was that clothes should be designed to facilitate whatever the person intended to do while wearing them. This scarcely seems startling, but no one apparently had taken time to think of the problem seriously. When defense and war needs arose, Miss Scott was ready to develop clothes for occasions when women would be engaged in farm, factory, or mechanical work.

She began by studying the bodily movements and the special protection required by each job. Then she designed coveralls, slacks, coats, and such other garments as would best suit the purpose. Again the designs were promptly adopted by manufacturers of ready-made garments who had waited only for Department of Agriculture experts to put science into their business.

The same functional approach was applied to children's garments. The principle of close adaptation to the child's actual needs was followed. The self-help features of the new garments, intended to develop the youngster's self-reliance, were an innovation. So also was the use of open-mesh material in the top of sun suits, so that the sun's rays could reach the skin directly.

A far more technical piece of research that was fundamental in a hitherto neglected field was the project on the proper types of sizing fabrics and their best use in both finishing and refinishing. Methods had to be developed also to prevent wrinkling and broaden the use of cotton. Therefore, the mathematical and physical relationship was worked out between the properties of starch pastes and the stiffness of fabrics produced by their use. Exact scientific determinations were also made for the first time of the correlation between the feel of fabrics and various measurable physical factors.

This pioneering and difficult work provided a scientific background for many popular publications. It promoted increased utilization of cotton. The end results, however remote they seemed at the start, proved of value both to commerce and to the public.

There has developed here a valuable scientific agency in which some scientists pull proteins apart to see what is inside while others prove that overcooking soya grits and flour deteriorates both the protein and the vitamin B content, and devise better recipes. Meanwhile, still others study methods of home food preservation, while 3,500,000 copies of the bureau's home-canning instructions are distributed in a single year.

Certain farsighted scientists on the staff look ahead into the home freezing of foods, and study the effects upon palatability and nutritive properties of this and of other methods of processing and packaging foods. The storage and ultimate food value of dehydrated beef, pork, eggs, soup mixes, and vegetables all come under careful consideration. Other workers scientifically investigate household appliances of all sorts, getting results of immediate value to both manufacturers and consumers.

Special wartime recipes were worked out to match current food supplies. Trends in the national diet are under continuous study. The effects of increased incomes on food-buying and eating habits is carefully recorded. The bureau also analyzes comparative farm and city family expenditures for medical care to give guidance to agencies making postwar plans for rural health improvement.

Finally there is the project on fabrics and clothing, involving the control of microbes which ruin clothing, sterilization and mildew-proofing of fabrics, rendering articles made of cloth relatively insect proof, and co-operative fur studies with other government agencies. Last but not least is the important ability to state highly technical findings in a form so popular that those who wish to scoff accuse the bureau of merely telling people what they already know!

The simplicity and directness of the language and the diagrams used prove deceptive, for great art and skill are displayed in this important field of wide popularization. That is why the total distribution of the bureau's popularized technical findings on textiles and clothing has amounted to eight or nine million bulletins, leaflets, and charts.

The bureau's economic studies interlock closely with the results of its laboratory research. Stiebeling was and is a genius at making laboratory results widely useful by developing their economic implications to the full. So they come to round out the contribution this small institution makes to the more efficient utilization of household goods and the improvement of living standards in American homes.[2]

[2] The interested reader will find more detail on this subject in the *Bureau of Home Economics*, Service Monograph of the U. S. Government No. 62, Brookings Institution, 1930.

CHAPTER 13

Science at the Milk Pail

Dairying and dairy products were not infrequently discussed in the annual books issued by the agricultural division of the Patent Office as well as in the reports of early commissioners of agriculture. But it was some time before work in this field formally began, and science drew its stool to the milk pail. This took place only after the head of the Department of Agriculture attained Cabinet rank.

In the Secretary's annual report dated October 26, 1889, the considerable growth of the dairy industry in the United States was noted, and it was announced that a proposal had been made to establish a dairy division in the Bureau of Animal Industry. It seemed necessary then to extend the markets for butter and cheese. The report for 1890 observed that it had so far proved impossible to organize such a division and to procure its necessary equipment.

In his own report to the Secretary dated June 30, 1894, Chief Salmon of the Bureau of Animal Industry declared that the dairy industry required immediate attention. However, Dr. Salmon thought that an expert at $2,500 a year, with two clerks, could do all that was required. Thus the Dairy Division was finally established in the Bureau of Animal Industry on July 1, 1895, staffed with a chief, an assistant, and two clerks. Its function was to collect and disseminate information on the existing dairy industry of the United States.

The first chief of this division was Henry Elijah Alvord. Incidentally Alvord had had the distinction of having been appointed general manager of Houghton Farm in 1881. This was the only attempt in the United States to establish an agricultural experiment station through the munificence of one man. The man was Lawson

Valentine, a philanthropic and public-spirited New York business-man of considerable wealth. The farm was in Orange County, New York, and carried on work similar to that of state stations at a cost of something like $20,000 a year to its proprietor.

Among other things extensive provisions were made for the breeding of dairy cattle and for work in dairy products, though no publications were issued on these subjects. The enterprise terminated with the death of Mr. Valentine in 1888, and Alvord returned to the Massachusetts Agricultural College as professor of agriculture. Later he became president of the Maryland Agricultural College and director of that state's experiment station.

His new division began, directly and co-operatively, to investigate the methods of preparation, chemical composition, and keeping qualities of creamery butter, as well as special methods of preparing and packaging butter for shipment to the tropics. It also studied and recommended methods of curing cheese at low temperatures, and it issued a special report on the handling of city milk supplies.

The passage by Congress on May 9, 1902, of an act to regulate so-called renovated butter charged the Secretary of Agriculture with important new duties. These concerned the manufacture of, interstate commerce in, and export of renovated butter. Details were assigned to the Dairy Division, giving it impetus for growth and incentive to undertake research.

A year later employees of the division were busy inspecting the plants where some 55,000,000 pounds of renovated butter were made annually. These were licensed establishments, but operation of the new law had not been found detrimental to the creamery-butter market as had been anticipated by many. The division at this time, as earlier, was procuring butter for the United States Navy. A year later the lines of research it intended to pursue were well outlined.

They concerned the dairy industry in semiarid and "short-grass" regions, the quality of cold-storage butter, the storage of cheese at different temperatures, and certain chemical investigations which had to be carried on in the laboratories of the Bureau of Chemistry, just as the division's bacteriological studies were made in the Biochemic Division of the Bureau of Animal Industry.

A year later these subjects were under investigation: the manufacture and storage of butter and cheese; dairying in the South; the manufacture of European varieties of cheese; the handling of city milk supplies; ice cream; skim-milk cheese; creamery and cheese-factory management; methods of carrying on market inspection of dairy products; and animal husbandry as related to dairy animals. In 1924 the division became the Bureau of Dairying by act of Congress, in response to pressure from the dairy industry. The name was changed to Bureau of Dairy Industry in 1926.

An early piece of work in this field that was not carried on in the Dairy Division should be mentioned here because of its importance and relevance. In 1902 studies began in the Division of Animal Pathology, under the direction of Theobald Smith, to determine the frequency with which virulent tubercle bacilli occurred in dairy products, for use of the tuberculin test in the nineties had shown tuberculosis to be much more common among dairy cows than had previously been supposed.

The studies revealed that virulent tubercle bacilli were common in all grades of market milk. Further investigation proved that cream, ice cream, butter, and cheese invariably contained tubercle bacilli when made from infected milk. The bacilli remained virulent in milk longer than the time required for this product to become unfit for human food by decomposition.

It was also found that the tubercle bacilli in butter, salted or unsalted, remained alive for months, and that they were a source of danger in fresh cheese, although rarely occurring in cured cheese. As a result of this investigation it was officially recommended that, to protect the public health, all milk be obtained from dairy herds that had been proved free from tuberculosis by the tuberculin test, or that the milk be pasteurized before it was used as food in any form.

A little earlier the fact was mentioned that the Dairy Division procured butter for the navy. Thereby hangs a tale. Early in this century Lore A. Rogers, who became one of the nation's foremost bacteriologists, began to study methods of butter making. This work was done in the old Dairy Division. At that time butter was made from ripened cream, the high acidity of the cream supposedly contributing to the keeping quality of the butter. Yet about three-quarters of the butter then stored acquired an objectionable fishy flavor and odor which reduced its sale price several cents a pound.

It was generally assumed that these flavors were caused by bacterial activity in the butter during storage. Dr. Rogers showed, however, that they were due to an oxidative process which was accelerated by the acidity of the cream used to make the butter. Hence it was unwise to use highly acid cream for butter making. Rogers first controlled deterioration in stored butter by reducing the acidity of the cream used in making it. Next he found that if butter were made from pasteurized, nonacid cream, it had exceptional keeping quality.

Initially Rogers' work was much ridiculed, especially in the trade journals. Cartoons appeared with the caption: "Not so fast, Mr. Rogers." However, the navy permitted Rogers to demonstrate his method by preparing large quantities of butter for its use. His demonstration proved a complete success and resulted in widespread adoption of his method. Ultimately Rogers' work revolutionized butter-making practice throughout the world.

It is conservatively estimated that the improved methods of butter making which resulted from this piece of research profit the American butter industry alone $5,000,000 a year. Some years it runs as high as $20,000,000—it all depends upon the price of butter and how extensively Rogers' method is used. Since the project cost about $20,000, that is a reasonably good profit. The fact that the navy wanted butter of superior keeping quality gave Rogers his chance.

There was an unearned increment here, too, for this work gave valuable information about the oxidative deterioration of fats generally which proved of great value in later investigations. It led to the protection of some food fats in such a way as to prevent light rays from starting oxidative processes in them. It led also to work on the keeping quality of whole-milk powder in wartime and resulted in the production and packaging of dehydrated whole milk of excellent keeping quality.

Rogers himself performed much more research of value, too. In 1939 he published a paper on the preparation of bacterial cultures by the freezing-high-vacuum method. It was so thoroughly forgotten that some one else later got a patent on the method, which is widely used today for the preservation of cultures and other biological materials. We shall hear much more of Rogers.

Rogers also worked with S. Henry Ayres and his associates on the bacteriology of milk pasteurization. This pioneering and fundamental research forms the basis for all sanitary and health regulations which govern the pasteurization and handling of milk in cities and towns in the United States today. The publications in which this work was reported have been widely used, for in them there was presented for the first time an exposition of the scientific principles underlying the pasteurization of milk.

Milk pasteurization was actually first recommended by a noted American health authority in 1875, only a decade after Louis Pasteur had found that heating would prevent the souring and abnormal fermentation of wine and beer. At first milk was heated secretly for the sole purpose of preserving it and preventing dealer losses. The method was regarded as unethical. But, as milk bacteriology and chemistry advanced, objections to this practice were overcome.

Before Ayres' work was undertaken, not only laymen but also physicians were extremely skeptical about the pasteurization of milk. The theory was held that this process menaced human health by destroying the lactic-acid-forming organisms in the milk and thus promoting the multiplication of putrefactive organisms which the former held in check. On studying the organisms which survived milk pasteurization Ayres found this not to be the case at all.

Instead, pasteurization merely tended to reproduce the condition of clean, freshly drawn milk. Nor was there any difference in the rate at which germs grew in fresh raw and in pasteurized milk, previous views to the contrary notwithstanding. The results of this work definitely removed the objections of physicians to milk pasteurization. The investigation was the most important single factor leading to the development of modern milk-sanitation regulations.

Ayres' work in turn had an unearned increment. It produced valuable information concerning the bacteria in milk and their varied forms. This proved most helpful in many later investigations. One of these was carried on by William Mansfield Clark, pioneer in hydrogen-ion research. His work revolutionized large sectors of medical and biological research. It had innumerable far-reaching industrial applications. Its value was stupendous even in strict monetary terms, though nothing was more remote than money profit when Clark undertook the work.

Clark came to the Dairy Division in 1910. He was first asked to investigate the chemistry of Swiss cheese. A little later his dissatisfaction with certain modified milk fed his infant daughter led to his first paper on the reaction of cow's milk as modified for infant feeding. That in turn led him to read S.P.L. Sørensen's classic paper on the hydrogen-electrode method of measuring hydrogen-ion concentration, a highly theoretical subject well in the preserve of pure research if ever there was one.

Meanwhile Rogers had asked Clark to look into the matter of gas production by a certain group of bacteria. This resulted in methods of differentiating such organisms, thus laying the foundation for classifying a group of bacteria of great sanitary significance. It then became possible for the first time to distinguish the fecal members of this group from closely related species which do not inhabit the intestines.

While at work on these various problems Clark time after time met questions about the meaning of acid and alkaline reactions. There were methods of roughly determining acidity and alkalinity, but he found them much too lacking in precision for his purposes. Sørensen's paper started him off on a new line of thought. In January, 1915, his paper discussing the reaction of cow's milk appeared. His basic interest now was the effect of acid on the growth of bacteria.

Existing methods of measuring acidity, however, measured merely the quantity, not the intensity, of the acid present, and every layman knows that the acid of sulfuric is quite a different thing from the acid of citric. Some acids seem "stronger" than others to all of us, but there was no way of measuring their strength. Physical chemists also knew that certain acids fell to pieces in solution, "dissociated" as they called it. The constituent components of these acids held themselves apart as units. These could be measured by determining the concentration of hydrogen ions in the solution.

That value, if it could be determined readily and accurately, would have far greater significance than the value determined by the ordinary methods of titration. Clark pointed out that it was the intensity of the acidity of a solution, the concentration of hydrogen ions in it, rather than its mere quantitative acidity which checked bacterial growth of any kind. Thus a few tenths of 1 per cent of hydrochloric acid, which dissociates strongly, would have the same effect on bacteria as a 20 per cent solution of a weaker acid such as citric.

Clark next proceeded to develop accurate methods for measuring the intensity of acidity in terms of hydrogen-ion concentration. He published a book on the subject which became standard text throughout the world. He founded a new science with almost incredible ramifications.

Clark also synthesized a graduated series of indicators, chemical substances which change color when they go from acid to alkali, or the reverse. By use of these, accurate hydrogen-ion determinations could be made rapidly. All this seems rather impractical and abstract. But today the laundry industry controls the reaction of its wash waters and rinse waters by means of the indicators Clark developed in the Department of Agriculture. Clark's findings are used in all of these industrial and other processes—and more: water purification; work on the erosion of metals; paper manufacture; the digestion of sewage for disposal; the disposal of industrial wastes; the manufacture and refining of beet and cane sugars; the manufacture of dyes and pigments; the manufacture of corn sugar, glucose, and candy; textile processing; clay casting; leather tanning; differential ore flotation; electroplating and electrotyping; chemical analyses, wherever carried out; the fermentation industries; the making of fruit jellies, and of flour, dough, bread, and crackers; the manufacture of milk products and the control of milk bacteria; canning foods; analyzing soils; the manufacture of pharmaceutical preparations; clinical pathology.

Clark's important paper which signaled the abandonment of the old titration method of adjusting reactions and the introduction of the new hydrogen-ion method appeared in the *Journal of Infectious Diseases* during 1915. His well-known book, *The Determination of Hydrogen Ions*, first appeared in 1920, the year he left the Department and went to the Hygienic Laboratory, which he left to head the department of physiological chemistry at Johns Hopkins University. In 1920 Clark began to publish papers on reduction potentials. This work led him to study the oxidation-reduction systems of the human body and proved to be of great importance.

A great deal more research of value has been carried on by Department dairy scientists, though most of the projects have been less spectacular than those of early days for obvious reasons. As science grows more complex and problems more difficult, it is less and less easy for an individual to make a big strike. The day of great basic discoveries also tended to pass merely because their effect was cumulative in broadening and filling out the field of scientific information.

Yet work like that on the physiology of milk secretion, carried on by Walter W. Swett and associates in dairy science ever since 1926, is very valuable. It has been shown experimentally that milk secretion is continuous and not, as the textbooks said, confined to the brief period during milking. This was ascertained by milking udders after they had been dissected from cows at slaughter and comparing the quantity of milk so obtained with that obtained at corresponding milkings of the same udders before death of the animal.

This investigation as a whole has completely revised many erroneous ideas about milk secretion and has provided a basis for much work since conducted on the physiology of lactation. Incidentally, among the hundreds of udders studied no case of cancerous growth was ever found, making it appear as if the cow's milk-secreting organ is immune to cancer. Such incidental and by-product leads are often of great value themselves.

The work that H. S. Palmer began in 1914 on carotene and other milk pigments and his many contributions to dairy science during the next quarter of a century brought him the Borden Award in 1939. William Mansfield Clark and others of the bureau's scientists have been recipients of this award.

Some of us may remember how milk and butter tended to get quite pugilistic some years ago, every time spring rolled around. Millions of gallons of milk are still rejected every year in the fluid-milk market because of undesirable odors and flavors derived from feed. Acceptance of such milk would affect milk consumption detrimentally, as the quantity of milk consumed depends upon its palatability.

J. A. Gamble and Ernest Kelley found that the flavors and odors from feeds and weeds eaten by cows pass rapidly through their bodies to their udders but are not, as was formerly supposed, absorbed by milk directly from the air. Further work by C. J. Babcock demonstrated that some of these feeds and weeds continue to impart a characteristic flavor to milk for much longer periods than others. As you may have guessed, garlic was among the most potent of these.

Garlic will flavor milk one minute after the cow has eaten the plant. This flavor takes at least seven hours to disappear, though other feeds impart their flavor to the milk for only an hour or two. Practical feeding instructions have been evolved which enable dairymen to utilize certain nutritious but highly flavored feeds—like silage, turnips, cabbage, kale, and sugar beets—without producing abnormally flavored milk. This seems a little thing, but it is a big help.

If such feeds are given the cows immediately after milking, their flavor passes off before the next milking. But strong garlic flavor can be found in the milk two minutes after the cow has merely inhaled the odor of the plant for ten minutes. The only practical way to prevent garlic flavor and odor in milk is to prevent the cows from eating the plant. If all dairymen observe the other feeding recommendations, however, this will add many millions a year to their aggregate income.

Turning from milk to cream, we find studies published in 1931 which tell how cream viscosity can be controlled. That is important because consumers tend to judge the quality of cream in the main by its viscosity or body, a quality they associate with richness. Though butterfat content and temperature are two important factors affecting viscosity, C. J. Babcock found that creams of the same fat content might vary in viscosity at the same temperature.

The butterfat in fresh cream occurs in individual globules. Any factor which affects the clumping of these globules also affects the viscosity of the cream. Aging cream will increase both clumping and viscosity, while pasteurizing it will lower both. Viscosity is also affected by methods of handling and storing cream.

It was of value to know that the best way to increase the viscosity was to store the milk at a low temperature for twelve hours before separating it, then lower the temperature still further at which separation occurs. Homogenization increases viscosity, freezing lowers it, and viscosity increases as the percentage of solids-not-fat increases. All this information proved of value in the important matter of viscosity control.

The bureau's research on ice cream has led to great improvement in the quality of ice cream during the last decade. A favorite diversion of Department employees used to be acting as official tasters for batches of ice cream made in different ways. In the beginning, commercial ice cream contained a low percentage of the valuable milk solids, and it was rarely made from pasteurized milk and cream.

Bureau workers found that most persons prefer ice cream that is rich in butterfat, sugar, and milk-solids-not-fat. However, when the manufacturers attempted to increase the milk-solids content of their product, it tended to become gritty or sandy in texture. Bureau scientists found that this condition was due to excessive milk sugar, which crystallized out when the ice cream was subjected to varying temperatures in the hardening rooms or in dealers' cabinets.

During the 1933–36 period Alan Leighton, Byron H. Webb, and Owen E. Williams, showed that the viscosity of skim milk could be reduced by adding cane sugar. Then, on concentration, the milk sugar could be crystallized out and removed. Commercial methods were then developed for thus removing much of the milk sugar from skim milk.

The process left as a by-product a condensed skim milk, low in milk-sugar content, which was admirable for increasing the milk solids of ice cream without producing sandiness. Raising the average milk-solids-not-fat content of ice cream by 1 per cent by use of this material would not only improve ice cream but would provide an additional market for more than one and one-half billion pounds of skim milk annually, and that highly nutritious by-product is too much neglected in this country.

Another milk product is cheese. C. F. Doane and E. E. Eldridge of the bureau did important work on the use of pure lactobacilli cultures in making Swiss cheese. This initiated work on the bacteriology of Swiss cheese, and that resulted in the use by domestic makers of three bacterial cultures, with control of the process that greatly improved the domestic product.

The manufacture of most milk products depends on control of bacterial growth, and basic work in that direction was done in this bureau, as we have seen. To exercise this control, one must know the conditions governing the growth, activities, and death rate of numerous bacteria. In this instance the fact was established that the quality of Swiss cheese depended largely on the growth, at the proper rate and in the proper sequence, of at least three species of bacteria.

To assist domestic Swiss-cheese makers in producing a high-grade product, the Bureau of Dairy Industry began to supply them with cultures of these bacteria to use as starters. About fifty million pounds of such cheese is normally made in the United States each year, an increasing percentage of which is produced by culture methods. As the cultured cheese usually sells for more than the noncultured, this research has a potential value of a million dollars a year to the dairy industry—a conservative estimate based on a price differential of only two cents a pound.

In 1921 K. J. Matheson published a paper on the manufacture of Roquefort-type cheese from cow's milk. This was the result of a long investigation begun in co-operation with the Storrs Agricultural Experiment Station in Connecticut. The work established the biological activities involved in the ripening of blue-mold cheese, the techniques of making such cheese from cow's milk, and the conditions essential to proper ripening.

All the blue-mold cheese now made in this country stems from the Matheson process. Of course, workers at Iowa State College at Ames carried the process further by showing how it could be applied to homogenized milk. They also began to grow blue mold on sterilized stale bread and to sell $8,000 worth of it a year at $2.00 a pound—a business the cheese makers refuse to let them drop. Others helped put the cheese in mass production, but Matheson of this bureau started it all.

In 1932 there appeared a paper by Dr. Rogers on the ripening of cheese in sealed packages. This was announced as the first successful method for providing a satisfactory retail package for natural cheese. The cheese was canned in a tin containing a special valve designed by Rogers, who is quite a mechanic—for instance, he spent years making a complete replica of the first home he and his wife occupied, complete in every detail, furnishings and all—just as a hobby.

Before the war the Rogers process was used successfully in packaging both Cheddar and Swiss cheese, some of it already sliced to sandwich size. The process expands the market for cheese by enabling consumers to purchase a well-ripened, palatable product of uniform quality, as desired. The trade likes it because brand names can thus appear on small units.

In 1936 the scientists of this bureau announced a new process for manufacturing Bel Paese—type cheese, a very soft, white variety of European origin. The copyright name was held by an Italian manufacturer who originated the product, but the type can now be made in this country by following the directions issued. The product is of uniformly high quality.

In 1943 the bureau announced its new method of dehydrating American Cheddar cheese. Development of this method made it possible to release much needed spray-drying equipment for the production of other wartime foods. George F. Sanders found that cheese of normal fat content could be dehydrated without loss of fat by first grating and then partly drying it by one method and completing the drying by another. The equipment was simple, inexpensive, and easier to operate than that used commercially.

A number of commercial companies immediately manifested interest in the process. One used it in preparing more than a million pounds of dehydrated cheese for incorporation into six times that much compressed cheese-soya soup stock for overseas shipment in 1944. The cost of cheese dehydration can be very materially reduced by use of this method, though the research itself cost less than $3,500. The end product contains all the cheese fat and other solids but weighs only two-thirds as much as the original cheese. It can also be compressed to two-thirds of the original volume.

Mention was made earlier of the fact that some of Rogers's

original work pointed the way to solve some spoilage problems. George E. Holm of the bureau and his associates have long studied the question. Much of their research seemed highly theoretical. But when war came, and with it quick need for whole-milk powder of good keeping quality to ship abroad, we were ready because this work had been done. Holm's investigations of milk proteins and the minor constituents of milk is also outstanding. He succeeded Dr. Rogers, who was long in charge of the dairy research laboratories.

Holm and George R. Greenbank gave close study to the oxidation of fats and the relationship between such oxidation and changes in flavor of butter and whole-milk powder. This resulted in many practical applications to a wide variety of fats and oils. In April, 1942, Holm received the Borden Award for his part in this work. He discovered that fats do not spoil unless a certain amount of oxygen is present to combine with them. By controlling the presence of this gas, he controlled spoilage.

In the field of medicine there should be mentioned the papers by Alice C. Evans on the bacteria of the normal udder, which began to appear in 1918. Miss Evans ultimately established a close resemblance between the organism causing contagious abortion in cows and the one causing Malta or undulant fever in human beings. This finding had great significance and gave Miss Evans a world-wide reputation. It forged an important connecting link between a disease of cattle and goats and one from which human beings suffer.

Then there was the test for prompt detection of mastititis streptococci, announced by R. P. Hotis in 1936. It was called the "Hotis test" after him. It offered a ready means of diagnosing a troublesome and costly disease, the quick detection of which is always urgent. Unfortunately Hotis died just after completing this work.

In 1931 there began to appear a series of papers by Harold E. Curran giving the results of investigations on the effects of heat, ultraviolet light, and other physical agents on spores. This research was productive of new data on factors which determine the viability of bacterial spores and the means by which their resistance may be overcome.

Studies of milk by-products have also been made in this bureau for a number of years. Some of the most distinguished were on casein. As early as 1919 Clark and his associates began to show how casein could be precipitated in small, firm granules from which the ash constituents could readily be washed. This involved application of Clark's work on the hydrogen ions. Application of these principles to the commercial manufacture of casein has made possible large-scale preparation of a very pure product.

Scientists of this bureau have also developed a method of grading casein according to its paper-coating quality, and further improved manufacturing processes. This has resulted in far greater domestic production and less reliance on imports.

E. O. Whittier and S. P. Gould have produced from casein a synthetic fiber having the appearance of wool. The process resembled but did not duplicate the previously announced Italian process; it was similar to that for making viscose rayon from cellulose and several public-service patents were obtained on it. The product was almost identical with wool chemically, except for a lower sulfur content.

Fortunately the fiber could be made from skim milk, four thousand pounds of which were required to produce one hundred pounds of the fiber. Development of this process made it unnecessary for American manufacturers to pay royalties on a foreign process, and in 1940 more than four million pounds of casein fiber superior to any of foreign origin were produced domestically.

Production has now risen to about 10,000,000 pounds annually. This uses up nearly 350,000,000 pounds of skim milk, hence increasing the farm market value of that product for which we long had insufficient outlets. Incidentally, while this research cost about $20,000, the initial payment for the use of the foreign patents would have been $1,000,000 and royalties of $500,000 a year would have had to be paid for an annual production of ten million pounds of fiber.

In 1928 there began to appear the first of a series of papers by Whittier and Rogers on lactic fermentation. An exceptionally efficient method of converting milk sugar, derived from cheese or casein whey, into lactic acid developed. As a direct result a large-scale commercial lactic-acid enterprise was established in this country. It is especially valuable when supplies of cane and corn sugar for fermentation have to be restricted. The work grew out of pure research on the fundamental factors which limit the growth of organisms that produce lactic acid from sugars.

More than ten billion pounds of whey is produced annually as a by-product in cheese manufacture and about one billion pounds more in the manufacture of casein from skim milk, mentioned above. Less than one-fifth of this annual production is used industrially, the remainder being fed to farm animals or wasted. Hence the process is ideal for using an only partially utilized by-product. It cost about $15,000 to develop and is worth nearly $500,000 a year in salvaging otherwise wasted lactose.

Another and somewhat minor method of utilizing cheese whey was also worked out in the bureau. It can be used to increase the food value of canned vegetable soups and of fruit-flavored whips. This affords housewives a convenient method of adding milk constituents to the diet while at the same time providing a new outlet for a dairy by-product.

Whey contains about half the food solids of milk and has excellent nutritive properties. Whey, whey powder, or whey cream can be used in place of whole milk to enrich many kinds of soups, and less difficulty is encountered with coagulation when whey is used.

Other acids than lactic can be prepared as dairy by-products, among them citric. In 1917 appeared J. N. Currie's paper on the use of a mold to produce citric acid, which led to the first commercial fermentation process based on the use of a mold. This was an outgrowth of work on molds and bacteria in the bureau, the process finally being used in the main to convert cane sugar into citric acid. The acid was formerly produced in Italy and Greece from lemons and limes and then imported here. Today we make our own citric acid domestically.

Then there was the work of James M. Sherman, R. H. Shaw, and E. O. Whittier, which began to appear in 1922, on a fermentation process to produce propionic acid commercially by the aid of bacteria. The process was covered by issuance of public-service patents. Salts of propionic acid are used in the main as preservatives against molds. These two processes may be regarded as unearned increments from basic research on dairy products and by-products.

An odd development was that in 1942 of a lacquer made from milk by Paul D. Watson. It proved to be an excellent substitute for the tin coating used on cans made to hold evaporated and condensed milk, also to ship fluid milk and cream. The lacquer was made in the main from lactic acid derived from milk, and a public-service patent was granted. Thus the cow was induced to provide her own substitute for a critical material. A number of commercial concerns undertook further development and application of this process. The material is also valuable for impregnating, gluing, and molding various articles.

During Secretary Wilson's administration the Dairy Division was carrying on important and useful work by promoting cow-testing associations and introducing the score-card system for improving market milk. The dairy-herd–improvement investigations of the bureau have done much to improve milk yields and prevent dairymen from losing money on unprofitable cows. Its researches on dairy-cattle breeding, feeding, and management have also been outstanding.

The dairy scientists began to develop a scientific and practical dairy breeding program about 1918. At that time one school of thought advocated line breeding, a second close inbreeding, and a third the mating of unrelated animals only. Since no scientific principles had yet been formulated for guidance and no experimental work had been carried out under controlled conditions, experimental breeding herds were then established and work with them has continued ever since.

Naturally, given the life span of cows, this is a long-time project. But it has been concluded that the most successful sire is pure in his genetic make-up for factors that govern the transmission of high milk and butterfat production. The production records of his daughters measure the sire's transmitting ability. If he demonstrates the ability to beget daughters which are better producers than their dams, that indicates the sire's make-up is desirable genetically.

Out of this prolonged study came the proved-sire system of breeding. Attention is centered on the use of sires of proved ability, in accord with what has just been said. For a quarter of a

Dairy farm at the Beltsville (Md.) Research Center

Administration wing and Chemical Laboratory wing, Northern
Regional Research Laboratory, Peoria, Ill.

century sires have been so selected at various field stations over the country. Remarkable progress has been made in developing strains or herds that approach purity in their inheritance of high production. The sires selected transmit high production to their offspring and need not be selected from the same family.

As a result of this work farmers and breeders have developed a lively interest in proved sires. Because there are few great sires, much work has been done towards prolonging the active lives of proved sires. Their superior germ plasm has been perpetuated in various ways. This led to study of the preservation of bull spermatozoa for artificial insemination and wide application of this practice. A few bulls have also been kept fertile much beyond the age at which they usually stop breeding.

T. E. Woodward and R. R. Graves carried on an inbreeding experiment with Holsteins which lasted for thirty years. No other such comprehensive studies have ever been reported. It was shown that, in skilled hands, inbreeding was a useful method of concentrating and perpetuating the germ plasm of superior dairy bulls. Moderate inbreeding, less than 25 per cent as measured by Sewall Wright's formula, was not harmful, though more intensive inbreeding was. Even if undesirable effects tend to appear, one outcross will wipe them out.

M. H. Fohrman and J. R. Dawson have been closely associated with breeding projects since they entered the bureau in the twenties. They have done work of value on correction factors, methods of taking uniform pictures of livestock for experimental purposes, the age and other factors influencing the fertility of sires, and methods of evaluating the inheritance of sires.

In the spring of 1946 the bureau announced preliminary results of its epochal long-time experiment on the crossbreeding of dairy animals. This project, undertaken somewhat on the hybrid-corn principle, was designed to produce more milk. It did, a 20 per cent increase having been chalked up already. This is not random crossbreeding, but the making of crosses between animals with proved ability to transmit productive capacity. Herds will not be mongrelized but will be vastly improved by it. Much more must be done before final conclusions can be drawn.

F. W. Miller did pioneer investigation in this country on artificial insemination. He also studied the factors influencing the viability of sperm cells, the influence of diet and exercise on sterility, and the extent to which transplantation of gonadal tissue aided in overcoming sterility. Miller and Fohrman collaborated on studies of the results of herd segregation in Bang's disease.

In 1935 a germ-plasm survey was conducted in order to supply material for the 1936 *Yearbook of Agriculture*. Information on the milk-production records of nearly one thousand herds of dairy cattle went under intensive study. This was the first application of a working plan of herd analysis to determine the quality of germ plasm in the herd through a study of all males and females that had contributed thereto. The method of herd analysis evolved then has proved invaluable since in understanding the laws of heredity as they apply to dairy herds.

After the scientists had studied dairy-cattle genetics, some means had to be found of explaining the principles of Mendelian inheritance to lay breeders. Oral presentation often proved confusing. Therefore, E. R. Graves designed his herediscope demonstration of dairy-cattle improvement. This ingenious device gave great impetus to the teaching of the principles involved, and it has been widely used.

Woodward, who was mentioned earlier, also did research on the effects of incomplete milking on the udder, on the relation of the cow's condition at calving time to her milk yield, on grazing to increase the yields of nutrients and maintain pasture stands, on the effect of different methods of storing hay and preserving silage to prevent loss of its carotene content and dry matter, and on the quantity of grain to be fed profitably to cows of different producing capacities. It is impossible here to do more than catalog the projects followed by one research worker, who retired in 1944 after thirty-five years of service, to show its astonishing scope.

On March 15, 1930, the first recovery of a fertilized ovum from the fallopian tubes of a cow threw new light on questions concerned with the times of ovulation and fertilization, the conditions favorable to fertilization and the characteristics of the ovum (or egg, cow egg in this case), all of which are vitally important to dairy scientists and breeders. A detailed study of female calves twin-born with males revealed important characteristics found in living animals that may be relied upon with reasonable certainty in determining which of such animals will prove to be freemartins, hence incapable of reproduction.

This work also is mentioned in the main to show the scope of the bureau's investigations which include study of the nutrition of dairy animals, on which the present writer worked in the bureau for about six years. Much of this work on dairy-herd nutrition is in the realm of pure research but offers most interesting possibilities; for instance, there are as yet unidentified growth-promoting factors in cows' milk that may be derived from feed, while evidence exists that certain plants contain gonad-stimulating substances.

Fairly successful efforts have been made to trace dietary constituents right through from the feed into the blood and the milk. Much of the work deals with refinements of method which make experimentation more reliable and less cumbersome. Much has been ascertained about the mineral, energy, protein, and vitamin requirements of dairy cattle. Other tedious studies, largely made by Ben H. Nicolet, have increased our knowledge of the composition and chemical reactions of casein and other proteins.

This work has provided useful tools in the study of wool processing and the manufacture of protein plastics and synthetic protein fibers. Nicolet has developed analytical methods which enable chemists to find out more about the inner structure of the proteins than they have ever known before. His methods have been widely used in other laboratories and have aided in the solution of many tough industrial problems. For his work Nicolet received the Hillebrand Award in 1944 and the Borden Award in 1945.

In the spring of 1946 A. M. Hartman and C. A. Cary of this bureau announced findings on an as yet unidentified food factor X, which plays an important role in rendering feed palatable to animals. Present in several milk products, in lettuce, egg yolk, beef and pork muscle, bluegrass, alfalfa, alfalfa and timothy hays, and, richly, in liver extract, it is so important that rats die on good protein diets if it be deficient. However, if X is injected into the animals, they find palatable, diets they hitherto disdained as "unpalatable."

When we come to the practical feeding of dairy cattle, we find that the first standards were developed in 1864. These have since been refined by many investigators. For many years it was tacitly assumed that, if cows were fed in a way to meet the requirements of an accepted standard, they would at the same time be fed most profitably. Until recently investigators have given the economics of feeding too little attention, while devoting themselves wholeheartedly to its physiological aspects.

In 1936 a co-operative feeding project was instituted with the Bureau of Agricultural Economics and ten state experiment stations. The idea was to find out how heavily it pays to feed cows at various prices for feed and product. At what feeding level do net returns attain their highest point? The yearly milk and feed records of nearly five hundred cows were obtained, making it the largest experiment of the kind ever conducted in this country. Carefully balanced groups of cows were fed at different levels, ranging from no grain at all to as much as they would eat.

Every increase in feed resulted in the production of more milk, but the increase in production tapered off as compared with the increase in feeding. It was thus possible to determine the optimum level. This depends upon the relative prices of forage, grain, and milk. It may range from no grain at all, where forage and milk are cheap and grain is dear, to giving the cows all the grain they will eat, when feed is cheap and the price of milk is high.

However, cows fed according to an accepted standard for an entire year usually became poor in flesh and failed to produce large quantities of milk. In fact standard feeding was well below the most profitable rate over the greater part of the United States. Hence ideas about feeding dairy cattle were considerably revised as a result of this work, to the profit of dairymen generally.

Investigations which may seem somewhat inconsequential to us yet had important economic results, such as the work of T. E. Woodward and J. N. Shephard on silage, which showed how it was possible to avoid the trouble and expense of using preservatives like molasses and acids. Then there has been important research on the carrying capacity of pastures, on the value of high-quality roughage for cattle, on the feeding quality of early-cut grass, and on milk production when the cows are fed this or that hay exclusively.

Much of this is long-time work, and it has required the establishment of many experimental herds. One definite finding that hay cut at early stages of maturity is markedly superior in all respects to hay cut when more mature is very important and useful. Moreover, there is no decrease in per acre yields by this method.

To raise a heifer calf to milking age costs at least one hundred dollars, yet about two million of them annually turn out to be unprofitable milk cows. Therefore, the bureau scientists are now making studies which will enable owners to discard potential low producers early in their lives.

The bureau has found that neither the abundance of the mammary veins on the surface of the udders, the size and length of the abdominal milk veins, nor the size of the holes through which the milk veins enter the body surely indicate whether the animal is or will be a good producer. Yet judges of dairy cattle have long given deep attention to these inconsequential points.

The bureau found during the war years that urea, which looks like fine stock salt and can be made from coal, air, and water, can supply dairy cattle with the nitrogen they require to make a good deal of protein for themselves. Several state experiment stations have been working on this matter, too. The bureau's scientists found that the milk production of cows fed urea declined only two-thirds as much in one hundred days of feeding as did that of cows consuming other feeds.

Farmers normally use about three billion pounds of whole milk a year merely for calf feed. It appears from work by Department dairy scientists that Holstein heifer calves do very well on skim milk, along with a grain mixture and timothy hay, and do not have to have whole milk at all. The scientists have continued to accumulate evidence that the practice of feeding poor-grade timothy hay to dairy cows is unsound, because the hay is a poor source of vitamin A and cows need their vitamins.

The bureau has shown that dairy-herd–improvement-association cows produce one hundred pounds of milk for every 99 cents' worth of feed they consume, whereas the figure is $1.32 per hundred pounds of milk for all cows in the United States. No wonder the bureau fosters dairy-herd improvement. It tabulates and keeps the records on thousands of sires, matings, and milk-production achievements.

World War II brought a speed-up of much research. The government's program for expanded milk production gave new emphasis to the relationships discovered between level of feeding and milk output and the discovery and use of good bulls. Bureau specialists went from factory to factory in a trailer laboratory to help improve the quality of the cheese made for Lend-Lease export. Feeding practices were recommended, after a survey, which increased the vitamin A content of market milk.

The fat and oil situation led to the study of oils from corn, soybeans, coconuts, and cottonseed as compared with butterfat. Bureau technicians found out how to replace some of the cane sugar in ice cream with other sugars, without damage to the quality of the ice cream. They aided the War Department ably in devising a method for producing butter that could be shipped to and used in tropical climates without deterioration. The dairy industry also was advised on the production, packaging, storage, and shipment of pure canned butter oil. Just very recently bureau scientists have shown a possible new field for the use of penicillin as a preserving agent, because of its powerful destructive action against bacterial spores.

Since 1910 the annual appropriations of the Bureau of Dairy Industry have averaged about $500,000 a year. They have not exceeded $800,000, as compared with our two-billion-dollar national farm income from dairy products. The research activities alone have been well worth the price paid. The bureau has had a relatively short but very active, useful, and productive career. War found it ready, as it had been in peace, to serve the dairy industry and the nation.

CHAPTER 14

Agricultural Engineering Triumphs

T̲HE MORE IMPORTANT AND FUNDAMENTAL agricultural implements had already been invented when the Department of Agriculture came into existence. Many methods of dealing with soil
erosion had also been foreshadowed. Yet there remained a great
deal for the Department engineers to do in making adaptations
and designing methods and equipment to meet special needs as they
arose. Not all of this work by any means was done in the divisions
of bureaus which, from time to time, worked in the field of agricultural engineering.

Entomologists devised sprays, nozzles, and power-spray equipment to meet their own particular problems. Soil conservation
workers did the same. Workers in forestry have had to design
rugged and powerful machines to assist in logging operations under
adverse conditions. But, nevertheless, there has long been a solid
core of agricultural engineering work *per se* in the Department.
While formal beginning may be said to have been made with the
initiation of irrigation investigations in the Office of Experiment
Stations in 1898, we find earlier mention of engineering.

Secretary Rusk in his annual report for 1890 discussed an appropriation of $20,000 Congress had made for the investigation of
the proper location of artesian wells to irrigate semiarid regions in
nine or ten Western states. Edwin S. Nettleton was then appointed
supervising engineer and Robert Hay geologist. Later an Office
of Irrigation Inquiry was set up under special agent R. J. Hinton,
to make special reports on irrigation financed by an additional
$40,000 Congress granted after it received the artesian-well report.

By 1891 Congress had appropriated a total of $70,000 for the
investigation of artesian wells, underflow waters, and the sources

and availability of irrigation. Field work continued, though a 300-page report had been prepared which funds were lacking to publish. Howard Miller was serving as an unpaid special agent to study certain wells in Colorado and Kansas. The next year the investigations were suspended. Charles W. Irish remained in charge of collecting and abstracting state and territorial laws governing water rights, but even this work lapsed later.

However, in his annual report for 1897 Secretary Wilson made note of a new appropriation of $10,000 for irrigation investigations. This time the work was assigned to the Office of Experiment Stations. A crisis existed in agricultural communities dependent on irrigation. Numerous irrigation districts were being established and settled by thousands of farmers, yet local laws and institutions were unsatisfactory, while correct irrigation practices were not observed and, indeed, remained to be determined.

Elwood Mead, state engineer of Wyoming, became consultant, and a general conference was held. It was decided to assemble information on irrigation laws, institutions, and practices. The work moved slowly, and little competent help could be obtained in this relatively new scientific field. Since more detailed investigations were required, Congress increased the appropriation in 1899, and an Office of Irrigation Investigations was established in Cheyenne with Mead in charge.

The main studies were carried on in California, Utah, and Colorado and they dealt with the basic principles of the use of water in agriculture. Soon study of sediment in canals and reservoirs began. In 1901 it was suggested that the government undertake extensive irrigation works, dam large rivers, make drainage investigations, and reclaim alkali soils; therefore, a laboratory of soil physics was instituted.

In his report for 1902 Secretary Wilson stressed the importance of agricultural engineering as related not only to irrigation, but to farming in general. During the past twenty years the capital invested in the manufacture of agricultural machinery had increased from $60,000,000 to $157,000,000, and the value of the product had doubled. Revolutionary changes had taken place in agricultural technology, yet the Department could offer no expert advice on such subjects.

Secretary Wilson thought that it should investigate the lay-out of farms, the arrangement of farm buildings, the placing of drains, the farm water supply and sewage-disposal arrangements, barn-ventilation systems, and the design of farm buildings. It was not long afterward that rural architecture began to be studied in the Bureau of Plant Industry. In 1902 the Office of Experiment Stations undertook study of farm lay-out and drainage.

It also instituted, as best it could, laboratory and field studies of farm implements and machinery. Recommendations continued that appropriations for such work be increased. Reviews of state work in agricultural engineering were published. The fact was stressed that though $100,000,000 worth of farm machinery was sold annually (1902), one-half of it went to buyers who could neither select nor use it wisely. It was felt both inside and outside the Department of Agriculture that that Department should provide technical advice.

By now drainage of agricultural land had progressed beyond the individual farm into the field of co-operative effort. Machinery for digging ditches was available, but landowners were unable to proceed with the necessary drainage work through lack of technical skill and information. The Department was now called upon for assistance in planning and organizing many early co-operative drainage districts.

In 1905 co-operative projects in agricultural engineering were carried on with the land-grant colleges and the experiment stations. It was suggested that the unit then called Irrigation and Drainage Investigations be renamed Rural Engineering. On October 15, 1907, drainage investigations were separated from irrigation studies. By 1911 it was stated that if drainage were carried out where needed and in line with facts unearthed by Department investigations, land values could be increased by one and one-half billion dollars and farm income by one-quarter of a billion a year.

Soon thereafter S. H. McCrory became chief of drainage investigations; and, on April 1, 1915, drainage and irrigation investigations were both transferred to a unit which came to be called, on the following July 1, the Office of Public Roads and Rural Engineering. Aid was still being given the states in setting up water laws and in educating farmers on the more economical use of irrigation waters. About this time the farm architectural work previously carried on in the Bureau of Plant Industry, the Office of Experiment Stations, and the Office of Farm Management, became an engineering project in the public roads agency.

Plans were next made to place all agricultural engineering in one division of the Office of Rural Engineering, with E. B. McCormick as chief. This division first studied the farm domestic water supply, farm sewage disposal, the construction of farm buildings, and farm machinery and equipment. Questions came in on a wide variety of farm mechanical problems.

At a meeting held in March, 1923, there was much discussion of using electricity in agriculture. Such use of power was declared to be a proper subject for federal research. Investigations were also being carried on of the ventilation of dairy barns, farm plumbing, the use of concrete in farm buildings, and the utilization of motor trucks and tractors. By 1925 farm power was costing three billion dollars a year, and a bulletin was issued on the service of power to farms.

In 1929 the Division of Agricultural Engineering reported work on irrigation, drainage, farmland development, mechanical farm equipment, and farm structures. Its engineers had developed equipment to reduce corn-borer hazards, machines for improving the distribution of fertilizer, devices to mount on airplanes for dusting cotton, seed-cotton driers, and new methods of cleaning drainage and irrigation ditches.

This division became the Bureau of Agricultural Engineering on July 1, 1931, with S. H. McCrory as its chief. It worked on irrigation, drainage, farmland development, farm-machinery investigations, and farm structures. The bureau was abolished in 1939 to become part of the Bureau of Agricultural Chemistry and Engineering, McCrory having been its chief throughout its existence. On February 23, 1943, the engineering research went to the Bureau of Plant Industry which then became the Bureau of Plant Industry, Soils, and Agricultural Engineering.

While the separate bureau existed, important work was done on the flow of water in irrigation and drainage ditches. These were fundamental studies. D. L. Yarnell, one of the engineers of the bureau, published his *Rainfall Intensity Frequency Data* in 1935.

It was of great value to irrigation and drainage engineers generally, and also to all who worked on soil erosion and on city water supplies. The work of the bureau's irrigation engineers achieved national recognition. The water-measuring flume developed by R. L. Parshall and the material F. S. Scobey published on the flow of water gained world-wide use.

A typical example of still earlier work of importance may be found in *Department Bulletin 512*, issued April 5, 1917. It is on the "Prevention of Erosion of Farm Lands by Terracing," and its author was C. E. Ramser, a drainage engineer. Before this investigation was made, no scientific data existed upon which to base the design of terraces used to prevent soil erosion. Terracing was carried on by rule of thumb. The bulletin gave the general engineering principles underlying the design and construction of broad-based terraces, and the rules to be followed to insure their proper functioning.

During the decade before 1933 some 15,000,000 acres were terraced on more than 300,000 farms. In 1933 it was estimated that such terracing resulted in an average increase in the value of the land of six dollars an acre. Hence at least $90,000,000 had been added to land values as a result of the publication of this work. Something more is told about these early investigations in the chapter on the work of the Office of Experiment Stations.

While the plow was invented long before this Department work was ever thought of, the engineers have done much to improve plow designs, resulting in lighter draft and better trash coverage. The work has been done in the main at the Tillage Machinery Laboratory, Auburn, Alabama, the only laboratory of its kind in the world, its purpose being to provide facilities for the comprehensive study of tillage tools under controlled conditions and in a wide variety of soils.

Here it is possible to test tillage equipment under various soil conditions within a very short period, without encountering any of the objectionable variables usually met in field testing. Commercial designers of tillage tools can get permission to use the laboratory's facilities. The reactions of plows to soils of different types have been studied here.

Basic information has been developed on improvements in tillage methods. Even better plow points have been devised. Work such as this carried on under carefully controlled conditions provides unusual opportunity for scientific testing of methods and machines which have been constructed for generations in accordance with tradition and rule of thumb.

Take the matter of fertilizer placement and distribution. For years commercial concerns manufactured implements for these purposes by rule of thumb. No one had thought to test what they would actually do under controlled conditions. When they were tested, it immediately became apparent that they neither delivered fertilizer at the rate claimed nor placed it where the plants could make best use of it. While much attention had been given the kind of fertilizer needed by specific crops, little had been paid to uniformity of distribution and placement of fertilizer with respect to seed or plant roots.

In 1929 something like five million fertilizer-distributing machines were in use by American farmers who achieved only about 50 per cent efficiency in operating them. Fertilizer-distributing machines were long made in many types and designs under the impression that delivery of the desired quantities of fertilizer was adequately controlled. Research showed, however, that the delivery rate was greatly affected by moisture conditions as well as by the physical and chemical properties of the fertilizer itself, and by minor changes in field operating conditions.

With the results of Department research as a guide, the manufacturers redesigned and greatly improved their machines, and fertilizer was prepared that would drill better. Next it was found that some crops thrive best with fertilizer applied in narrow bands at each side of the row at planting time, and that yields could often be increased 20 per cent by proper fertilizer placement. Commercial production of a wide variety of fertilizer-placement implements which did the job right followed this disclosure.

This work has been of very considerable monetary value to farmers, for, when the implement places the fertilizer where it should be and in no more than the necessary quantity, yields have increased from 25 to 40 per cent—no mean accomplishment, when it is realized that no additional fertilizer need be used.

For a long time the engineers have made fundamental studies

of farm buildings. The basic principles of ventilating dairy and other barns have been worked out. It is no more than natural that farm research workers should be called upon for this service. It is rather odd, however, that the building industry had never carried on useful research on building rural homes and that the fundamental principles remained to be established.

It was found, for instance, that temperature differences between the floor and breathing height in houses cannot wholly be overcome by making changes in the heating equipment. However, the changes can be neutralized by scientific use of storm sash, weather stripping, and insulation. On the other hand it was discovered that the gable ventilators so long put in many houses by pious builders had no effect in reducing summer temperatures or increasing comfort in the house.

Studies of low-cost homes for the South showed that the use of ordinary window shades would reduce the temperature in the house in summer by three or four degrees. Slatted blinds on the outside proved even more effective, though the conventional high ceilings long used in this region did not prove to be a comfort factor. Cottonseed hulls could be used for insulating purposes so as to reduce winter fuel consumption 16 to 25 per cent.

Four regional farm-building services were developed to promote uniformly standardized building practices on farms. Acceptable building plans were worked out with the land-grant colleges, suitable for use under local conditions. Varied studies of comfort factors in farmhouses led to new, practical recommendations for heating, ventilating, remodeling, and reconstructing farm homes economically and efficiently.

At times the engineers have made studies which notably reduced farm fire losses. Largely as a result of applying the safety measures they recommended, farmers reduced fire losses by about forty million dollars a year, according to estimates of the National Fire Protection Association. A further indication of the value of these results is seen in considerable insurance-rate reductions on structures like grain elevators, starch factories, and grain-threshing machines.

Much of this work concerned the cause and prevention of dust explosions in threshing machines, flour mills, and elevators. Research was carried on over a period of years. It resulted in great reductions in both dust-explosion and farm-fire hazards generally. The benefits extended to many industries engaged in processing farm products.

. Now let us see what the engineers have done to aid in the production of a few specific crops. The principles and methods of dusting cotton from airplanes in order to reduce damage from boll weevils were discovered and patented in the course of the Department's pioneer work on cotton production. Cotton ginning itself has been placed upon a more scientific basis through the work of the Department's Cotton Ginning Laboratory at Stoneville, Mississippi.

The development of the variable-depth cotton planter in 1935 makes it possible to get a good stand whether the weather is dry, wet, cold, or hot. Use of this machine, designed by Department engineers, eliminates most of the poor stands and thus saves both labor and seed. Several manufacturers have employed the basic principles in making machines now in use on many cotton farms.

The Cotton Ginning Laboratory was established in 1930 under an act of Congress authorizing investigations in this field. Its operation now comes under the Bureau of Plant Industry, Soils, and Agricultural Engineering. Losses from poor ginning have been estimated at more than $15,000,000 annually. Poor ginning leads to low-quality cotton from the standpoint of spinners, and loss to growers. The laboratory's work covers all phases of picking, handling, ginning, cleaning, and packaging cotton.

This laboratory is equipped with virtually all standard types and makes of ginning machinery. If good mechanical driers are used, as recommended by the laboratory, for the proper conditioning and drying of damp, green, or wet seed cotton, the value of the ginned lint rises 70 cents a bale on short-staple and $2.50 a bale on long-staple varieties. The germination and milling quality of the seed is also enhanced. Mechanical driers developed and patented by the workers at the laboratory are now widely used.

Many tests have also been made of gin-saw speeds and seed rolls, because here as elsewhere manufacturers had put out machines which would not operate as directed, or else had given directions which were wrong. Increasing the saw speed and ginning with loose seed rolls was found to increase the gin capacity about 20 per cent. In terms of value this meant an additional turnout of $2.50 a bale for long-staple and $1.50 a bale for short-staple cotton. There was also a profit of $4.00 a bale on long-staple cotton by the use of loose instead of tight seed rolls.

The work of this laboratory has attracted wide attention. Large groups of growers and ginners from the important cotton-growing states visit it regularly, spending several days. It serves as a training school for state extension specialists, who come for a week nearly every spring. It disseminates useful information over the entire cotton belt. Selected samples of cotton ginned at the laboratory are used in actual spinning tests by co-operative federal-state testing laboratories.

Other subjects of study are gin-saw design and maintenance; the use, repair, and replacement of brushes; packaging with various bale coverings and using different bale densities; the handling of seed to maintain purity; the reduction of power waste; and such special problems of an individual or regional nature as may arise. The laboratory's recommendations in all fields are widely used by ginners, farmers, and manufacturers of cotton-ginning machinery. Just recently the laboratory showed how 35 per cent of shipping space, with comparably less bale covers and ties, could be saved by inexpensive methods of compressing bales to greater density.

Studies of beet-production machinery, made by Department engineers, have been quite as successful. They have resulted in great improvements in planting, blocking, thinning, and harvesting this crop. A method has been devised for cracking sugar-beet seed balls into single-germ segments so as to get a higher percentage of single plants. Increased efficiency and the elimination of much stoop labor has resulted.

It is now practicable both to thin and to harvest sugar beets mechanically, the former with one-tenth to one-half the usual number of workers and the latter with one-sixth former labor requirements. This advance has resulted from co-operative work of Department engineers and workers at the California and Colorado agricultural experiment stations.

Mechanical thinning experiments were started some years ago when labor was plentiful; when labor became scarce, they assumed prime importance. Mechanical harvesting was also beneficial during war. A commercial trial of nonstoop thinning, as developed by the Department, resulted in savings of $4.50 per acre for the entire sugar-beet crop. Mechanical harvesting also leaves the by-product, the tops, in better condition for cattle feed than hand labor, while the machine misses fewer beets. A new beet topper and a single-seed sugar-beet planter which requires less seed and cuts thinning costs are both developments of this research.

The Soil Conservation Service in its contouring and terracing work turned to that thin mantle of soil over virtually solid bedrock upon which so many of our potatoes are produced in Aroostook County, Maine. Here an entire agricultural industry depends upon retaining and building up a vital layer of thin soil. Special potato machinery was devised by J. W. Slosser of the service, which greatly aided in this project. Slosser worked in the main by making deft revisions of standard equipment.

The heavy planter was changed to prevent side-slipping on steep fields and to place seed and fertilizer more accurately. The two-man potato sprayer was reconstructed so that it did better work while only one man operated it. New design for the digger enabled it properly to separate potatoes from vines and soil.

All these changes were inexpensive, but they rendered the standard equipment used for this highly mechanized operation far more efficient and conducive to soil conservation. Then contouring alone increased potato yields 30 bushels an acre, which more than paid for the research in one season. The Presque Isle (Maine) Experiment Station helped in this work.

Work of the Department engineers has gone far towards making both the beet and potato crops highly mechanized. Improvements have also been made in potato-storage houses, which make it possible to store the tubers with less rotting both of them and of the timbers in the storage house. Application of the results of this research, based in the main on control of temperature and moisture, save northern farmers many thousands of dollars annually.

The method requires less artificial heat, and it is not necessary to watch the potatoes so closely as when former storage methods were used. The potatoes shrink a great deal less. Proper design

U.S.D.A. photograph by Forsythe

The Persian lamb comes to America
Resting in the arms of Miss Ann Wickard, it is a link in the chain
between the sheep originally imported from Bokkara and future
fur-bearing sheep that will thrive on American farms

and construction of the potato storage houses were basic. Plans were then worked out for storage of different sizes of potatoes, to meet localized conditions in the North. This so-called "shell-cooled" storage method actually gave us many more potatoes than we should otherwise have had during war scarcity.

Co-operative work on the development of machinery for use in growing and harvesting flax was fortunately carried on in Oregon for some years before the war. It resulted in improvements in all machines used—pullers, de-seeders, cleaners, tow shakers. An experimental cleaner devised through research and used in one co-operative mill in Oregon in 1942 made unsalable tow readily salable, bringing one group of farmers $31,000 extra income.

War gave impetus to the fiber-flax industry in this country. Production grew very considerably. The improvements devised by the Department engineers and crop men, in collaboration with the Oregon Agricultural Experiment Station, were largely instrumental in effecting the tenfold increase in acreage when the war cut us off from our usual sources of fiber and linen.

Department engineers also worked out the proper requirements for small-grain combines. In one instance after another it will be seen that the research of the engineers consisted in controlled testing of machinery sold by commercial concerns, the discovery that the machines would not perform as claimed, or that the directions sent with them were in error, and the making of required changes.

Outlines of the work by W. M. Hurst on small-grain combines appeared in *Agricultural Engineering*, a publication of the American Society of Agricultural Engineers, for June, 1935. Many of the small combines now in use all over the country have been built according to the eleven principles propounded by Hurst in this article.

New principles have also been developed for the better handling of high-moisture silage. Grass silage became a common feed in recent years, and the requirements for silos to hold it had to be discovered. The engineers rose to the occasion as usual. They have also devised improved farm practices and machinery for the control of the European corn borer. Improved husking rolls have likewise been developed for picker-huskers which reduce shelling loss from a former 5.65 to a mere 1.95 bushels of corn per acre. Finally there is new machinery for harvesting and putting up the above-mentioned grass silage more economically.

Engineering work has resulted in improved orchard-heating equipment as well as in better domestic oil burners for household use. The carefully controlled tests made some years ago of household oil burners were richly productive of facts used in redesigning them, and undoubtedly many American citizens benefit from this research, wholly ignorant of the fact that Department of Agriculture scientists had so big a hand in it.

Work on spraying machines was mentioned in connection with cotton. Much other dusting and spraying machinery has been redesigned as a result of work by Department engineers. The usual findings were made that commercial machinery deviated from specifications. Variations were then made in the capacity of dusting nozzles and in machinery used for mixing and spreading powdered insecticides, fungicides, and diluents. This resulted in better and more economical control of crop pests.

Year after year this valuable but little-heralded work goes on. During the war engineers instructed farmers in keeping their machinery in better repair, as well in doing a better job with it. Many new machines had to be devised for producing, harvesting, and processing crops which had not been grown here, at least extensively, before the war.

Improved mechanization was of great aid to peanut growers. Homemade egg coolers were designed. Studies of metal grain bins and corncribs reduced damage from insects and moisture. Proper fertilizer placement still further increased yields from many crops. New mechanisms continued to be devised for the cotton industry. Shortages of materials hitherto used for storage structures made necessary the building of storages from noncritical materials.

Thus, though we little realized it, the agricultural engineers served the farmer and through that function served all of us as well. The divisions of Agricultural Engineering are located at Agricultural Research Center, near Plant Industry Station, Beltsville, Maryland. They are the divisions of Farm Power and Machinery, Farm Electrification, Mechanical Processing of Farm Products, and Farm Buildings and Rural Housing.

CHAPTER 15

Something Could Be Done About It

Mark Twain is credited with having said that, while everybody talked about the weather, nobody did anything about it. However, something could be done about it, and the Weather Bureau, which formed part of the Department of Agriculture from 1891 until mid-1940, did it.[1] Certain fundamental laws obviously governed the development of weather conditions. It seemed possible to ascertain what they were and to remove the element of unpredictability for meteorological conditions. That was what the weather specialists aimed to do.

Moreover, their work has a very distinct economic value every time that crops or property can be protected from sudden freezes, or that ships, property on land, and human lives can be saved as a result of advance warnings about high winds. In the old days the reports of the Weather Bureau were often replete with calculations of huge sums which it declared, with no little justice, had been saved as a result of its forecasts.

The United States took a leading part in organizing and carrying out the series of so-called "International Observations" made in 1884-88. It was the first country to have a well-organized network of pilot balloon observations coming in regularly, a feat which it accomplished in 1917-18. The bureau published the first Northern Hemisphere Map, based on current daily reports by telegraph and cable; it actually had manuscript maps based on telegraphic data as early as 1906.

---

[1] A document prepared in the Weather Bureau and sent in manuscript form proved of inestimable value in the preparation of this chapter.

The first extended forecasts were issued on the Saturday of each week around 1911. Ours was the first country to use telegraphic circuits for the exchange and distribution of synoptic weather observations—comprehensive reports in summary form. We first used the radio in 1909 to obtain ship reports in order to forecast storms and hurricanes.

It was Weather Bureau scientists who devised the practice of using heaters in citrus and other fruit orchards to protect crops against frost and freezing. Savings from this technique have undoubtedly attained huge sums.

The United States took a prominent part in making meteorological observations by means of instruments attached to kites and of others carried aloft by hydrogen-filled balloons. Our work with radiosondes, complex instruments the nature of which will be explained later—in essence they radio down how upper-air conditions are—is of the highest standards.

The employment of weather information in very practical ways by agriculture, commerce, manufacturing, navigation, and transportation by air has been developed here to an extent found in no other country. The prediction of river stages and the issuance of flood and low-water warnings are characterized by extensive distribution, high accuracy, and the great speed with which reports go out.

Our Weather Bureau was a pioneer in extending forecasts that looked ahead more than a day or so. As early as 1911 some forecasts were being issued for three to six days in advance. This could be accomplished when reports from Alaska strongly indicated the approach of some pronounced change in the weather.

Even in Patent Office days the Agricultural Division had developed an interest in the weather. Commissioner Mason's report for 1855 not only contained meteorological data from different parts of the United States, but also an article by Secretary Joseph Henry of the Smithsonian Institution entitled "Meteorology in Its Connection with Agriculture." Commissioner Holt's report for the following year also carried a long article by Professor Henry on the general principles of science applicable to meteorology, plus the customary weather data.

Meteorological data furnished by the Smithsonian Institution regularly appeared in the annual reports of the Commissioners of Agriculture from 1863 until 1872. Commissioner Newton himself wrote that "the state of the weather at different points of the country might be daily communicated by telegraph and immediately spread over the whole country with beneficial results."

Commissioner Watts, however, stopped the Department's publication of the Smithsonian's meteorological data and suggested that the work be turned over to the Signal Service of the army. In response, Congress, on June 10, 1872, appropriated money with which "the War Department was directed to collect and publish meteorological information for the benefit of agriculture." But the work had actually started in the Signal Service on November 1, 1870, as the result of approval of a Congressional joint resolution on February 9, 1870.

This was done in the main because army personnel at widely scattered posts throughout the country provided a ready-made network of stations where weather observations had already been made to a limited extent. The plan of organization was largely devised by Cleveland Abbe, who directed the technical and scientific work of the new service. The name of the Signal Service was changed to Signal Corps in 1880.

A group of civilian scientists assisted Professor Abbe with the technical functions, supplemented as time went by with commissioned officers of the Signal Corps who were assigned to meteorological work. They became proficient largely through instructions by a number of meteorologists outside the corps. The training of enlisted personnel assigned to duty as weather observers took place at Ft. Myer (formerly Ft. Whipple) Virginia, until 1886. Many of the men thus trained remained in the Weather Bureau after it became part of the Department of Agriculture on July 1, 1891.

This transfer was made pursuant to an Act of Congress passed October 1, 1890, when Mark Harrington was chief of the bureau. The work remained in the Department of Agriculture until Reorganization Plan No. IV, effective June 30, 1940, placed the Weather Bureau in the Department of Commerce. The head of the bureau was a presidential appointee. We here consider the research activities of the bureau which were carried on until its transfer from the Department of Agriculture.

During its sojourn in the Signal Service (later Corps) the Weather Bureau engaged the services of a number of distinguished scientists, Edward Bennett Garriott among them. He took a leading part in compiling international weather observations which were later published in bulletin form, and also in the early development of forecasts for periods more than a day or two ahead. Like Cleveland Abbe, he remained with the bureau when it was transferred to the Department of Agriculture.

As director of the Cincinnati Observatory, Abbe had proposed the development of storm predictions for the Lake Region. Also, with the help of the Western Union Telegraph Company, he had developed a telegraphic weather bulletin or forecast which was not just a collection of data. Very soon after that the federal weather service came into existence.

Abbe joined the service in 1871 and served until his death in 1916. He edited the *Monthly Weather Review* and the *Bulletin of the Mt. Weather Observatory*, a research station for work on balloons which was supplied with some of the most hideous buildings that ever desecrated the Virginia landscape, and was later summarily discontinued on a change of administration. As a matter of fact airplane observations seemed at this time ready to replace balloons. Abbe created much popular interest in meteorology and did useful bibliographical work.

Then there was resplendent General Adolphus Washington Greely, with his pugnacious facial alfalfa and his glittering medals, he of the Greely Arctic Expedition of 1881–84. (See "Epic of the Arctic," *Reader's Digest* for January, 1946.) The scientific data he obtained on this expedition are generally acknowledged to be the greatest of all single contributions to our knowledge of this region. He became chief signal officer in 1887.

Greely completely reorganized the weather service, making it the outstanding meteorological organization in the world. This led to its separation from the Signal Corps and its incorporation into the Department of Agriculture, whither Greely followed it. Greely initiated the *Weather Crop Bulletin*, the use of self-registering instruments of various sorts, the flood service, and the use of the telegraphic code, while he greatly expanded the observational network.

William Jackson Humphreys was a renowned physicist and served as professor of meteorological physics in the bureau from 1905 until 1935, having entered it after it became part of the Department of Agriculture. He also edited the *Monthly Weather Review* and contributed vastly to the bureau's physical research. His *Physics of the Air* is an outstanding work.

Willis Luther Moore is still remembered as having been chief of the Weather Bureau from 1895 until 1913. He was not a scientist, though he at times pretended to be. He was, however, an excellent organizer and administrative officer; he thus developed a bureau that stood in advance of many other federal agencies.

His successor, Charles Frederick Marvin, who served 1913–34, conducted experiments which resulted in many basic tables used by the bureau. He made important investigations of instruments to register wind velocity, rainfall, air pressure, sunshine, and snowfall, and also carried on extensive studies of the use of kites for investigating upper-air conditions. Largely because of the work of Marvin and his colleagues, the bureau had more refined instruments for observational work than any other in the world.

We turn now to consider some of the outstanding research carried on in this bureau. A great deal of it is so highly technical as to appear almost esoteric and mystical. It will be best to classify it under certain heads used by writers in that bureau when discussing its research, first of all the forecasting and warning services.

Forecasts of weather and warnings of severe storms, floods, cold waves, and so on have been a prime concern of the organized weather service since its inception. That this service has saved the American public millions of dollars goes without saying, even if the bureau has quit bragging about this accomplishment in monetary terms for some time. Yet its pointing with pride was doubtless justified even years ago when it did so.

To make such prognostications, a pool of sound overall surface data must exist. Observations at various centers must be collected promptly, collated centrally, and the results disseminated fast. It is for the inauguration of this service that Cleveland Abbe and his associates were mainly responsible. Since accurate observations depend upon accurate instruments which at first did not exist, a high degree of inventiveness was requisite.

This required the combined effort of several related service units and the work of many skilled and gifted individuals. Improved forecasting his resulted down the years through increasing the number of stations at which observations are made and the kind and precision of the instruments utilized. As early as 1896 surface observations began to be supplemented by those made in the upper air. Kites carrying meteorographs were first used, C. F. Marvin being an active leader in this field.

By 1918 airplane flights were being undertaken to carry the instruments, and they entirely replaced kites by 1931, reaching their peak of usefulness in 1937, when the radiosonde became practical. Pilot-balloon observations taken with theodolites, giving wind directions and velocities high aloft, began to be of substantial benefit to forecasters about 1918, and by 1940 some 133 stations were making daily observations of this character.

The radiosonde has the marked advantage of providing quickly a record of temperature, relative humidity, and atmospheric pressure aloft by means of a radio receiver and other ground equipment devised to intercept and record the signals made. This equipment is the result of work by Weather Bureau scientists in co-operation with those of the Bureau of Standards, other scientific agencies, and manufacturers.

Outstanding development in upper-air observations came with the perfection of this instrument, the first experimental flights with which were made 1936–37. In July, 1938, six regularly reporting stations for such observations were established; by 1940 some thirty-five stations were making at least one observation daily. Radiosondes have now not only superseded kites but airplanes also as media for upper-air soundings.

The original forecasting service was devoted almost entirely to shipping, commercial, and agricultural interests. As its scope widened, increased saving of life and property resulted. It is known that warnings of one destructive hurricane alone kept $30,000,000 worth of shipping safely in port. Flood warnings have had similar monetary value. In 1926 forecasts began to be made available to the Post Office Department to guide its mail flyers. By 1930 commercial aviation required such service and has continually required more as it expanded.

The development of the polar-front theory gave great impetus to upper-air observations; this led to air-mass analysis. Surface observations alone proved inadequate for the application of air-mass analysis to forecasting, because such a relatively small part of the mass was under observation. Frequent upper-air observations from a close network of stations became obligatory and, partly through the use of radiosondes and pilot balloons, became a reality by 1940.

Many leaders in Weather Bureau personnel have been engaged both in advancing the cold-front theory by use of air-mass analysis and in making practical applications of these new and useful concepts. By means of these observations, which involve the upper air as well as surface air, the advance of great air movements from above and the storms and other conditions accompanying them can be predicted much longer ahead than was hitherto possible.

The flood service, a part of this work since its inception, parallels the general weather-forecast service but requires special techniques. Daily or special reports of precipitation over given watersheds and gauge readings of rivers and their tributaries are both required. Then from forecasts of precipitation and computations of runoff, and other factors, quite accurate forecasts may be made of river stages and prospective damage to life and property. The work of H. C. Frankenfield, long chief of the bureau's River and Flood Division, stands out here.

Early in the century he set the example to be followed by officials of the various river-district centers to whom were entrusted the details of such forecasting and the necessary close contact with the public. Recent progress in procedures of this nature has been accomplished by Merrill Bernard and his associates. Hardly a year goes by that a major flood does not require this valuable protective service, which is so well co-ordinated as to add what amounts to genius to judgment, discretion, and scientific training.

For many years special service has been provided which enables growers to protect their valuable fruit and orchards from frost and freeze. This service is especially intensified in the citrus districts of Florida, California, and Texas. Floyd D. Young directed its beginning in California in 1913. Orchards are heated sufficiently to prevent or minimize damage when severe frost is forecast. This is usually accomplished by oil-burning equipment placed between the trees. So precise are the predictions that growers can judge quite exactly the heating required, thus preventing waste of fuel, labor, or time.

Young continued active in the direction of this service for many years, constantly extending its scope and helpfulness. Many valuable crops have been saved and much undue damage has been prevented as a result. Young's *Farmers' Bulletin 1588* on "Frost and the Prevention of Frost Damage" is the classic publication in the field. Deciduous-tree fruits and small fruits such as cranberries and strawberries are protected from frost damage by adaptations of the method used for citrus fruit.

Forecasting is also of great aid in preventing forest-fire damage. Protection is made possible through an accurate knowledge of current weather, humidity, temperature, wind direction and velocity, and visibility, coupled with forecasts of changes which will affect the degree of fire hazard. Forecasts of wind, precipitation, and lightning storms aid the Forest Service in determining the start, progress, and control of forest fires. Forest Service and Weather Bureau have a long history of close collaboration in such forest conservation measures.

We have now reached the general subject of climatology and crop-weather service. Climatology is a science based on regular, daily observations of the weather, temperature, wind, precipitation, and other conditions reported by the wide network of weather stations. No effective service in this direction began in this country until the Weather Bureau was established and, though early observations were intended in part for climatological use, they were made in the main for forecasting purposes.

But, in 1887, under the direction of General Greely, real growth began. Stations were established to make observations directly for climatological use. This network was further augmented by the act of Congress which made the bureau an agency of the Department of Agriculture. Growth of these stations has been steady, and, in recent years, upper-air, marine, and airway observations have been added to the data accumulated. Thus the study of the nation's climate has been extended to contiguous bodies of water and to the atmosphere high above the surface.

The first comprehensive work on climatology published by the Weather Bureau appeared in 1903, and was under the supervision of A. J. Henry. Revisions have appeared every decade or so, the form of the publication has been altered, and separates have been issued covering entire states or, more often, the divisions of a state. Another useful monthly and annual publication is *Climatological Data*. Development and growth of this work has represented the combined efforts of many people over the years.

A special service of the Weather Bureau of long standing is the issuance of bulletins on current weather and temperature conditions as they affect agricultural pursuits and farm operations such as soil preparation and the seeding, growth, cultivation, and harvesting of crops. The principal publication of this character is the *Weekly Weather and Crop Bulletin* issued by the central office of the Weather Bureau in Washington.

This publication summarizes weather conditions for the past week in the entire United States. It contains precipitation and mean-temperature statistics for the week, with departures from normal. There is also included a general summary of crop conditions and of work as affected by the current weather, with individual reports from each state. J. B. Kincer and W. A. Mattice directed the success of this publication over a long period.

The Weather Bureau was continually pioneering in new types of meteorological research. Not only did it have to decide how it should go about ascertaining fundamental principles, but it must design instruments for making precise observations of altogether new kinds. This was delicate work requiring the greatest possible skill. The design and perfection of such instruments could alone fulfill observational requirements and enable the bureau to increase the scope and reliability of its service.

C. F. Marvin did outstanding work in this field, more especially before his appointment as head of the bureau loaded him with administrative duties. Before that he had served a long time as chief of the Instrument Division. The design or radical improvement of all the following instruments stand high among his achievements, though he also did outstanding research in the field of solar radiation and on other problems. The instruments and the date of their perfection by Marvin and associates follow:

Photographic sunshine recorder, 1891; mercurial sunshine recorder, 1893; tipping-bucket rain gauge, 1894; nephoscope, instrument for observing clouds, their direction and velocity, 1896; kite meteorograph, instrument for simultaneously recording temperature, moisture, etc., and accessories, 1897; Weather Bureau—design anemometer, for measuring wind velocity, 1900; weighing rain and snow gauge, 1900; automatic river gauge, 1904; mercurial barograph, self-registering instrument for measuring the variations in atmospheric pressure, 1904; kiosk, where the weather instruments are placed downtown for you to see, 1907–1908; hair hygrometer, instrument for measuring the degree of moisture in the atmosphere, 1908; pyrheliometer, instrument for measuring sun's heat and energy, 1910; shielded rain and snow gauge, 1910; float rain and snow gauge, 1913; sounding balloon meteorograph, a meteorograph which calls the ground observer up and tells him what's what, 1919; various seismographs, for recording location and intensity of earthquakes.

This is indeed a formidable list, requiring a great degree of skill and scientific knowledge, as well as inventiveness of the first order. Furthermore, any individual who undertook work of this kind must know in advance that it would not make him rich. As a matter of fact, it was unlikely to gain him much popular renown. In spite of their undeniable achievements, the Weather Bureau and the weather man are bound to remain obscure and impecunious.

More recently B. C. Kadel and S. P. Fergusson have taken up the work dropped by Marvin around 1914 when he became chief of the bureau. They are responsible for a special wind-measuring device for use at airway observation stations and wind-velocity and wind-direction indicators for the same service, refined instruments to measure evaporation, and improved instruments to measure wind volocity, rain and snow fall, and to foretell weather more accurately. They have also refined and redesigned many electrical instruments and other devices for use in balloons and airplanes.

Other personnel outside the Instrument Division have also contributed much to the betterment of devices, mainly as a result of their field observations. Here exacting performance of equipment was demanded and improvements suggested themselves. J. Cecil Alter was active in the research and development of effective wind shields for precipitation gauges, for instance. His work was carried out in experimental installations in Utah, where he long served.

O. L. Fassig was responsible for the first Weather Bureau ombroscope, an instrument which automatically determines the beginning and end of a rainfall. Fergusson rebuilt this instrument in 1920. Snow-sampling apparatus was developed by Marvin and associates as a result of field experience in stream flow at Wagon Wheel Gap, Colorado. This equipment is useful in making surveys of snow depth and density by means of which to estimate the runoff that will result from the spring snow melt. Such information is of great value in several Western states which depend on this water for irrigation and power.

Finally, there is research in the general field of weather science. But, because the Weather Bureau is primarily a service organization, meteorological investigations have been limited and have been directed in the main toward improvement of service. However, the science of meteorology has benefited substantially through the analyses of meteorological observations and the applied physics and mathematics utilized.

The objective has been a better understanding of atmospheric circulation, which, in turn, might afford a logical explanation of how storms and allied phenomena build up and evolve. Cleveland Abbe was an early contributor to this research. But many others also had a hand in it.

A particularly valuable study was the *Report of the Barometry of the United States, Canada, and the West Indies*, made by Frank H. Bigelow, which, though published in 1900, continues to be a standard reference work. W. J. Humphreys' *Physics of the Air* set a high standard for meteorological textbooks prepared from the standpoint of physics and mathematics; Humphreys is likewise credited with the first explanation of the existence and characteristics of the stratosphere, in 1909.

C. F. Brooks, while with the bureau, 1918–21, and since, as an outstanding figure in meteorological education, added much both to theory and to practice. He assisted in preparing the climatic section of the *Atlas of American Agriculture*, 1918–22, for which J. B. Kincer, later chief of the Climate and Crop Weather Division, was primarily responsible.

The most significant recent scientific development is in the use of the polar-front theory and of air-mass analysis, work instituted by F. W. Reichelderfer, present director of the Weather Bureau, and carried on by him with the assistance of C. J. Rossby, H. R. Byers, H. Wexler, and others. The work developed out of attempts by Norwegian scientists to study the air currents during World War I and to devise improved methods of weather forecasting when ocean weather reports no longer came in.

Most weather changes are related to the boundaries between air currents which have different temperature and humidity conditions. There is almost constant conflict between warm, moist currents, usually from the south or west, and cold, dry currents from the north or east, in the Northern Hemisphere at least. This so resembles the tide of battle that the Norwegians began to call the boundary between these air masses a "front." This led to development of the polar-front theory and the air-mass method of weather analysis.

It became necessary then to devise means of finding out what conditions were high above the surface in these air masses. Upper-air soundings had been taken in manned balloons as early as 1784. Indeed, crude temperature soundings had been made as early as 1749, by sending a thermometer aloft on a kite. Benjamin Franklin was active in this field. Beginning in 1900, unmanned balloons began to be used which carried instruments to record air conditions during ascent. Then came box kites and airplanes. Finally, in 1938, the system of radiosonde observations began.

This instrument is sent aloft along with an extremely lightweight radio which transmits signals translatable in terms of air pressure, temperature, and humidity. The assembly is released in a small gas-filled balloon which carries it up fifty thousand feet or more. A radio receiver on the ground records the signals. During its descent other instruments in the balloon record wind direction and velocity. Daily air-mass analysis can readily be made by the use of such equipment.

The recording of such upper-air data does not, of course, replace surface observations nor the surface weather map. They may do so eventually when the radiosonde observation network extends more widely over oceans and continents, but for the next few years these observations will serve to complement the partial picture given by surface maps and observations. At least conjecture about what is happening in the upper air is thus replaced by exact observation.

These new developments undoubtedly have already made and are destined to make meteorology a much more reliable science than ever before. Even while fighting its way against obstacles, the Weather Bureau has aided amazingly in the protection of life, crop, and property values. It has never been a joke to people who really understood its practical accomplishments. It is destined to be still less the butt of inane witticisms in future.

CHAPTER 16

Men on Wheels

THE FEDERAL GOVERNMENT had to undertake extensive research on and subsidy of public roads because men persisted in traveling on wheels.[1] You may not know, however, that some of the most influential of these men were cyclists of the Gay Nineties on bicycle wheels. Their entreaties had a good deal to do with arousing new interest in public roads.

Under authority of legislation approved March 3, 1893, work in the field of public roads began in the Department of Agriculture, and an Office of Public Roads was established. As a matter of fact the unit was called the Office of Road Inquiry until 1898, when it began to designate itself Office of Public Road Inquiries. Finally, in 1905, the agency became the Office of Public Roads, in 1918 the Bureau of Public Roads, then, on July 1, 1939, pursuant to Reorganization Plan No. I, it was transferred to the Federal Works Agency where it became the Public Roads Administration.

General Roy Stone directed the organization until June, 1898, when he joined the staff of General Nelson A. Miles for service in the Spanish-American War. He returned to Public Roads for a few months in January, 1899. Martin Dodge of Cleveland served as director during Stone's absence and after his resignation. M. O. Eldridge, later assistant traffic director of the District of Columbia, was attached to the organization soon after its creation, became assistant director, and played an active part in its early leadership.

The road work grew from 7 employees in 1896 to a 165 in 1912. The appropriation grew accordingly. Then Congress appropriated $500,000 for the construction of post roads, on condition that the

---

[1] Manuscript material prepared in Public Roads Administration proved of very considerable assistance in the preparation of this chapter.

states would match each dollar of federal money with two of their own. The expenditures and the road building were to be supervised by the Department of Agriculture.

The Federal Highway Act of November 9, 1921, providing for the construction of the federal-aid system of public highways gave the agency its largest and most important task to date. The act, as amended, authorized the Secretary of Agriculture to direct payments to the states by the Secretary of the Treasury, on a specified basis, for the construction of public highways. Road construction in the national forests was also increased. Thereafter the agency absorbed and redistributed a large bulk of Department appropriations which finally subsidized road building to the tune of hundreds of millions.

Again we are concerned with research carried on during the time that the agency formed part of the Department of Agriculture.

Following the Revolutionary War there was marked interest in highway improvement. Several turnpikes were built; and, in 1806, the federal government embarked on the construction of a national pike from Baltimore westward across the Appalachian Mountains to Ohio, Indiana, and Illinois. Then came interest in canals, and the United States passed through a considerable period when there was little interest in road building.

About 1830 the railroad era dawned, and work on the national pike ceased. In the eighties farmers began to complain about mud roads, but they were ill-organized and attracted little attention. But in 1885, bicycles of modern types began to appear on highways and the cyclists joined the farmers in urging better roads. Three years later Commissioner Colman stressed the urgent necessity for a well-regulated system of public highways.

At that time the dean of the Engineering Department of Vanderbilt University, Nashville, had undertaken to investigate highway systems. He tendered his results to the Department of Agriculture, which lacked funds to take over the study. A National League for Good Roads was organized and held its first meeting at the Columbian Exposition in Chicago, in October, 1892. At that time almost all rural roads were of unimproved dirt construction. They were cared for superficially by county and local officials, and highway travel between major cities was all but unknown.

Nevertheless, a hundred road-improvement associations and boards of trade were represented in Chicago. Plans were discussed for local, state, and federal legislation on roads, as well as for the creation of a national commission of road inquiry. At this time the League of American Wheelmen became increasingly active in demanding that something be done about poor roads and started publication of a monthly called *Good Roads*.

It was because of such agitation that there was inserted in the Agricultural Appropriation Act for the fiscal year ending July 1, 1893, a paragraph appropriating $10,000 for road-management inquiries and the investigation of road making, with publication of the results. Thus a special agency was created in this field with Roy Stone, New York civil and mechanical engineer and veteran Civil War general, as special agent and engineer for road inquiry, taking office October 3, 1893.

Stone directed a small group working on roads during a period when the modern road-construction movement was just beginning, motor vehicles were not a factor in transportation, and the science of road building was as yet undeveloped. The activities were largely educational in character. Stone conceived the idea of building object-lesson roads throughout the country. He aroused interest in good roads, stimulated the creation of agencies for road construction, and a small beginning was even made in study of road-construction methods.

But the scope of the work was as limited as its appropriation. For some years it was merely advisory and co-operative, though specimens of road material were collected, national roads were mapped, surveys were made of state road work, and numerous conventions were attended. Gravel highways and macadam and other stone roads were studied principally. Publications were issued containing hints on earth roads, digests of road laws, the proceedings of road meetings, and accounts of state aid to counties for building roads.

The small staff was seeking to become expert in an unexplored field. Highway engineering was then unknown and there were neither state nor county highway departments. Various experimental roads were built in different states, costing from $900 to $3,500 per mile, and the difficulties farmers encountered in moving crops to market over poor roads were stressed. State and county aid to road improvement, which started in New Jersey in 1891, was recommended. Discussion was rife, and some states began to consider taking control of their own main highways.

In 1896 a National Road Parliament was held at Atlanta; it was attended by delegates from thirty-two states. The Office of Road Inquiry constructed a sample road on the Atlanta Exposition grounds. Demonstrations were made of the effort required to haul loads over different types of surfaces. The testing of road materials was soon undertaken in earnest, and the building of short stretches of road as object lessons continued.

Stone wanted to construct at least one object-lesson road in every state to demonstrate how easily heavy loads could be carried over good surfaces. Various projects got underway in New Jersey, New York, Rhode Island, and Pennsylvania. These roads not only had educational value but they also provided useful experience for later road-construction projects.

By 1902 several expert road engineers were employed, and the physical and chemical testing of road-building materials was being done in a scientific manner. Early in his administration Secretary Wilson wrote: "Good roads save time and expense. Steel rails are perhaps the coming material where hard rock is not convenient." Considerable experimentation with steel roads was undertaken.

Ease of traction was sought, the stock argument being that the cost of a quarter a ton-mile to haul farm products on existing roads could be reduced drastically by hauling on smooth surfaces. Some sixty years experience with steam engines hauling freight over steel rails suggested that steel trackways might be used on highways. The steel concerns were naturally interested in developing a new market, and search began for a co-operator willing to pay $3,500 for materials to build a mile of steel road.

None was found. But, in 1895, five hundred feet of track was put down on the outskirts of Cleveland. A description of the road reads: "This road is composed of inverted channel bars placed in such a position that they become a tramway or trackway. A broken stone surface had been prepared for the horses to walk upon, and to enable the teamsters to take their wagons on and off the road at will."

In 1898 short sections of steel-track road were built in three states. But the report of the experiments also wrote the obituary for steel roads by saying: "Imperfections were naturally found which can easily be remedied if steel again becomes so cheap that the manufacturers can take the matter up and make rails of special shapes." Exit steel roads.

In no year before 1901 did the expenditures of the road agency attain $10,000, yet seeds were planted which began to sprout in almost every state east of the Mississippi. Little had been done across the big river, in the main because of high travel costs from Washington, D. C. The annual report for 1900 describes co-operation in the construction of object-lesson roads in a dozen states.

The railroads, which wanted to develop the territory they served, as well as the road-machinery manufacturers, were ready with assistance on road-building programs. The latter loaned equipment with the hope of selling it later. Financial assistance came from many institutions and local groups. The financing of a section of road was often undertaken somewhat as a small community later undertook to raise money for hospitals or community houses, except that little aid came from public treasuries.

The railroads went so far as to run special "good-roads trains," in which education was carried forward. From 1901 until 1912 they criss-crossed the country, stopping at thousands of small cities, towns, and villages to spread enlightenment on the advantages of good roads. Eldridge and others in the Department of Agriculture bespoke the good-roads gospel with true evangelical fervor.

Road-building methods which have since been brought to high efficiency in modern practice were sometimes tried in those early days, only to be put aside and forgotten until revived by later generations. In 1899, an earth road at Menomonie, Wisconsin, was rounded up, sprinkled with crude oil, and consolidated by traffic. This was the forerunner of many different types of bituminous-treated soil roads.

An object-lesson macadam road was built at Port Huron, Michigan, in July, 1900, as a demonstration for the League of American Wheelmen, who were in convention. A steam traction engine with wide wheels was used as a roller, and also to pull a road grader and dump wagons. Many years were to elapse before trucks and tractors provided almost unlimited power for highway work. Then an era ended in 1904 and a new one began. Motor traffic appeared, and it tore up macadam roads in no time.

Logan Waller Page headed the federal road-building organization from 1905 until his death in 1918. During this period motor vehicles were rapidly increasing in numbers, methods of highway construction had to be revolutionized, and all branches of government were creating machinery for control over road construction. Page assisted many states to organize their highway departments. He took a leading part in the long debate over federal-aid highway legislation, and he directed co-operative relations with the states during the first two years after the act was passed.

Few of us stop to think that the automobile quickly became the outstanding commercial success it was largely because of huge federal subsidies poured into our network of highways and the research on highway construction performed for many years in the Department of Agriculture. The automobile had to have something equivalent to the modern road to make its operation successful and its performance good. Had the automobile industry been compelled to finance the highways which were absolutely essential to the success of this machine, the price of the automobile would have been prohibitive, and its use could never have spread as rapidly as it did.

Until the motor car arrived there had been little significant change in methods of road construction employed here for over a century. Either gravel or macadam surfacing gave satisfaction for the traffic normal to country roads of the time. Other types of road had been developed and used experimentally; others still, such as the shell roads of the tidewater states and the sand-clay roads of the South, were suggested by the ready accessibility of certain materials rather than by any difference in the demand of traffic using them. In all cases a fragmental mass was bound together more or less firmly by a natural cement.

But the peculiar effect of the automobile on water-bound macadam roads changed conditions. Road builders then rose to meet the challenge with tars and asphalts as substitutes for natural binders. These materials were borrowed from the stock in trade of the city-street builders. They were first used to lay the dust, then as protective surface coatings, next as binders introduced into roads of the macadam type by penetration, and finally as hot admixtures in accord with the bituminous concrete principle. The automobile problem was thus solved.

In 1904 there were in the entire country only about eighteen miles of bituminous rural roads, all in Massachusetts and Ohio. By 1914 there were 10,500 miles—or nearly three-quarters of the aggregate length of all roads of higher type than macadam. The Office of Public Roads played an important part in this transition.

In 1906 it established a chemical laboratory in which to examine, among other things, the properties of tars, asphalts, and oils. Here its workers really explored a new realm. Samples of bituminous material were obtained from many sources and subjected to such chemical and physical tests as seemed requisite. At the same time materials from the same sources were being used in a variety of ways on short sections of experimental roads.

Results on the test roads indicated the kind of materials which stood up well. Correlation of this actual service data with laboratory tests aided in selecting useful materials and indicated test limits to be used in specifications. As knowledge of bituminous materials developed, preliminary tests of proposed mixtures were made in the laboratory. Only the most promising were selected for more expensive field tests.

There were many failures in the first years of bituminous road building. The wrong consistency, the wrong mixture of materials, or the wrong treatment of materials caused these failures. As troubles developed, however, the laboratory experts were called in to diagnose and to prescribe preventive measures or a cure. Gradually a body of knowledge accumulated which brought scientific practice to bear on these matters.

The thousands of miles of fine roads we have today are the result not of any single great discovery but of years of detailed work by many individuals in the laboratory and on experimental roads. However, F. H. Jackson has been engaged in research work of this sort since 1905. His particular field is the physical testing of road materials, the design of concrete mixtures, and the placement of concrete for road surfaces and structures.

Since early days the strength and durability of concrete as used in roads has increased enormously and Jackson is one of the many who had a hand in making this improvement. He has aided in the establishment of highway-testing laboratories and in standardizing laboratory-test procedures. For many years he represented his agency on committees of national organizations dealing with the testing of highway materials.

Parallel to the development of bituminous roads, another type of surface was brought into significant use in agricultural areas. Some person unknown became interested in those sections of natural dirt road which remained fairly smooth in wet weather, and he sought the cause. It was finally discovered that such sections were in the main composed of sand with just enough clay to bind its particles together.

Then some road officials began surfacing roads with material from natural sand-clay deposits. But William L. Spoon, road expert of the Office of Public Roads, was apparently the first to realize the full possibilities of this type of construction, and to circulate information among the growing number of would-be road builders. *Farmers' Bulletin No. 311* on "Sand-Clay and Burnt-Clay Roads" was issued in 1907. In rather didactic style it gave instructions and rule-of-thumb methods for combining sand and clay to surface roads.

In the light of present knowledge about soils this was a very elementary treatise. But it was the guide to building thousands of miles of low-cost road and it is doubtful whether a more technical publication would have been either so effective or so valuable. Spoon's methods were well fitted to the equipment and funds then available. Early attempts to treat sand-clay and gravel roads with bituminous material to lay the dust and smooth the surface failed. But in time the bituminous research workers found what materials to use and how to apply them. Now thousands of motorists ride over surface-treated sand-clay, gravel, and soil roads, knowing only that the surface is bituminous.

Modern highway research really dates from the passage of the Federal-aid Road Act of July 11, 1916. The act initiated the cooperative federal-state program of road construction that has played the most important role in providing us with a system of main highways. The act placed heavy responsibilities upon the Office of Public Roads both in the matter of supervising expenditures and in that of guiding a great road-construction program.

At first 3 per cent of the federal-aid funds was set aside for administrative expenses, including research; in 1921 this was reduced to 2.5 per cent. A periodical magazine, *Public Roads,* has been issued as a distribution medium for research reports ever since May, 1918. Important research began at the Arlington Experiment Station after World War I. A large program has been carried on ever since, its major lines being physical properties of soils as they affect highways, bituminous materials, nonbituminous road-building materials, pavement surface, and bridge design.

Some of this research investigation has had a decisive influence on the development of highway transport. The highways of the land were in bad shape at the close of World War I, because of neglect, heavy traffic, and increasing use of trucks equipped with solid tires. Public demand grew for restricting vehicle loads to existing road capacity, but vehicle manufacturers, sensing the great field ahead for highway transport, said, "Build the roads to carry the loads."

Either course would have seriously retarded the development of our transport system, which, in 1942, moved over fifty billion ton-miles of freight in rural sections alone. The Bureau of Public Roads therefore undertook to determine the impact of vehicle wheels on road surfaces and to ascertain the difference in pavement stresses caused by variations in vehicle loads, tire equipment, and speed. The results of this fundamental research did as much to make the motor-car industry a financial success as any other factor.

It was soon demonstrated that solid tires are much more damaging to pavements than pneumatic tires. So, one by one, the states drove solid tires out by high taxes or else prohibited their use directly. Tires of this sort thus rapidly disappeared from the highway. During his early years with the bureau, Leslie W. Teller conducted many studies on the impact of motor-vehicle wheels upon pavements.

His findings had much to do with the disappearance of solid tires. They also had important application to road-surface design.

Later he made extensive studies of stresses in concrete pavements due to wheel loads and temperature effects. His studies formed a basis for the rational design of concrete surfaces. Teller is an outstanding authority in this field, though far less known to the public than many early automobile designers. Yet he was quite as important to the development of the automotive industry as they.

Tests and investigations relating to the structural action of pavements under loads continued through the years. They furnished a rational basis for state legislation restricting the weight and speed of vehicles and a guide for engineers in pavement design. In carrying out this work, especially refined instruments had to be devised and considerable mathematical calculation was required.

The study was basic, both for road making and for the commercial success of the automobile industry. The results facilitated the construction of a road only expensive and durable enough to withstand the impacts it was likely to receive. As a result of this work it also became possible to modify load stresses and tire construction so as to mitigate materially wear and tear upon more expensive roads. The genesis of the balloon tire may be found here.

Chester A. Hogentogler had immediate charge of the early work of devising methods to measure the impact of motor vehicles on highways. He entered the service in 1919. Later on he undertook studies which resulted in a new soil science for highway construction. When he began his work, our knowledge of soils was limited almost entirely to agricultural aspects.

Tests have been devised and methods of applying the results worked out to fit a number of phases of highway work. Among these are the construction of low-cost surfaces of granular materials and the placement of consolidated fills so that the surfacing does not have to be delayed until settlement takes place.

The soil and impact studies began together. The initial purpose of the former was to devise ways of preventing road failures attributable to the character of the subsurface soil. It was already known that sandy soils provided good road support while clay soils did not. Beyond this the field was almost wholly unexplored. Therefore, thousands of soil samples were taken where failures occurred, as well as from near-by areas where the road stood up.

As no standard test procedure existed for examining such samples, many tests were devised and tried out to differentiate between soils causing failure and those that did not. Gradually a standard test procedure was evolved. A system of soil classification was created for the use of road-design engineers, so that road surfaces might successfully be placed on given soils and corrective measures applied to poor soils.

The information about soils which was thus developed had a much wider field of application than to road building alone. There was an unearned increment of this research also. The soil expert may now take samples of materials from several local deposits, each of which is unsatisfactory for road surfacing, and, guided by the test data, combine two or more of them so as to produce an excellent road base or surface. The materials must have certain qualities indicated by the tests.

Runways for the Washington National Airport were constructed by this method. Engineers operated a field testing laboratory and constantly supervised the mixing of materials used.

It is also possible now to build excellent roads for light and medium traffic at very moderate cost. Soil science has been developed to the point where it is possible to predict the settlement that will take place after twenty or thirty years, when a highway is placed across a swamp, and what the annual settlement will be.

Fills are now being placed on ordinary ground and surfaced with high-type pavements immediately. Formerly one had to wait one or two years for settlement before risking a permanent surface. Unfavorable soils are rejected. The tests make it possible to control the water content of the soil to permit a high degree of consolidation. Checks are also obtained in the consolidation obtained with special rollers. This knowledge was used successfully in constructing certain access roads to military establishments and war industries needed for immediate use.

Studies by public-roads scientists have resulted in an altogether new science of soil mechanics. They have shown what the various kinds and types of soil would do under varying pressure conditions, what factors contribute to soil stability, and how these react under heavy loads. Here is an unearned increment for the building industry.

For this research supplied the industry with valuable facts from which to determine the best manner of laying the foundations for large structures. It now became possible for construction engineers to circumvent both pavement and foundation failure by giving careful attention to the fundamental principles of soil mechanics established by the scientists of the Bureau of Public Roads.

Finally, the bureau carried on important economic studies. These are traffic and transportation surveys, studies of highway finance, highway planning, highway maintenance, the movement of vehicles at intersections, motor-vehicle taxation statistics, and the determination of the effect of highway traffic upon the abandonment of rail lines. The agency works in close co-operation with the American Association of Motor Vehicle Administrators.

Once more we find that a research agency which seems remote from us has affected our personal lives. For the scientific work of the Public Roads Administration is of great importance to all who own or drive automobiles, pay taxes, or inhabit modern buildings. Once again we find that unknown men of sound scientific training have continuously served us unaware.

CHAPTER 17

Birds and Beasts

WHILE IT WOULD BE UNTRUE to say that the birds and beasts held a convention and, as a result, a new agency came into existence in the Department of Agriculture, something remotely resembling that did happen. For a long time certain people have feared the extinction of various species of birds and animals, and some have felt that this might catastrophically upset the biological balance of nature. Many societies have been formed in this country to promote the study and protection of wild life.

Some of these societies were local in scope, others national. Among the latter was the American Ornithologists' Union, founded in 1883. This society undertook detailed studies of the migratory movements and food habits of North American birds and aroused considerable interest in the subject. But funds proved inadequate to conduct the inquiries on a sufficiently broad scale. Therefore the union memorialized Congress in 1885 to establish a division of economic ornithology in the Department of Agriculture to take over accumulated data and pursue the work further.

Congress responded with an appropriation of $5,000. The Branch of Economic Ornithology was then established on July 1, 1885, in the Division of Entomology. A year later it became independent as the Division of Economic Ornithology and Mammalogy, and in 1896 its name was changed to Division of Biological Survey. This was in recognition of the surveys it made of the major biological regions of the continent. In 1905, in the administration of Secretary Wilson, the unit became the Bureau of Biological Survey. Reorganization Plan No. III transferred this bureau to the Department of the Interior, July 1, 1939, where it merged with the Bureau of Fisheries to become Fish and Wildlife Service.

When the agency was created, Commissioner of Agriculture
Colman invited the American Ornithologists' Union to recommend
someone to head it. At a special meeting of the council of the union,
Dr. C. Hart Merriam, chairman of the union's Committee on Migration and Geographical Distribution, was nominated for the post by
Henry Weatherbee Henshaw. He got the job and held it for
twenty-five years when Henshaw himself succeeded to it, serving
for six years.

When about to retire, Henshaw recommended Dr. Edward
William Nelson as his successor, and Secretary Houston gave him
the post. Nelson retired in 1927 and was succeeded by Paul G.
Redington, who was followed by "Ding," the cartoonist with such
a fervent interest in wild life—Jay N. Darling, who served 1934-35.
In 1935 Dr. Ira N. Gabrielson became chief, and, after Biological
Survey left Agriculture, he assumed office as director of the Fish
and Wildlife Service.

The agency has had a remarkable history, though we shall stop
here with the date of its transfer from the Department. Under its
six chiefs it has probably done more outstanding work in the field
of wild-life conservation, and carried it on more scientifically,
than any other single organization in the world. Its list of personnel
throughout its history reads like a "who's who" in biological
science.

The unit began work when our American wild-life paradise
had been well depleted. Buffaloes, antelopes, wild turkeys, and
passenger pigeons no longer appeared in myriads. Fur-bearing animals had largely disappeared in the process of founding great
American fortunes. The inroads of civilization, disease, and wanton
slaughter had combined to reduce the nation's wild life to a piti-
ful remnant of its former numbers. The heath hen, the passenger
pigeon, and the Carolina parakeet had vanished, and migratory
waterfowl and big-game animals seemed on the way out.

Today conditions are much better, largely because of the work
of scientists in this agency. A complete review of their accomplishments would fill several volumes, not only one, and we have but a
brief chapter. Food-habits investigators, migration and distribution experts, refuge managers, taxonomists, predatory-animal and
rodent-control workers, law-enforcement agents, all have con-

tributed a great deal of information to the detailed knowledge on the life histories, habits, distribution, and status of various forms of wild life.

All this knowledge was acquired in the effort to preserve a great natural resource. Survey scientists collected more than 136,-600 specimens of mammals alone in North America during their years of research. This, the largest collection of its kind on earth, includes the smallest mammal on the continent—a three-inch shrew —and the largest existing meat eater, a Kodiak bear. Much of the early work was exploratory and necessarily dangerous. This period witnessed a succession of field surveys that rival in interest the early explorations of the West but were for a quite different purpose.

As Paul Redington has written: "The expeditions were conducted by field naturalists whose names are known throughout the scientific world. Their energy and resourcefulness enabled them to overcome difficulties that in no wise suffer in comparison with exploits that in other settings have formed the basis of romantic tales of absorbing interest. Through deserts whose very names were resonant of desolation and death, through unhealthful tropical jungles, to the summits of mountains carrying perpetual snow, through unexplored mazes of southern lakes, down dangerous unmapped rivers, through untrodden mountain passes, forests and subarctic wastes, by canoe, raft, packtrain, and snowshoe, in sun and storm these men labored."

Yet every day these men unearthed new facts about the distribution or habits of wild life or some new specimen of scientific value. Co-ordination of such exploratory surveys enabled the agency to prepare and publish maps of the natural life zones of North America and to issue important scientific reports on the classification, distribution, and habits of American wild life. Voluminous data were also accumulated on the food habits of wild birds and mammals so that we could tell which destroyed crops and which destroyed insects or rodents that live on crops.

Many of the results of these investigations reached the public in bulletins and circulars issued by the Bureau of Biological Survey, or in numbers of the *North American Fauna*, a series of technical reports it also published. The beginning of the new century placed increasing responsibilities on the bureau. Certain game-preservation functions were added by passage of the Lacey Act in 1900. Three years later the first of a growing system of bird refuges was established by executive order of Theodore Roosevelt.

Passage of several Alaska game laws extended the wild-life conservation work. Passage of the Migratory Bird Law in 1913 and of its successor, the Migratory Bird Treaty Act of 1918, as supplemented in 1929 by the Migratory Bird Conservation Act, authorized the system of migratory bird refuges. The last two measures were designed to carry out provisions of a treaty for the protection of birds that migrate between this country and Canada. This treaty was negotiated with Great Britain and proclaimed by President Wilson in 1916.

The first appropriation for the fiscal year 1886 provided "for the promotion of economic ornithology, or the study of the interrelation of birds and agriculture, and investigation of the food, habits, and migration of birds, in relation to both insects and plants." C. Hart Merriam, who first headed, and practically comprised the staff of the unit, had been on the Hayden Survey in 1872 and assistant to the United States Fish Commissioner in 1875. It was during the first twenty-five years of the agency's existence that Merriam developed his theory that accumulated temperatures during the breeding and growing seasons govern the geographic distribution of plants and animals.

Merriam elaborated this theory in many publications. One of these, *Life Zones and Crop Zones of the United States*, as well as various editions of the *Zone Map of North America*, were distributed by the Department of Agriculture. In 1891 President Harrison appointed Merriam as United States representative on the joint British and American Fur Seal Commission. Merriam was also a member of the United States Board on Geographic Names for twenty years and its chairman for eight years.

It has been said that Merriam named more animals than Adam did. For many species and subspecies were first described by Biological Survey workers and many carry names honoring the discoverers or their colleagues. Systematic collection of specimens and related data involved extensive work by field naturalists from the very start. In organizing and orienting this early field work,

Merriam was much influenced by the concept of life zones advanced by Humboldt and others.

The idea was to map natural-life zones from data on the distribution of both plant and animal life. This distribution would be determined, in turn, by temperature as influenced by altitude, latitude, and exposure, and modified by humidity and other factors. The breeding, growing, and fruiting seasons were especially important. Dr. Merriam resigned in 1910 and died on March 19, 1942, the last of the founders of the National Geographic Society. Mt. Merriam, California, is named for him.

In its second year's existence the agency had its appropriation doubled and its scope enlarged to include the study of mammals as well as birds, but still in relation to agriculture, horticulture, and forestry. Merriam now wrote reports as the Ornithologist and Mammalogist, and was aided by A. K. Fisher and a single clerk. Fisher was a former district superintendent of the American Ornithologists' Union migration study.

In his annual report dated June 30, 1897, Merriam said he had suggested as early as 1889 that there should be a biological survey in the Department. Although Congress had authorized the division, in 1890, to undertake a comprehensive investigation of the geographic distribution of plants and animals, the change of the unit's name to Division of Biological Survey was unauthorized until July 1, 1896. It was then organized in three sections.

A. K. Fisher had charge of economic ornithology. He retired in 1931 after more than forty-six years of service. His main studies were in the fields of bird migration and the food habits of birds of prey, the latter being published in a bulletin entitled "Hawks and Owls of the United States." Fisher was a member of expeditions to Death Valley, to Alaska, and to the South Seas. The last trip was productive of his *Report on Birds Recorded by the Pinchot Expedition of 1929 to the Caribbean and Pacific,* written in collaboration with Alexander Wetmore.

Fisher remained in charge of economic investigations until relieved of administrative work in 1927. Many forms of animal life —mammals, birds, reptiles, amphibians, mollusks, and insects have been named in Fisher's honor. He was one of the founders of that famous American Ornithologists' Union which started the work.

How the process of producing penicillin starts—by pouring a pure culture of the mold into a bottle containing the medium for its growth

Checking the progress of *Penicillium notatum* growth in the battery of milk bottles

Vernon Bailey had charge of the section on geographic distribution. *American Men of Science* rated him among the thousand leading scientific men of the country beginning in 1910. He achieved wide recognition for his studies of the geographic distribution of mammals, birds, and plants. He conducted biological surveys in many states and published many reports embodying his findings. He was also widely recognized for his efforts in behalf of the humane treatment of animals, especially because of traps he devised to capture them alive and unhurt.

A native of Michigan, Bailey was first employed as a special agent by the Department of Agriculture in 1887. He was president of the American Society of Mammalogists and a fellow of the American Association for the Advancement of Science. Many of the country's small mammals, including those important to farmers, were unknown to even the ablest naturalists until Vernon Bailey devised practicable traps and trapping methods for catching them.

The section on game protection, in 1896, was supervised by T. S. Palmer. Palmer retired on July 31, 1933, after forty-four years of service, as against Bailey's forty-six. He was a native of California and a graduate of the University of California in 1888, coming to the Department the following year. In 1895 he took a degree in medicine at Georgetown University. In his early field studies he visited most of the United States. From 1917 he was secretary of the American Ornithologists' Union.

Palmer was widely known for his game-protection activities. He was outstanding also as a zoological historian and biographer, and an authority on the names of mammals. Monumental among his published works is his *Index Generum Mammalium*, issued in 1904 as *North American Fauna No. 23*. Honored abroad as well as at home, he was instrumental in initiating legislation governing the importation of wild animals and birds, and was always foremost in serving the best interests of wild life.

The food habits of birds and mammals almost immediately came under the scrutiny of the newly established unit, the English sparrow, ricebird, blackbird, and gopher being the main objects of study. It was soon found that many birds and mammals supposed to destroy crops were inclined rather to destroy the insects that fed on crops. Hence there was a job of protection as well as one of eradication.

Meanwhile, knowledge of American wild life was so rudimentary that tremendous amounts of data had to be assembled on the range of animals, their life histories, habits, and abundance. Specimens had to be collected by the hundreds. When agricultural and livestock interests required federal help in the control of rodents and predators, the agency got this job also. Taken up in the national forests in 1907, the work expanded until it became one of the major functions of the Biological Survey.

Studies of birds demonstrated their usefulness, and surveys revealed the serious depletion of valuable wild life. Need for conservation became apparent, so the Biological Survey became its advocate. When the treaties with Great Britain and Mexico made migratory-bird protection a federal obligation, the bureau got the administrative and regulatory work. Finally the bureau served well in the later land-utilization programs of the Department of Agriculture.

Recommendations for the protection of useful and the control of injurious species were based squarely upon research. *Biological Survey Bulletin No. 1* was a comprehensive report on the first species to be studied exhaustively. It appeared in 1889, was by Walter B. Barrow, and the subject—"The English Sparrow in North America, Especially in its Relations to Agriculture." The work has been described as the most important treatise ever published upon the economic relations of any bird.

Oddly enough the final technical report of the Bureau of Biological Survey issued before it left Agriculture also dealt with the English sparrow. It was *Technical Bulletin 711*, on the "Economic Status of the English Sparrow in the United States," by E. R. Kalmbach. It was based on examination of a larger number, some eight thousand, of stomach contents than had been analyzed for any other bird species.

While the title sounds as if the problem were to find out how well the sparrow was doing financially, it was actually to discover whether the bird was harmful or beneficial from a crop standpoint. The only way to determine this is to examine stomach contents of many individuals and see what the birds eat. The sparrow turned out to be less of a menace than had been previously supposed, although those in charge of public buildings may be reluctant to believe it.

A. K. Fisher's classic work on *The Hawks and Owls of the United States in their Relation to Agriculture* was mentioned earlier. It appeared in 1893 as a 210-page book with 26 color plates. It clearly demonstrated that, contrary to popular notions, most of the hawks were either beneficial or neutral, not harmful. Its conclusions were effectively substantiated with scientific data.

Fisher's work thus early pointed the way to basing our attitudes towards wild life on carefully determined facts. In the same year the first similar report on mammals appeared, Vernon Bailey's *Biological Survey Bulletin No. 4* on "The Prairie Ground Squirrels, or Spermophiles, of the Mississippi Valley." This careful work changed public attitudes towards many birds and mammals.

Through the course of the years a staff of food-habit analysts, the dean of whom was F. E. L. Beal, reported upon group after group of birds. Some which were supposed to be pests turned out to be highly beneficial. This work resulted in eventual adoption by every state of the American Ornithologists' Union model law, or equivalent legislation, for bird protection. Laws such as this in conjunction with the migratory-bird treaty acts give this country the best code of bird protection in the world.

Data on bird migration collected by the union and later reported by its members, and other observers all over the country, made possible the publication in 1888 of a *Report on Bird Migration in the Mississippi Valley in the Years 1884–85*. This report was prepared by Wells W. Cooke. Largely through his devoted efforts, unparalleled masses of data on bird migration and distribution were accumulated.

Professor Cooke became known finally as the father of bird-migration studies in America. He published six monographs on the range, and movements of birds of as many different families. In 1915 the bureau issued his general treatise on *Bird Migration*. This was later revised and enlarged as a technical bulletin on *The Migration of North American Birds* by Frederick C. Lincoln.

Information on the geographic distribution of birds continued to be accumulated, classified, and used in the preparation of distribution maps and notable publications. Among them was the outstanding series on *Life Histories of North American Birds*, by A. C. Bent, published by the Smithsonian Institution, and the American Ornithologists' Union check lists of North American Birds.

Closely related observations on the numbers of birds were also kept from the start. In 1915, Cooke published a *Preliminary Census of Birds of the United States*, a line of work continued in the bureau by his daughter, May T. Cooke, and others. While censuses in the meaning of actual counts have been abandoned as impracticable, the inventories of waterfowl, organized annually by Mr. Lincoln since 1935, have been very successful in indicating population trends.

In 1920 the Bureau of Biological Survey took over the work of the American Bird Banding Association. Since that time it has accumulated invaluable data concerned with all studies of the migration, distribution, and abundance of birds. The work has also facilitated the annual formulation of regulations for the taking of migratory waterfowl.

Dr. Harry C. Oberholser, internationally known ornithologist, who in his early days with the agency, organized this bird-banding work, retired in 1941. It was he who directed the first nationwide migratory-waterfowl inventories. He was the author of some eight hundred technical and popular publications on birds and had been the first to describe or to name scientifically 650 bird forms, in addition to several birds named in his honor by other ornithologists.

Oberholser was born in Brooklyn, came to Washington in 1895, enrolled at George Washington University, and there took his bachelor's, master's, and doctor's degrees. He entered the Division of Ornithology and Mammalogy, February 1, 1895, and was still with the organization when it went to the Department of the Interior. Well known as an educator, lecturer, and writer (his *Birds of Louisiana* and *Birds of Texas* are outstanding), he could also identify wild-bird species by examining their bones or feathers, and was often called to give expert testimony in court in cases involving wild-duck bootleggers and similar characters.

Bird banding was itself designed to aid in the correct identification of birds. Identification of many small animals was also desired by many individuals and institutions. Biological Survey carried on much work of this kind. By 1890, a Department report said that the division "is in effect a biological survey, and should be so named, for its principal occupation is the preparation of large-scale maps of North America, showing the boundaries of the different faunas and floras, or life areas."

In 1897, after the proposed change in name had been made, the Department of Agriculture *Yearbook* declared that: "The colored maps prepared by the Biological Survey furnish the first rational basis the American farmer and fruit grower had ever had for the intelligent distribution of seeds, and the only reliable guide he can find in ascertaining beforehand what crops and fruits are likely to prove successful on his own farm, wherever it may be located."

The basic value of the information assembled in these biological surveys was really stupendous. The surveys were at first carried on through intensive investigations by expeditions of naturalists to areas of critical importance. In 1889, such an expedition to San Francisco Mountain in Arizona and the area of the Little Colorado Desert gathered material that led to the recognition of seven life zones and the publication of a provisional map.

This survey was followed by the Death Valley Expedition in 1891, and later by intensive investigations of other regions, including Mount Shasta in California, the Yukon River Region in Alaska, and some areas in Canada and Mexico, along with others in this country. Results of this work were published in the bureau's series of *North American Faunas*, many of which had general as well as biological importance.

Edward A. Preble's 574-page volume, *A Biological Investigation of the Athabaska-Mackenzie Region*, published in 1908, thus made valuable contributions to the geography of the region. These were later recognized by the Canadian government in naming for Preble an island in Great Slave Lake and a bay of Great Bear Lake.

The series included not only many biological surveys but also the results of the taxonomic investigations made, and a few special reports. One of the largest and best of the systematic monographs was W. H. Osgood's *Revision of the Mice of the American Genus*

Peromysous, which appeared in 1909. A bibliographical work which was never surpassed in its field was T. S. Palmer's *Index Generum Mammalium: A List of the Genera and Families of Mammals*, appearing in 1904.

The North American Fauna series continued throughout the stay of the Biological Survey in the Department of Agriculture. It comprised more than fifty numbers and constituted a set of scientific monographs rarely if ever equalled. They brought world recognition to their authors and their agency alike. Originally the bureau's scientists not only made fundamental investigations but also devised many new techniques which were widely adopted by other scientists.

At all times the bureau has sought only to control harmful species while protecting the beneficial and desirable sorts. Practical application of the knowledge its scientists developed was widespread. It found few forms of wild life to be either wholly good or wholly bad, viewed from the vantage point of genus Homo sapiens, earth shaker and master of the atomic bomb.

The survey helped millions to discriminate between the preponderantly harmful and the chiefly beneficial groups of birds and mammals. Methods to control injurious forms of wild life were objects of study from the start. Widespread publication of information favored expansion of control activities. This was especially true after $125,000 was appropriated for predatory-animal control in the national forests and on the public domain, for livestock protection. That was in 1915.

Later the work increased through state co-operation. It was extended in organized fashion to destructive birds in 1930. Here the scientists' study not only made control activities more efficient but also served to restrict them to species and even to individuals that were actually doing damage. Time and time again scientific findings yielded facts contrary to popular assumptions regarding the good or harm done by wild birds and mammals.

On the other hand, desirable wild life has been protected consistently and its welfare promoted. The foundation for improved conservation was placed by demonstrating the usefulness of many forms of wild life and arousing popular interest in its protection. Discovering and recommending methods for improving the habitat of game birds, waterfowl, and song birds featured the survey's program for many years. These activities were especially effective because they were based on scientific fact.

For example, regulations to restrict the take of hunters were greatly improved when founded upon the proved needs of wild-life forms rather than upon the consensus of opinion among those with political or narrow sporting interests. The establishment of game refuges proved more successful because the areas chosen for them were selected upon a sound scientific basis, taking into account the food habits and other characteristics of the wild life they were designed to protect.

Because it was so thoroughly equipped with knowledge about wild life and experience in this field of administration, the survey became the government's principal instrument for an extensive wild-life restoration program. This program gained renewed impetus in the nineteen thirties as part of a great movement for the conservation of natural resources embodied in the Department's land-utilization program.

As the survey began with the American Ornithologists' Union, it was fitting that Ira N. Gabrielson, who was its chief when it left the Department, should have been a fellow of the union. He had spent in the service of the Biological Survey all but three of the years since he graduated from Morningside College, Sioux City, Iowa, in 1912. He had had a wide and varied experience and was an ideal selection as director of the Fish and Wildlife Service, where this work continues to be energetically pursued.

CHAPTER 18

Fraud in Foods and Drugs

T HE WORK CARRIED ON by the Food and Drug Administration rather naturally originated in the Department of Agriculture, for this Department has employed chemists since its creation and it has always been largely concerned with the American food supply. Fraudulent fertilizers early attracted the attention of the several states and also that of the Department, while food adulterations came to the attention of Department chemists early in its history.

The Commissioner of Patents, on the basis of an appropriation of one thousand dollars made by Congress in 1848, engaged the services of Lewis C. Beck, a member of the faculty of Rutgers College, to conduct an investigation on breadstuffs of the United States. Beck's report appeared in the report on agriculture issued by the Patent Office in the same year. The report for 1849 (pages 49–82) called attention to widespread adulteration of flour with alum, potato starch, and other substances.

It was around 1873 that the Commissioner of Agriculture directed the Department chemist, William McMurtrie, to devote his time exclusively to the examination of agricultural products. This was because Commissioner Watts had been annoyed by private individuals who desired the chemist to test wines, patent medicines, and ore samples. As there were then loud complaints about fraud in commercial fertilizers, the chemist analyzed a number of these and the results were published.

Around 1878 Commissioner Le Duc's chemist was requested by the city government of the District of Columbia to analyze cream puffs and coffee suspected of being poisoned, as well as supposedly adulterated bologna sausage and tea. The chemist also examined certain coffee and tea substitutes, some baking powders, butters, and oleomargarines, and a tonic called "Boneset." In publishing the analysis of the last-named, the chemist made clear that it was a misrepresented article.

The rather extraordinary work begun in 1871 by Thomas Taylor of the Division of Microscopy, has been mentioned hitherto. Taylor not only investigated cranberry rot, mushroom culture, grape mildew, peach yellows, and black knot of plum, but he also devised a microscopic method of detecting adulterants in butter and other fats. When this division was dissolved, that part of the work went to the Division of Chemistry.

The *Annual Report* of the Commissioner of Agriculture for 1880 contained a paragraph explaining why the Department of Agriculture could not prohibit food adulterations. This paragraph was printed because frequent letters came in asking whether the Department could not undertake this function.

For many years, then and thereafter, there was constant public agitation for the passage of a stringent law making it a crime to manufacture spurious articles or to adulterate genuine ones. At that time the government already regulated imported articles, drugs in particular. Publication of the paragraph mentioned indicates an interesting trend in public opinion destined to result in passage of the first Federal Food and Drug Act a quarter of a century later. Many bills were introduced and came to nothing before this occurred because the opposition was powerful, wealthy, and ever on the alert.[1]

In 1883, as was noted earlier, Dr. Harvey W. Wiley became Department chemist and the following year a Division of Chemistry was created. At that time cottonseed oil was a common adulterant of butter and lard; coconut shells, olive seed, rice bran, sawdust, and other foreign substances were used to adulterate spices; candies abounded in poisonous coloring matter and added metallic substances; honey was adulterated with glucose or cane sirup; chicory was a common adulterant of coffee; and brick dust, sand, copper, and gypsum appeared in tea. Poisonous preservatives were used freely in meat and other products.

Almost immediately Wiley began his classic investigations on

[1] Cf. "Congressional Opposition to Pure Food Legislation, 1879–1906," by Thomas A. Bailey, *American Journal of Sociology*, July, 1930, 52–64.

food adulterants, which were mentioned in the chapter on agricultural chemistry. By 1900 these researches, published in a succession of bulletins, had had far-reaching influence. Wiley also was an excellent publicist and a skilled agitator, and though he had to develop his methods of analysis as he went along, he always found time to propagandize his findings in print and by word of mouth. He was a one-man movement all by himself, and he carried others with him.

While public agitation for a law to control foods and drugs had gone on for many years, it crystallized under Wiley's skillful touch. The politicians got in line, Congress took action and, in 1906, the first Food and Drug Act was passed. While it was imperfect and contained many loopholes, it was a step in the right direction. Some thirty to thirty-five years later these loopholes were fairly well stopped by passage of the Food, Drug, and Cosmetic Act and of the Wheeler-Lea Amendment to the Federal Trade Commission's organic act, which aimed to put truth in advertisements, a field, like cosmetics and medical devices, untouched by Wiley's act.

When the Food and Drugs Act was passed, the Bureau of Chemistry, of which Wiley was then chief, was charged with its enforcement. In 1927 this regulatory work, which had been superimposed upon the bureau's research work to the disadvantage of both, was placed in a unit to itself called the Food, Drug, and Insecticide Administration, and later just the Food and Drug Administration. This new unit absorbed the work of the Insecticide and Fungicide Board, which had been set up in 1911 to enforce the Insecticide Act.

The change of name to Food and Drug Administration became effective in 1930. Reorganization Plan No. IV transferred the administration to the Federal Security Agency, June 30, 1940. This was soon after the passage of the Food, Drug, and Cosmetic Act. We are concerned here with research performed by the unit during the time it was in the Department of Agriculture.

The research carried on by scientists in this line of work almost entirely concerned itself with methods of chemical, biochemical, microanalytical, physical, and bacteriological analysis. The work aided materially in the detection of fraud and adulteration, and new methods had constantly to be devised to detect new and subtle forms of sophistication. Such research had definite and considerable monetary value to consumers, though it is all but impossible to estimate this in terms of the dollar. It likewise aided producers by weeding out unfair competition.

In the chapter on chemistry Wiley's famous "poison squad" was mentioned. Later the Remsen Referee Board worked on the physiological effects of benzoate of soda, sulfur dioxide, and saccharin, when used in foods in the ordinary way. Investigational techniques of value were developed.

So rapid was progress in the field of food processing and preservation that, even in 1907, the analytical methods available to the chemist for examining foods were few and inexact. The same held for drugs. Today, as a result of the labor of more than a generation of federal scientists and their numerous collaborators in this field, one of the finest collections of analytical methods extant has been developed.

In Wiley's time the Food Research Division was located in Philadelphia and was directed by Mary E. Pennington. Dr. Pennington did pioneer work on problems concerned with the preparation, processing, and storing of foods, especially poultry and fish. These studies were undertaken primarily to educate the food industries in the use of such processing and storing methods as would enable them to meet the requirements of the Food and Drug Act.

Here is an early example of the constructive type of endeavor that has long engaged the food and drug specialists. Not only have its scientists developed methods for the detection of frauds and adulterants, but they have undertaken research investigations designed to enable manufacturers to meet the increasingly stringent requirements of laws regulating foods, drugs, and cosmetics. This educational technique was bitterly attacked by Wiley in his later years, when he worked for *Good Housekeeping*, though he himself initiated it.

The work of the Association of Official Agricultural Chemists also early resulted in the development of highly accurate and specialized methods of analysis for fertilizers, foods, drugs, and related products. Men like R. E. Doolittle and A. F. Seeker made outstanding contributions. The sugar investigations carried on by C. A. Browne and his coworkers, the microscopical work of Andrew L. Winton, and W. D. Bigelow's work on food products were all outgrowths of regulatory requirements. They also had definite scientific value.

Work of this kind is never-ending. Over and over again new methods of food processing, preservation, handling, or storing, as well as subtler and more refined techniques of fraud and adulteration have compelled chemists to exert themselves to develop new methods of analysis and detection before they can take legal action with evidence that will stand up in court. This has required much ingenuity and exacting research.

Outstanding is the work of the food chemists in the development of quick and accurate analytical methods for determining mere traces of lead, arsenic, and flourine left on fruits and vegetables as spray residues. These workers have also developed refined methods of extraordinary precision for the quantitative determination of fruit acids. These methods have had decisive diagnostic value in the examination of fruit products to determine compliance with the law.

Work on methods for estimating volatile acids as a measure of partial decomposition of food products was difficult but helpful. Methods have also been developed for the objective measurement of quality factors in canned fruits and vegetables. Novel methods of far-reaching application have likewise been developed for the identification of various genuine and imitation fruit flavors.

Application of these and other methods has checked many abuses in the way of substituting highly concentrated imitation flavors for genuine food ingredients in food products. The economic significance of this work to fruit growers has been large.

For many years the microscopic work in this field was carried on by Burton J. Howard. His mold-count method is not only the standard regulatory means of determining the presence of decomposed tissues in tomato products, but it is also used by processing plants as a factory-control method to insure the production of sound products.

Later John D. Wildman developed a mold-count method for detecting butter made from moldy and decomposed cream. Again a control procedure was devised which materially improved the general quality of an important food product. Extensive research has been carried on upon methods for the determination of decomposition factors in cream and butter generally. The microscopists have developed many methods which now prove in court that such products contain disgusting contaminants, in many cases, which are esthetically offensive if not active menaces to health.

Such methods of detecting and identifying filth present in food are based usually upon an oil-flotation technique. They are particularly valuable because the presence of such matter in minute particles would otherwise go undetected. Some judges have been moved to comment that contamination of food products with microscopic filth is one of the worst forms of law violation.

In 1924 whole counties of blueberry growers were threatened with ruin because of the presence of the blueberry maggot in their products. Here was a case where the microscopists under Howard went to work to save an industry. They first developed microscopic methods of detecting the maggots, and, as a result, most of the berries were being rejected for market.

But they went further. To save the growers, they devised a mechanical device which proved to be the salvation of the Maine blueberry-canning industry. It separated the sound from the maggoty, wormy, or otherwise unfit berries. A public-service patent was procured. The device was thus made available to and was largely adopted by the packers, who thereafter had no further trouble with the law on this score.

In the drug field one of the finest pieces of research performed by the chemists was that by Marvin R. Thompson, which won him the Ebert Medal at the seventy-eighth meeting of the American Pharmaceutical Association, May 5-10, 1930. This was a basic study of ergot. Thompson's investigations stimulated further work on the biological assay of ergot preparations, and accelerated the search for biologically active substances in ergot which were not identical with those already known.

Somewhat later the same medal was awarded Lloyd C. Miller for his work on the assay of digitalis. Considerable work of permanent value was likewise performed by the late Herbert O. Calvery and associates on chronic lead and arsenic poisoning. Oddly enough this research was being carried on right while the administration was being criticized for having dropped all research work! Those who made this criticism simply did not understand the administrative advantages of separating regulatory work from the research carried on in the Bureau of Chemistry proper.

A further outstanding piece of research was the study on the toxicity of certain glycols and their derivatives. The results of this work will aid in forestalling another tragedy such as that which occurred in 1938, when about a hundred people were killed by innocently using a sulfanilamide preparation a manufacturer had sent to market containing poisonous diethylene glycol.

E. M. Nelson of the administration is one of the outstanding as well as one of the most reliable workers in the field of vitamins. He and his associates have developed many improved assay methods. They have also carried on significant research in collaboration with the Children's Bureau of the Department of Labor on the relative antirachitic value of cod-liver oil and viosterol.

Nor have the bacteriologists been idle. They perfected a method for determining the effect of chemical antiseptics on phagocytosis —the ability of the blood to mobilize its infection-fighting forces —which has had wide application. Initial publication in 1940 was followed by several other publications on the subject.

In general, the scientific work carried on by the staff of this agency has had broad social, industrial, and economic value. It did much to prevent unfair competition in trade, as well as to protect consumers from physical or economic injury by misbranded, adulterated, or deleterious food and drug products. It aided the agricultural industry to produce foods of better quality, and it directly protected farmers from unwise investment in misrepresented veterinary remedies. The research on methods required to achieve these results constituted much basic investigation of the highest standards.

PART IV : VALUES

CHAPTER 19

Value of Pure Research

FOR MANY YEARS NOW the value of pure, as opposed to applied, research has been hotly debated. Was it worth while for scientists, going where curiosity led them, simply to piece together the mosaic of scientific knowledge regardless of immediate applications and monetary considerations? Was it sufficient merely to solve particular problems as they arose and to rather ignore the search for basic principles?

The development of the atomic bomb should end this debate forever, because nothing so spectacularly tremendous has ever before developed from pure research. When such research can be so accelerated that the progress of a quarter of a century is packed into two or three years, the cream of the scientists in several countries working successfully to develop a relatively small bomb capable of destroying a city of a quarter of a million persons, who can say that pure research is of dubious value?

It was only on the last day of December, 1939, that Waldemar Kaempffert, scientific editor of the New York Times, announced that he regarded the splitting of the uranium atom as the outstanding scientific achievement for that year. Who had accomplished this? Why had they done it? The atom had been under close investigation by pure scientists for a number of years. Their concept of its nature and organization changed constantly, but none of them thought in terms of making money, of destroying cities, or of revolutionizing monetary systems. Yet that is what their work was destined to do.

Some of these scientists had discovered a neutral particle in atoms seven years earlier, and had named it a "neutron." In 1939 Dr. Liese Meitner, a German Jewish refugee in Sweden, continued work begun by Dr. Otto Hahn in Berlin, and released tremendous stores of energy from atoms of uranium by splitting them with neutrons. Later she continued her experiments with Dr. Otto Robert Frisch in Copenhagen. But in 1934 Professor Enrico Fermi, who later became a refugee from Rome at Columbia University, had found that the bombardment of uranium with neutrons appeared to produce entirely new radioactive elements.

Fermi started in to make some of these elements. We only knew ninety-two kinds of atoms then; he made a ninety-third, a ninety-fourth, a ninety-fifth, and a ninety-sixth, giving them such esoteric names as eka-rhenium, eka-osmium, eka-tridium, and eka-platinum. In 1938 Mme Curie-Joliot was at work on new elements. Savitch, Strassmann, and Professor John R. Dunning of Columbia all had a hand in this work. Complex mathematical calculations indicated that if the nucleus of uranium were annihilated it would manifest itself as a tremendous quantity of energy.

All of this sounded very remote, very impractical, but neither Hiroshima nor Nagasaki could be brought to think that in August, 1945. Nor in the future, when billions of dollars in capital investment become obsolete and monetary systems tumble because a new and stupendous source of energy has become economically practicable, can those who lose and those who benefit thereby regard that background research as remote or impractical.

The same case can be made out for penicillin. Somebody made about $1,280 available to Professor H. W. Florey of Oxford University to equip a laboratory to develop a chemical approach to pathological problems. Later a sum of $5,000 was granted for "A Chemical Study of the Phenomenon of Bacterial Antagonism," certainly a formidable subject one would expect to yield little of immediate moment.

But, partly by accident, Dr. Alexander Fleming of St. Mary's Hospital, London, discovered that penicillin, produced by a mold, was antagonistic to bacteria. The equipment at Oxford was used to make pioneer studies of the clinical value of the drug. The fact that certain Department of Agriculture scientists had for years maintained a very large collection of molds and related microorganisms, enabled the Regional Research Laboratory at Peoria quickly and effectively to increase yields and lower prices.

What was that worth in dollars? The drug is truly priceless.

Take as another example the laboratory of physical chemistry under Dr. Edwin J. Cohn, established—of all places—at Harvard Medical School in 1920. It was an odd sort of laboratory for a medical school to have and its research was profoundly pure and unruffled by practice; but in the end it supplied methods of separating blood plasma into components which proved of extraordinary value in surgery and in wound treatment.

It found the value of albumin in shock. It isolated blood-clotting factors, plasma antibodies, and produced a transfusion unit which occupied one-sixth the space and weighed one-seventh that for whole plasma. All sorts of practical clinical value has accrued and more will accrue from this purely theoretical investigation, which turned into a process of mining blood for its valuable constituents in therapy and prophylaxis. Once the basic knowledge is at hand, application comes easy.

Then, in this immediate connection, we have at Orlando, Florida, the research laboratories of the Bureau of Entomology and Plant Quarantine which so quickly branched out into an enormously intensive research program on insecticides and fungicides and insect repellents. Once again twenty-five years of research was highly organized and concentrated into two or three years, and practical results—DDT among them—flowed freely from what had a little earlier been highly theoretical investigations.

The conclusion is inescapable that any soundly conceived research project is bound to produce knowledge which will, at least in the long run, and often quickly under emergency conditions, produce results of tremendous practical import and value. Our minds naturally revert to the quiet monk, Gregor Mendel, whose fundamental discovery in the field of genetics was locked away in an obscure Swiss journal for fifty years, yet finally came into its own.

Sometimes basic-research workers appear to concentrate most intensively on problems that appear to have no possible value to humanity, but the utility of the seemingly useless knowledge they accumulate is frequently astounding.

Many years ago Karl Wilhelm von Nägeli, a brilliant Swiss botanist, was studying the fresh-water alga belonging to the genus

Spirogyra, known to laymen as "frog spittle" or "green slime." This alga grows in ponds and slow streams. To the naked eye it looks like fine, long, green silk thread. But it is easy to see the living cell in operation, and that is why the plant is often selected for laboratory study.

True, a visiting committee of farmers might not have been suitably impressed with the activities of a scientist who frittered his time away on frog spittle. They would probably have been as disgusted as was Nägeli when he could no longer get his alga to grow in his carefully prepared solutions which he was sure contained everything a well-mannered alga could want in precisely the right proportions to render it healthy and happy.

However, the alga disconsolately died every time. Day after day Nägeli tried to find out why. At long last it occurred to him that minute traces of copper from his bronze laboratory spigot caused the water he used to kill the alga. The quantity of copper involved here was so minute that no known method of chemical testing revealed it, but optical tests indicated it was present to the extent of one part per fifty million parts of water. That tiny bit of copper killed the alga, a fact Nägeli dutifully recorded in a little pamphlet and then went on to other things and later to his reward.

His pamphlet remained untranslated and almost forgotten for half a century. Then an indignant cress grower appeared at the Department of Agriculture and complained that he and others like him were being put out of business because some sort of disease was killing the cress. So Dr. George T. Moore was sent to investigate. He found that Spirogyra was smothering the cress. Then he thought of Nägeli's forgotten pamphlet.

Arrangements were made to add one part of copper per fifty million parts of water in the cress beds. This destroyed the alga without injury to the cress. That led to further study of the use of copper in destroying objectionable algae of various kinds which impart undesirable odors and flavors to water in certain reservoirs. Methods were worked out of using copper for this purpose, and they became standard practice in sanitary engineering.

Next, it was observed that certain species of disease-causing bacteria in the water, those of the colon group for instance, could be destroyed by the introduction of small quantities of copper

322

without endangering those who drank the water. However, the copper killed certain types of fish. Hence a test was made with chlorine which proved effective in killing the bacteria without injuring the fish. Such use of chlorine became standard practice at certain reservoirs. It was also observed that traces of copper killed mosquito larvae. Then Colonel Gorgas suggested that some Department of Agriculture personnel be sent to him to help clean up the Isthmus of Panama, and Karl Kellerman was assigned.

Another step which followed elsewhere was study of the important role of copper in nutrition. Diets deficient in copper were found to produce secondary anemias. A trace of copper was discovered essential to both plant and animal growth. So much for Nägeli's penchant for monkeying around with frog spittle.

It is very difficult to tell where a simple scientific discovery will lead, or what its ultimate ramifications will be. It is therefore usually well worth while to make the discovery by all means. Research with growth-regulating substances or plant hormones is another case in point. This was quietly carried along for years without anything very spectacular happening, though it was known that many different substances would affect the roots, stems, buds, and flowers of various plants in peculiar ways.

The thing assumed considerable theoretical interest. In some cases the natural behavior of the plant could be altered completely. But in the course of time it was found that apple trees, treated with an extremely dilute hormone solution, would hold their fruit without premature dropping. So the spraying of apple trees with hormones became standard practice in many orchards. It has very considerable value in preventing fruit from dropping before it has reached good size and color.

That single application of this research will easily save all the money spent on all the hormone research carried on by the Department of Agriculture. It is even useful to keep the berries on holly trees at Christmas! Yet all this was not even dreamed of when the work began. It was simply a by-product of a job in pure research. Now hormones are also used to stimulate root development in cuttings of plants which ordinarily root with great reluctance. It seems as if blossoms might be dusted with hormones to improve the quality of the fruit which comes later.

The *Journal of Agricultural Research* has been mentioned before. It is a journal of pure research which some persons tend to deride as being filled with complex and forbidding technical papers that have little or no practical value when published or at any time thereafter. As an example, a paper appeared there in 1924 which recorded the daily fluctuations of the carbohydrates in the leaves of corn and sorghum. It was soon forgotten.

Why should anybody ever have interested himself in such a thing in the first place? Who cared how much sugar a corn leaf contained at different times of day? Then, years later, members of a university dairy department found that silage varied markedly in acidity and they could not tell why. Finally they came upon the paper mentioned above. Then they discovered that they could control the acidity of silage by paying attention to the time of day when the sorghum or corn was cut to make it. Thus theory passed into practice.

The first paper telling about the use of derris root, containing rotenone, as an insecticide, appeared in this journal in 1919, and from that paper flowed an entire insecticide industry. The paper by Clara H. Hasse, which identified the cause of citrus canker and resulted in control methods which prevented this disease from wiping out the citrus crop in Florida, Alabama, Mississippi, and Texas, appeared in this journal in 1915.

The original papers on the nature and control of apple scald, which was causing apple growers tremendous losses, appeared in this journal between 1919 and 1923. The disease was shown to be physiological and caused by respiration products given off through the skin of the fruit; wrapping the fruit in oiled or waxed paper prevented it entirely.

The basic paper from which present methods of control of the oriental fruit moth developed appeared in this journal in 1932. The paper describing the use of spore-forming bacteria to cause milky disease of Japanese beetle larvæ, and the one on which was based the use of lead arsenate to treat the soil and free it from the beetle grubs, both appeared in the journal. Other papers that appeared therein have been mentioned earlier.

When it comes to strictly monetary value of Department research, much has already been said, and much more could be said.

The discovery in the Bureau of Entomology and Plant Quarantine of a method to prolong the life of peach trees by controlling borers cost possibly $85,000 and is worth about $3,000,000 a year, if used to increase the crop of one-fourth of the country's peach trees a mere 6 per cent.

The discovery that celery leaf tier could be controlled by the use of pyrethrum powder, made in the same bureau at a cost of something like $67,000, can largely prevent a loss from this insect of $1,000,000 a year for this one crop. Methods of controlling the alfalfa weevil which have been developed in this bureau at a cost of something like $500,000 are worth at least $1,000,000 a year. Rotenone root powders were found effective in protecting the raspberry and similar crops from worms at a cost of $38,000, and can prevent a loss to growers of $200,000 annually caused by degrading or condemnation of infested fruit.

The preharvest apple spray, mentioned a little earlier, developed by Dr. L. P. Batjer of the Bureau of Plant Industry, Soils, and Agricultural Engineering, seems destined to produce a dividend of 400 per cent on the investment, for it should add $4,000,000 a year to the income of fruit growers; and Batjer and Paul Marth originally used it to keep berries on Christmas holly trees! The one piece of research, one single discovery, out of hundreds underway, thus promises to return to the taxpayers four times the cost of the entire division in which it was made.[1]

The bureau just mentioned has estimated that twenty-two of its research accomplishments bring the American public about a quarter of a billion dollars added income annually. If only 5 per cent of its research projects work out practically, and that is a conservative estimate, this will pay $100 for every dollar expended on research by the bureau. Returns of 500 to 10,000 per cent on the investment in research are not at all uncommon, while govern-

[1] Readers interested in the monetary returns derived from small investments in research should apply to the Co-ordinator of Research Publications, Agricultural Research Administration, Department of Agriculture, Washington, D. C., for copies of some of the Research Achievement Sheets. These, printed on both sides of one sheet of heavy paper, give complete accounts, with references, costs of projects, value of the discovery in monetary terms, and other pertinent information, regarding a great number of scientific investigations that have been carried on to the taxpayer's profit.

ment research does much to stimulate investigation by private enterprise.

No greater broad vindication of Department research in the fields of both the natural and the social sciences ever surpassed the production record of the agricultural industry during World War II, when—with labor, supplies, insecticides, fertilizer, and equipment all scarce—sufficient additional food was produced, as compared with the 1935–39 period, to feed fifty million additional persons. Moreover, it has been shown that, with certain adjustments of the farm-production and the dietary patterns, we could readily produce enough food, using the newer agricultural technology to its highest potentialities, to provide for a population twice the size of that we now have.

During the 1942–45 period it at last became possible for agriculture to use to the full the vast reservoir of scientific knowledge and technological know-how which had been accumulated during the nineteen thirties, but which was then held back from use because of drought and depression. For it was greater mechanization, more lavish use of fertilizers, lime, and soil conservation practices, the adoption of improved crop varieties and more productive strains of animals and poultry, improved control of insects and plant and animal diseases, and the social and economic know-how that enabled us to provide proper incentives to farmers to produce what was needed when it was needed which made wartime increases in production possible.

Total cultivated acreage was increased only slightly. There was no plow-up of unsuitable land destined later to erode. The farm population had dropped from thirty to a mere twenty-five million. Farmers had 8 per cent fewer workers in 1944 than in 1935–39, and these were but 85 per cent as effective as those of prewar times. Yet an absolute, irrevocable, and irreversible break was made with the immediate past, and farm output for human use—with due allowance made for abnormally good weather—jumped 20 per cent above 1935–39. That is in essence and in reality a triumph of agricultural research such as history has never before witnessed.[2]

[2] Space is unfortunately lacking to give a full account of this most extraordinary revolution in American agricultural technology and productivity, but readers interested in further details are strongly advised to procure and

Pure research therefore has important practical aspects, and applied research pays huge dividends on the investment therein. But many farmers remain poor and the profits do not seem to go to the right people, you say. The solution of that problem would involve us too much in economic reform for the present context. However, I would like to repeat the paragraph with which I ended my contribution to the *Yearbook of Agriculture*, 1940, entitled "Science and Agricultural Policy." It read thus:

> In the past we have assumed the permanency of our economic and social frame of reference and have insisted upon trying to cram into this frame, willy-nilly, the vast knowledge and potentialities the natural sciences have provided. Henceforth we must decide to take the knowledge natural science has given us as our frame of reference and deliberately, consciously, and scientifically devise the kind of social and economic system that will enable us to use it most fully and beneficially for promoting the public welfare.

read the following publications, issued by the Department's Bureau of Agricultural Economics, in the chronological order in which they were issued: *Technology on the Farm*, a special report by an Interbureau Committee and the Bureau of Agricultural Economics, August, 1940; *Using Resources to Meet Food Needs*, Raymond P. Christensen, (processed) May, 1943; *Farm Production in War and Peace*, Glenn T. Martin and Martin B. Cooper (processed), December, 1945; *Changes in Farming in War and Peace*, Sherman E. Johnson (processed) June, 1946.

APPENDIX

The Publication of Research

THE ACT creating the Department of Agriculture stated that the "general designs and duties" of the Department "shall be to acquire and to diffuse among the people of the United States useful information on subjects connected with agriculture in the most general and comprehensive sense of that word." Obviously, the Department was established not only to make investigations and acquire information, but in some manner to acquaint the public who paid for its activities with their nature and accomplishments.

Soon after 1836 the annual reports of the Commissioner of Patents began to contain material of interest to agriculturalists. In time, this grew to the extent that a man especially qualified in agriculture was employed to edit and, in part, to write what eventually became an annual book on purely agricultural matters. This book contained articles by outside writers, reports, and replies to correspondence. Initially the annual publications of the Department of Agriculture followed the same pattern.

The Department also issued scientific and technical reports. Publications of this sort really began when Congress in 1828 authorized the printing as a document of Count Von Hazzi's *A Treatise on the Rearing of Silkworms*. Two years earlier the House had ordered published the 220-page document on the growth and manufacture of silk, produced by Secretary of the Treasury Rush in response to its resolution of May 11, 1826. It also appeared in 1828. The first publication issued by the Department in 1862 was a pamphlet on "The Present Agricultural, Mineral, and Manufacturing Conditions and Resources of the United States" by the first head of the Department, Commissioner of Agriculture Isaac Newton.

In 1862 there was also issued a research publication by the

Department's first chemist, Charles M. Wetherill, a "Report on the Chemical Analysis of Grapes." Other publications followed, becoming more technical and specialized as science itself progressed and proliferated.

By the time the head of the Department assumed Cabinet rank, it was realized that the publication policy required more attention. The necessity for increased publication of agricultural information in popular form was realized to be urgent by Secretary of Agriculture Jeremiah M. Rusk, who assumed office in 1889. In addition to the rather popular annual agriculture book, containing as it now did reports from those in charge of various lines of investigation, the Department had tried publishing monthly reports. But even this did not supply the need for getting popularly expressed technical information to those requiring it, quickly enough to do the most good.

As W. O. Atwater had also seen this difficulty he proposed that a series of farmers' bulletins be instituted to solve it. This was done. George William Hill was appointed to supervise editing and publishing, and the issuance of popular publications was begun. Rusk's successor, J. Sterling Morton, established a Division of Publications. Thereafter there was a gradual evolution to the point where specialized editors were employed to bring Department publications to approved standards.

For a long time, however, the technical publications continued to be issued not only by the bureaus but by the sections and divisions that in some cases later became bureaus. The complexity of this publication policy ultimately became so great that it proved too confusing to be continued. In 1913 the bureau series of publications was largely consolidated into the Department series. In 1926 the Division of Publications became part of the newly created Office of Information.

During the first seventy-nine years of its life the Department issued 253 series of publications, including 43 periodicals, all of which are now defunct. The total number of separate publications—not copies—in the numbered series was 10,516. These were issued from sixty-six bureaus or administrative units of one sort or another, many of which have since been reorganized, transferred, or abolished.

At the outbreak of World War II the Department was issuing 98 series of publications, including 16 periodicals. These were exclusive of the publications prepared by bureaus which were transferred to other Government agencies from 1939 on.

Today the farmers' bulletins, leaflets, and Agricultural Information Series (AIS), an outgrowth of the War Information Series, with folders of various kinds, contain popularized scientific information. But most of the research and technical material which is published as such now appears in the *Journal of Agricultural Research*, and in such series as technical bulletins, circulars, miscellaneous publications, statistical bulletins, soil surveys, the hydrologic bulletins, and the land use and erosion surveys.

As has been noted elsewhere, the annual *Yearbook of Agriculture* is now a huge anthology of one-half million words, giving cyclopedic information about an entire field of science. Distribution of yearbook separates offers another broad avenue for the dissemination of scientific information.

Although the passage of time had brought many changes in the administrative phases of the Department's publication program, the form and structure of its technical and scientific publications have remained fairly well stabilized for a number of years. Their content, however, has undergone extensive modification.

First published in an era when professors of agriculture were just taking their place on college faculties and were recognized authorities in a very broad field, the early agricultural bulletins bore evidence of this in their tendency to generalization and relative linguistic simplicity, although scientific work of great value was performed and its results disseminated in those early days. In time, as science progressed and specialized, and each specialty developed its own technical nomenclature, the content of these publications changed. The number of professionally interested readers naturally becomes smaller as the specialty itself narrows.

The Department's technical bulletins contain reports of the more comprehensive types of investigation. Each publication is a separate and independent entity, with a more or less complete statement of the study and the findings on the subject considered. Though these bulletins are in a numbered series, they may differ entirely in subject matter from one to another. Department circulars and miscellaneous publications are semitechnical in character, some leaning towards the popular and others towards the technical.

The editions of technical bulletins and circulars for free distribution by the Department normally range from 2,500 to 3,500 copies. To these are added the necessary copies for the depository libraries and a sale stock. In the fiscal year 1941–42 (we assume this to be the latest fairly normal peacetime year), there were distributed free 593,865 copies of technical bulletins and circulars, while the Superintendent of Public Documents sold 53,448 copies.

The *Journal of Agricultural Research* is a leader in its field. Two thousand copies are issued for free distribution, but in the fiscal year 1940–41, 672 subscriptions to the journal were sold, as well as 18,825 copies of reprints or separates of articles that appeared therein. In addition, the bureau or station of origin is given 250 reprints of each article published. This journal was originally started through the influence of Karl F. Kellerman, who had concluded that neither scientific reviewing journals nor libraries gave to bulletins the attention they accorded to material published in indexed journals.

A long-time historical trend is involved in the issuance of Department publications. For many years a large part of our public has looked to the Department of Agriculture for accurate and unbiased scientific information on a wide variety of subjects. This is traditional. Late in 1889 Secretary Rusk wrote that the Department had received nearly 40,000 letters of inquiry for information between January 1 and October 1 that year. These letters, he said, came "from all sections of the country, from all classes and conditions."

As Secretary Rusk held, it is ill advised for a government agency to keep secret the knowledge it gathers or creates. He wrote that, "Time and expense, ability and experience, lavished on the work of this Department can have no practical results unless we can lay their conclusions promptly before the people who need them." In recent years, of course, all modern forms of communication have been invoked to aid this process, including the press, exhibits, the radio, and the motion picture.

Some of the more popular Department publications have been issued in huge quantities, mounting to two or three millions. In the fiscal year 1941–42, members of Congress themselves distributed nearly 5,000,000 farmers' bulletins and leaflets, and almost 400,000 publications in other series. They also requested 6,874,250 copies of Department lists of farmers' bulletins and leaflets to send to their constituents. Meanwhile, the Department's Office of Information received over 900,000 requests for information or publications, of which 279,000 emanated from offices of members of Congress. Again we adhere to semi-peacetime figures. The publication program increased enormously under the spur of war.

In that fiscal year about $225,000 was expended for the publication of scientific and technical material and about $406,000 for the publication of popular material. The printing of forms, certificates, instruction pamphlets, reports, periodicals, and other administrative material required, if the planning and regulatory functions of the Department pursuant to acts of Congress are to be properly carried out, absorbs the bulk of the printing funds. In the fiscal year mentioned, the sum required for this purpose alone was $1,155,000.

Because of the continuous pressure on its printing funds, it has not been possible for the Department to publish all the technical and research material written by its staff of specialists. During the fiscal year 1941–42, a total of 1,974 articles or addresses, mostly technical, were issued through outside journals. To provide for the further distribution of 265 of these, about 200 reprints of each were purchased. On the other hand, there were sent to the Government Printing Office during that fiscal year only 237 technical and scientific manuscripts, or 12 per cent as many, for issuance as technical bulletins, circulars, miscellaneous publications, statistical bulletins, soil surveys, and articles in the *Journal of Agricultural Research*.

The Department of Agriculture is a research and an educational institution as well as a planning and regulatory agency. It is continually creating scientific knowledge. To give this knowledge power, it must be published.

INDEX

Abacá, introduction and importance: 110

Abbe, Cleveland, weather service work: 277–78

Abortion: in cattle, control, 158–59; contagious, organism, relation to cause of undulant fever, 253

Acidity, cow's milk, determination: 246–47

Adams Act, grants to states for research: 176

Aerial photography, development and use: 127

Aerosol method of insect control, description: 66–68

Air-mass analysis, weather forecasting: 281, 286

Aircraft: manufacture, glue requirements, 137; wood, increase, 145

Airplanes: use for locating insect damage, 63–64; use for application of insecticides, 63–64, 68, 77; use in weather observations, 280

Agriculture, first federal aid: 10

Agriculture and Statistics, Bureau of, recommendation for: 21

Agriculture, Department of: major research agencies, 5–6; creation by President Lincoln, 6, 21–22; annual report, appropriation for distribution, 16; creation, recommendations, 21, 23; research, 1862–89, 23–33; organization 1889–1934, 36; new bureaus and agencies, 1901–34, 36

Agricultural: research institutions, 5–6; marketing facilities, study, 35; research, basic, expansion, 39; chemistry, accomplishments, 45–57; products, chemical analysis,

methods, 47; experiment stations, state, 173 ff.; engineering, accomplishments, 263–74; machinery, investment and value, 1882–1902, 264; industry, wartime accomplishments, 326

Agricultural Adjustment Act of 1938, provisions: 38

Agricultural Colleges and Experiment Stations, Association of, organization: 175

Agricultural Engineering, Division and Bureau of, work: 266

Agricultural Research Administration, creation, 1942: 37

Agricultural Research Center, facilities: 6

Agronomy research: 183–85

Agrostology, Division of, establishment: 35

Alaska Agricultural Experiment Station: 178, 187

Alcohol, industrial, manufacture from agricultural commodities: 47

Alfalfa: varieties, resistance to pea aphid, 62; breeding for disease resistance, 98; weevil, control, 325

Algae, destruction with copper: 321–22

"Alkali disease" of livestock: 202

Alvord, Henry E., dairy research: 241–42

American Ornithologists' Union, activities: 300, 301, 304, 307 ff.

Anderson, Clinton P., secretary of agriculture, 1945–: 35

Animal: diseases, investigation, appropriations, 1869 and 1881, 148; fibers, sterilization method, 237

333

Carotene, needs and sources: 230, 248

Carsner, Eubanks, work on sugar beets: 94–95

Casein, research: 254–55

Cattle: growers, returns from control of pleuropneumonia, 5, *see also* stockmen; industry, annual losses from cattle grub: 72; grub, damage and control, 72–73; tick fever, introduction and control, 150–51; dips, development and tests, 153; tuberculin testing, 159–60; foot-and-mouth disease, damage and control, 160–61; importation, sanitary regulations, 161; cattle-liver flukes, damage and control: 161–62; phosphorus-deficient, treatment, 162; breeding for better beef: 185–86

Cattle-tick: fever, control, cost and returns, 5; transmission of protozoan causing fever, 151

Cedar, host of apple-rust fungus: 91

Celery: mosaic, control, 97; leaf tier, control with pyrethrum, 325

Cellulose, decomposition by soil bacteria: 202

Cereals: investigations and diseases, 85; breeding for disease resistance, 97–98; introduction by Mark Carleton, 103

Chace, E. M.: work on dehydration of foods, 50, 56; work on citrus and citrus by-products, 50–51, 56

Cheese: investigations, 242, 243, 250–51; tubercle bacilli occurrence, 243; Swiss, chemistry, 246; blue-mold, production by Matheson process, 251; cultured, production and value, 251; Roquefort-type, manufacture, 251; Swiss, bacteriology, 251; Bel Paese-type, manufacture, new process, 252; ripening in sealed packages, 252; Cheddar, dehydration, new method, 252; whey, utilization, 254–55; improvement for Lend-Lease export, 262

Chemical research, expansion under Agricultural Adjustment Act: 38

Chemist, first in Department of Agri-culture—Charles M. Wetherill: 24–25

Chemistry: early importance to agriculture, 11; agricultural, early reports, 14; agricultural, early investigations, 24–26, 31–32

Chemistry and Soils, Bureau of, work: 196, 198

Chestnut, introduction and breeding for blight resistance: 141, 142

Chickens: pullorum disease, tests, 153, 166; importation and improvement, 166

Chicks, incubators for, design: 167

China, soil conservation: 214–15

Chinch bug, annual losses: 62

Cinchona: seed, introduction and importance, 110; research in Puerto Rico, 188

Citric acid, domestic production: 255

Citrus: by-products laboratory, establishment, 50; orchards, damage by fluted scale and control, 60–61; fruit, vapor-heat treatment for insect control, 66; breeding, work of W. T. Swingle, 85, 104; decay, prevention, 107; canker, cause and control, 324

Civilian Conservation Corps, forestry operations: 143, 144

Clark, William M., hydrogen-ion research: 245–48

Clemson, Thomas G., agricultural activities: 18–19

Climatic and Physiographic Division, work: 211

Climatological Data, publication: 283

Climatology reports: 282–83

Cline, McGarvey, establishment of Forest Products Laboratory: 131

Clothing, research: 219, 235–39

Clovers, improvement: 98

Cobb, N. A., work on nematodes: 109

Coccidiosis: *see* caecal coccidiosis

Cold: waves, warnings by Weather Bureau, 279–82; front theory, weather forecasting, 281, 286

Collier, Peter, chemical investigations: 26, 31, 42

179, 223; requirements, calculation, 224–26; preparation, research, 231–34; research, accomplishments, 188–89, 312–18; adulterants, list, 313, 315; examination methods, 315; decomposition, detection by mold-count method, 316
Food adulteration: early research, 31–32; work of Harvey W. Wiley, 47; research, 312 ff.
Food and Drug Act, work of Harvey W. Wiley: 45 ff., 313–14
Food and Drug Administration, accomplishments: 312–18
Food, Drug, and Cosmetic Act, passage: 314
Foods: analyses, 179–80; research, 217–35; freezing and processing, 239; see also nutrition
"Foods: Nutritive Value and Cost," by W. O. Atwater: 222
Foot-and-mouth disease, damage and control: 160–61
Forage: range, types in national forests, 115–16, 117; plant investigations: 117, 127–30; on range, survey methods, 129; grasses, improvement, 184
Forest: commissioner, first, appointment, 31; insects, control with orthodichlorobenzene, 71–72; research, accomplishments, 112–46; products, investigations, 115, 117; range research, 117, 127–30; influences, study, 119; range, grazing practices, 129–30; pathology, research, 141–46
Forest experiment station: Arizona, 118, 140; Philadelphia, 118–19; southern, 123
Forest fires, prevention: legislation, 114; and control, 123–27
Forest Products Laboratory, work, description: 115, 130–40
Forest Service: creation in 1905, 115; present organization and work, 118, 119
Forestry: research, first, 31; federal appropriations, 1898 and 1946, 141

Forestry, Bureau of, formation in 1901: 115
Forestry, Division of, establishment in 1851: 113, 115
Forests: burned-out, protection with mustard plants, 112–13; national, program, 114, 116 ff.
Fowl paralysis, investigations: 168
Frankenfield, H. C., flood-warning service: 281
Freezing: fruits and vegetables, for preservation, 56; weather forecasts to orchardists, 281–82
"Frost and Prevention of Frost Damage," by F. D. Young: 282
Frey, Ralph W., work on leather: 51
Fruit: dehydration, processes, 56; flies, control by vapor-heat treatment, 66; pollination, studies, 90–91; protection by freezing-weather forecasts: 281–82; moth, oriental, control, 324
Fruits: odorous constituents, 49; preservation by freezing, 56; refrigeration, 106; harvesting and transportation, 107; fungi diseases, control, 109
Fuel-fired furnace processing of phosphoric acid: 205–206
Fumigation, vacuum, value in insect control: 65–66
Fungi, studies by C. L. Shear: 109
Fungicides, research: 321
Fur farming in Alaska: 187
Furfural, production from corncobs: 52

Galloway, Beverly T., work in botany: 84–85, 88
Game protection: 302, 310
Gapeworms, control with barium antimonyl tartrate: 166–67
Garlic, effect on flavor of milk and control: 249
Garments, sizing: 237–38
Garriott, Edward B., weather service work: 278
Germ-plasm survey, dairy cattle: 258
Gibbs, Dr. H. D., discovery of process for making phthalic anhydride: 49

INDEX

Gisborne, Harry T., forecasting
fire weather: 124
Glass resistant to sun glare,
invention: 126
Glover, Townend, agricultural
activities: 16–17, 24, 58
Gluconic acid, production, new
method: 52
Glue: tests for various properties:
136–37; new uses, 137
Glycols, toxicity: 318
Goldenrod: source of rubber, 56;
rayless, source of tremetol, 169
Good-roads trains: 292
Gore, Howard M., secretary of
agriculture, 1924–25: 35
Grain: varieties, effects of soil and
climate, appropriation, 1848, 14;
combines, improvement, 273
Grange, founding: 27
Grapes, chemical analysis, 1862: 25
Grasses, work of F. Lamson-
Scribner: 84
Grasses of the United States, by A. S.
Hitchcock: 86
Grasshoppers, control by poisoned
bait: 61
Grazing: unrestricted, effects and
prohibition, 128; rotation
practices, 128–29
Great Lakes Region, storm
predictions: 278
Greely, Adolphus W., weather
service work: 278
Guayule, wartime project of Forest
Service: 140
Gullying, control: 216
Gypsy moth, discovery, 1880: 79

Hall, Maurice C., hookworm
research: 4, 155–56
Haller, Mark H., work with
strawberries: 82
Hansen, N. E., plant introductions:
101
Harter, Leonard L., work on plant
diseases: 81
Hassall, Albert, index catalogue of
animal parasites: 157
Hatch Act, provisions: 33, 149–50,
173, 175–76

Hawaii Agricultural Experiment
Station: 178, 186–87
"Hawks and Owls of the United
States," by A. K. Fisher: 304, 307
Haze cutter, invention for smoke
detection: 126–27
Haze meter, use in smoke detection:
127
Hazzi, Count von: "Treatise on the
Rearing of Silkworms": 8, 328
Heel fly, damage and control: 72–73
Hemlock bark, value in tanning
extract: 51
Herediscope, description and use:
258
Hessian fly, damage and control:
39–40, 62
Hexachloroethane, use in control of
cattle-liver flukes: 162
Highway: acts, see Federal-aid Road
Act and Federal Highway Act;
systems, investigation, 289–91
Hillculture Division, work: 211
Hitchcock, A. S., work on grasses: 86
Hogentogler, Chester A., road
research: 297
Hogs: cholera control, work of
Marion Dorset, 152, 153–54;
genetics, impetus by research, 163;
southern, improved feeding
practices: 164; see also swine
Holloway, David P., commissioner
of patents: 19–20
Holm, George E., milk-spoilage
problems: 253
Home canning, studies: 232
Home economics, research, accom-
plishments: 217–40
Home Economics, Office and
Bureau of, work: 218–40
Honeybee, research: 75–77, 90
Hookworm, occurrence, damage
and control: 4, 154–56
Hormones, plant, research: 323
Horsepower, early farm uses: 9
Horses: venereal disease, control,
165; parasites, control, 165–66
"Horse doctor bill": 149
Hosiery, cotton, designs: 237
Hotis test, purpose: 253

Oats: breeding for disease
resistance, 97–98; new varieties,
development, 183
Oberholser, Harry C., research in
ornithology: 308
O'Brien, Ruth, work on textiles and
clothing: 235–36
Oleomargarine Act, passage in 1884:
44
Oleoresin production, studies: 120–23
Onions, breeding and production: 82
Optics, research of G. M. Byram:
126–27
Oranges, navel, importation from
Brazil: 27, 86–87
Orchard-heating equipment,
improvement: 274, 276
Orchardists, aid by freezing-
weather forecasts: 281–82
Organic compounds in soils,
identification: 202
Oriental fruit moth, control: 324
Ornithology research: 300–11
Orthodichlorobenzene, value in
control of forest insects: 71–72
Orton, William A.: supervision of
work on sugar from corn, 42;
plant breeding for disease
resistance, 92
Osteomyelitis, control by sterile-
maggot therapy: 60

Pacific Northwest Forest and Range
Experiment Station: 125–26
Page, Logan W., road-building
work: 293
Palmer, H. S., work in dairy science:
248
Palmer, T. S., wild-life research: 305,
310
Paper plastics, development: 135
Paradichlorobenzene, value in
control of peach-tree borer: 71
Parasites: importation for insect
control, 60–61; animal, occurrence
and control, 154–67; animal, index-
catalogue by Albert Hassall, 157
Patent Office: agricultural reports,
15 ff.; Agricultural Division, first
agency, 6, 7, 10

Patrons of Husbandry, founding: 27
Pea aphid, damage to alfalfa and
control: 62, 69
Peach-tree borers, control: 71, 325
Peach yellows, work of E. F. Smith:
84, 89
Peanut by-products, new uses: 56
Pear blight, studies by M. B. Waite:
90
Penicillin research: 54–55, 262, 320–21
Phagocytosis, effect of chemical
antiseptics: 318
Phenothiazine: value in control of
livestock parasites, 5, 165; uses on
humans and animals, 52
Phosphate investigations: 205–206
Phosphoric acid, manufacturing
processes: 205–206
Phosphorus: feeding to cattle, 162,
206; production, new processes,
205–206
Photoperiodism, discovery and
importance: 107–108
Phthalic anhydride, process for
making: 49
Physics of the Air, by W. J.
Humphreys: 285
Phytopathology, impetus by B. T.
Galloway: 84, 88
Pinchot, Gifford, work in forestry:
114–15, 140–41
Pine, white, blister rust, control:
141, 142
Pineapple disease, cause and control:
186–87
Pines: breeding for high gum yield,
123; seedlings, damping-off
disease, control, 144
Piper, C. V., introduction of Sudan
grass: 105
Plant: explorer, first—Daniel J.
Browne, 16; introductions, 16, 27,
85–87, 94, 98–105, 184; explorations:
16, 83, 85, 94, 98, 99–105; diseases:
81 ff., 93, 195; science, accomplishments: 81–111; bacteriology, work
of E. F. Smith: 84, 88–89; pathology, basic discoveries: 87–92;
breeding for disease resistance:
92–98; nutrition, balance-sheet

Terraces, use to control soil erosion: 267

Textiles, research: 235–39

Thom, Charles, work in soil microbiology and penicillin: 203

Tick fever, cattle, occurrence and control: 148, 150–51

Ticks: problem, solution, basis for control of other diseases, 152; on sheep, eradication, 165

Tiemann, Harry D., work on kiln-drying of lumber: 132–33

Tillage Machinery Laboratory, Auburn, Ala., work: 267–68

Timber: resources, depletion, problem, 113 ff.; saw, reduction prior to World War II, 116; tests, work of H. S. Betts, 131–32; heart rot, studies: 143–44

Tires, impact tests: 296–97

Tobacco: mosaic virus, transmission by aphids, 91; soils, investigations, 198

Tomato: breeding for wilt resistance, 95; plants, protection in transit, 106

Trace elements, definition and importance: 3

Tractors, steam, first trials: 18

Trees, breeding for specific purposes: 138

Trembles, occurrence and control: 168–69

Tremetol, cause of milk sickness: 169

Trichinae in pork, discovery and control: 157–58

Trichinosis, occurrence and control: 157–58

Tropical fruit culture, work of Wilson Popenoe: 102

Tropical-plant introduction garden, Puerto Rico: 188

Tubercle bacilli, occurrence in dairy products: 243

Tuberculin, discovery and production: 159–60

Tuberculosis, bovine, eradication: 159–60

Tung trees, cultivation and importance: 107

Turpentine production, studies: 120–23

2, 4-D, discovery and uses: 110–11

Typhus epidemic, 1943–44, control by DDT: 68

Udder, bacteria, studies: 253

Undulant fever, organism, relation to cause of contagious abortion: 253

United States Agricultural Society, 1852–62: 21

United States Entomological Commission: founding, 58; report on cotton insects, 63

United States National Herbarium, maintenance: 82–83

Upper-air observations, weather forecasting: 275, 281, 286

Uralloy, production: 135

Vaccine for: hog cholera, development, 154; brucellosis, development, 158–59; equine encephalomyelitis, development, 166

Vacuum fumigation, value in insect control: 65–66

Valentine, Lawson, agricultural experiment station: 241–42

Van Deman, Henry E., work in plant science: 86

Vapor-heat treatment, citrus fruit, for insect control: 66

Vasey, George, work in botany: 82–83

Vedalia beetle, importation and control of fluted scale: 61

Vegetable: fats and oils, work of G. S. Jamieson, 50; rehydration, processes, 56; preservation by freezing, 56; oils, new uses, 56, 262; refrigeration, 106

Vegetation, influences on rainfall: 194–95

Vehicle wheels, impact tests: 296–97

Velva Fruit, development: 56

Veterinarian: first, appointment, 30; first in Department of Agriculture —Daniel E. Salmon, 148

Veterinary Division, establishment: 30, 148

UNIVERSITY OF OKLAHOMA PRESS

NORMAN